# LINEAR PROGRAMMING
# AND THE THEORY OF THE FIRM

# LINEAR
# AND THE

With Contributions by

**SHERRILL CLELAND**
*Kalamazoo College*

**HANS H. JENNY**
*The College of Wooster*

**CHING-WEN KWANG**
*University of Notre Dame*

**C. MICHAEL WHITE**
*University of Southern California*

**YUAN-LI WU**
*Marquette University*

# PROGRAMMING THEORY OF THE FIRM

**KENNETH E. BOULDING**

*Professor of Economics*

*AND*

**W. ALLEN SPIVEY**

*Associate Professor of Statistics*

THE UNIVERSITY OF MICHIGAN

*The Macmillan Company*

NEW YORK

*First Printing*

*Library of Congress catalog card number: 60–7415*

The Macmillan Company, New York
Brett-Macmillan Ltd., Galt, Ontario

Printed in the United States of America

# PREFACE

This volume is the joint product of a seminar for college teachers of economics in smaller colleges, sponsored by the Ford Foundation and held at the University of Michigan, Ann Arbor, in the summer of 1958.* The main object of the seminar was to examine some new developments which were relevant to the theory of the firm, and which had largely grown up in the last ten or fifteen years outside of professional economics. The new mathematical discipline of linear programming, the somewhat looser collection of related techniques known as operations research and an even looser collection known as management science constitute one phase of this development, much of which hinges on the techniques of "finite mathematics" rather than on the calculus of continuous functions. A second important but still more loosely defined development is in the area of the theory of organization, cybernetics and information theory, the sociology of enterprise, and the ethical theory of responsible behavior. These various developments have caused a good deal of excitement among mathematicians, engineers, and even philosophers and sociologists, but the excitement has been slow in reaching the professional economists, and has scarcely touched the undergraduate teaching of economics. As most of the participants in the seminar were actively engaged in teaching economics to undergraduates, one of the main problems of the seminar was to determine how much of these new materials might profitably be incorporated into the undergraduate economics curriculum.

The seminar was greatly helped by Dr. W. Allen Spivey of the University of Michigan, who presented the material which is mainly incorporated in his chapters in this volume. Toward the end of the seminar the idea of a symposium sprang spontaneously out of the work of the group. In its inception it was hoped to develop two parts—the first on the more mathematical aspects such as linear programming, the second on the more sociological and ethical aspects. Unfortunately the proposed second part proved to be much more

* The following Fellows participated in the seminar: Patrick M. Boarman, Sherrill Cleland, William E. Gordon, Hans H. Jenny, Harold L. Johnson, Ching-wen Kwang, John Vandenberg, C. Michael White, James G. Witte, jr., and Yuan-li Wu.

difficult than was anticipated, and the first part turned out to be longer and more substantial. It was decided therefore to incorporate in this volume for the most part only those essays which related fairly directly to more mathematical aspects of the program. The second part therefore essentially remains for the future, though Professor Cleland's essay is in a sense a bridge towards it, and I have incorporated some ideas from the unpublished essays of Professors Boarman and Johnson in my introductory chapter. Professors Witte, Gordon, and Vandenberg, whose work is also not represented in this volume, made valuable contributions to the discussions out of which this volume arose.

The published essays speak largely for themselves. In my introductory chapter I have tried to place these new developments in the light of their historical setting, and to show perhaps that they are not quite as revolutionary as they look at first sight. Dr. Spivey's monograph is the core of the volume, and will, I believe, open the door to these new developments to numbers of students and professional economists whose mathematical timidity or unsophistication has prevented them from pushing over this not too formidable threshold. The essay by Dr. Wu and Dr. Kwang builds a valuable, and hitherto unbuilt bridge between the old marginal analysis and the newer techniques. Dr. Jenny widens the path still further in the direction of operations research. Dr. White raises the problem of broader criteria of maximization in the firm, and finally Dr. Cleland points up the nature of the shift from the simple skeletally organized firm of economic theory to the large-scale, managerial organization which dominates the scene today.

Our united thanks are due to the Ford Foundation, which initiated and supported this and a number of similar ventures.

K. E. BOULDING

# CONTENTS

*Chapter 3 (continued)*

*Chapter 4* **An Analytical and Graphical Comparison of Marginal Analysis and Mathematical Programming in the Theory of the Firm**
YUAN-LI WU
CHING-WEN KWANG

| Chapter | *THE PRESENT POSITION* |
| :---: | :--- |
| *I* | *OF THE THEORY OF* |
| | *THE FIRM* |

*by* KENNETH E. BOULDING

## HISTORICAL BACKGROUND

The theory of the firm, as an explicit segment of economic analysis, is of surprisingly recent origin. Some notion of the pursuit of maximum advantage on the part of the individual decision-maker is implicit in the classical economics of Adam Smith and Ricardo, but there is little or no attempt on the part of these writers to spell out the consequences of the principle of maximization in any detail. In Adam Smith there are some luminous insights into the advantages and disadvantages of large-scale organization—he recognizes, for instance, that the large organization can only thrive if its operations can be reduced to "strict rule and method" (*The Wealth of Nations*, Mod. Lib. Edition, p. 714). Nevertheless, he regards the corporation mainly as a restrictive and monopolistic device, and the Joint Stock Company as an institution suited perhaps to the limited fields of banking, insurance, canals and waterworks which require large capitals, but with very limited application to the general run of economic activities. Consequently, in the classical economics the "firm" is a shadowy entity, and the entrepreneur even shadowier—or at least is shady where he is not shadowy! Where a profit opportunity arises, capital and labor flow together into an enterprise from all sides as if into a vacuum, and organize themselves into a process of production apparently without effort and without guidance. Where profits and wages are low, capital and labor disengage themselves from the disadvantageous occupation and flow hungrily but easily toward greener pastures. The firm is thus an aggregation of capital and labor rather than an organization, and most of the problems which are connected with it simply do not arise.

The theory of the firm as we know it today originates historically in the work of Cournot ([43][1] 1838), though in view of the relatively small impact of

[1] Throughout the text, numbers in brackets refer to the Bibliography [pp. 217–24].

work in his own day we may perhaps date the introduction of the theory of the firm into the main stream of economic thought a generation or more later, with the "discovery" of Cournot by Jevons and the explicit development of the theory of maximizing behavior by Edgeworth [57] and Marshall [118]. It took another generation and a half until the marginal analysis was fully and explicitly developed by Harrod [75], Joan Robinson [140], and Chamberlin [29] round about 1930. The hundred years of development from 1838 to 1938, however, merely made more explicit and usable what was already in Cournot, where all that is essential in what has come to be known as the marginal analysis is found in embryo, expressed in the formulae of the differential calculus.

## THE MARGINAL ANALYSIS

The essential principles of the marginal analysis are so simple as to be almost trite. The firm is thought of essentially as an input-output process, whereby certain inputs of factors of production—labor and land services, capital services, raw materials, and so on—are transformed into outputs of salable product. Inputs are generally bought, outputs are generally sold, though there may be both inputs and outputs which are furnished or consumed by the owner or entrepreneur himself and hence do not enter into an explicit market. Because of their explicit or implicit market prices, however, inputs and outputs can be *valued*—that is, expressed as a sum of "dollars worth" or of any other convenient measure of value. Costs are then the value of input, revenues the value of output, and corresponding to the process of transforming inputs into outputs there is a corresponding process of transforming costs into revenues. The excess of revenues over costs is the *net revenue*, which is taken as a measure of profit.

A *position* of a firm is a set of values of all the variables which are relevant to it, such as quantities of input and output, prices of these inputs and outputs, revenues and costs associated with these, and so on. Out of the set of all conceivable positions we must first define a set of *possible* positions by ruling out all those sets which are inconsistent with the *constraints* which its nature and environment place on the firm. Thus, if we have an output of 500 bushels and the price at which they can be sold is $3 per bushel, the revenue from this output must be $1,500; it cannot be any other number whatever, so that, for instance, a set of values consisting of 500 bushels of output, $3.00 price per bushel and $1,499 revenue is not possible. In addition to these purely definitional constraints which take the form of mathematical identities, there are empirical constraints which describe the limitations placed on the firm by its internal nature and its external environment. There is, for instance, the production function, which tells us which combination of quantities and kinds of inputs and outputs are possible and which are impossible. Qualitatively, seed potatoes, labor and land will not produce cabbages; quantitatively $x$ units of seed, $y$ of labor and $z$ of land will not produce more than $q$ units of product. This is the principal internal limitation. Then there are external limitations in the form of market functions. These take forms such as "if $q$ units are to be sold they must be sold at a price of no more than $p$." In the case of what is known as a "perfect market" the maximum price at which a product can be sold does not depend on how many units are sold; where there is an "imperfect market" the price is lower the more units are sold. Both these, however, are cases of the general concept of a market limitation. Even if we include selling costs the idea of a market limitation remains; the limitation merely takes the more complicated form: if a price $p$ is charged, and a selling cost of a specific kind $s$ is made, a maximum of $q$ units of product can be sold. There will also be market functions of input, showing how much input of a given item can be bought at each price and buying cost.

The production function and the market functions together define the set of all feasible positions of a firm of a given nature and context. The *optimum* position of the firm is then defined as that position out of the set of all possible positions for which the net revenue is a maximum. If the set of possible positions is bounded by a differentiable function and the optimum position is not at the boundary of the set, the optimum position is distinguished by the fact that the "marginal conditions" are satisfied. The marginal conditions are that for each of the continuous variables which define the firm's position at the optimal point, marginal revenue is equal to marginal cost. Marginal revenue is the increase in total revenue which results from a unit increase in some relevant variable, such as quantity of output or input: marginal cost is the increase in total cost which results from a unit increase in the same variable. If marginal revenue is greater than marginal cost, increasing the variable will raise revenue more than it raises cost and will raise net revenue: the position is not optimum. If marginal revenue is less than marginal cost, then *decreasing* the variable will raise net revenue, and the position is also not optimum. If marginal revenue is not equal to marginal cost, therefore, the position cannot be an optimum. It is, then, a necessary condition for an optimum that marginal revenue should be equal to marginal cost. This is not a sufficient condition, as it holds for a minimum as well as a maximum value of the net revenue. The condition may break down also when the functions are not continuous.

## THE PROBLEM OF THE MAXIMAND

So far all we really have is mathematics, and fairly elementary calculus at that. The jump into economics comes with the assumption that the optimum is the equilibrium—that is, that there is a tendency for firms to move to their optimum positions—and with further assumptions about the general shapes of the production and market functions. Here we go immediately to more debatable ground which has already been the scene of extensive controversy. The controversy extends to many different aspects of the problem. There is first a controversy about the *definition of the position* and the *measure of the optimum.* The "net revenue" which is supposed to be maximized in the Robinson-Chamberlain theory is a curious quantity of which no accountant or businessman ever heard. Furthermore, the firms are creatures without past or future, balance sheet or net worth. The first natural extension of the elementary marginal analysis would seem to be in the direction of taking explicit account of the time and capital-assets dimensions of the firm. This has been attempted by Tintner [160], Hicks [78], Hotelling [85], Friedrich and Vera Lutz [103], and the writer [23], to name but a few authors in this field. The general pattern here has been to regard the position of the firm not merely as a set of variables at a given date, but as a set of subsets of variables, each subset characterizing the firm at a given date within some relevant sequence of successive dates. The optimum position of the firm then is that set of dated variables over its whole relevant life history which maximizes some quantity which measures its profitability over its whole relevant life. A still unresolved controversy revolves around *what* quantity is the measure of whole-life profitability. The weight of the majority inclines toward taking the present value of the future net revenues at market rates of interest as the measure of the optimum. A minority incline toward the "internal rate of return," or the rate of profit (per cent per annum) which is actually earned on the investment in the enterprise as a better measure. The controversy is, however, swallowed up in a larger one about whether any "objective" measure of the optimum is possible, for if no objective measure is "realistic" the argument about which of two wrong measures is right loses a lot of interest.

The "subjectivists" argue, in effect, that the decision-maker orders the possible positions which he reviews according to some subjective ordering or utility function, and simply picks out what seems to him at the time to be best, according to this subjective criterion. Thus the theory of the firm becomes thoroughly amalgamated with the theory of consumer behavior or of the household: like the household, the firm maximizes utility, if anything. If the firm will sacrifice "profits" (no matter how measured) for anything else, whether prestige, or good public or labor relations, or a quiet life, or liquidity, or security, or what have you, then it is clearly not maximizing profits. And if it is not maximizing profits it must be maximizing "utility," which is simply a more elaborate way of saying that it does what it thinks best. This can hardly be untrue, but it is also not very helpful unless some content can be poured into the empty utility functions.

## CRITICISMS OF MARGINALISM

In view of these difficulties it is not surprising that a vigorous controversy developed around the question of the "realism" or usefulness of the marginal analysis. To a considerable extent the dissenters have been labor economists such as Richard Lester [37], inspired in part by rebellion against some of the conclusions which seemed to emerge from the marginal doctrine. According to the marginal analysis, net revenue is maximized when the addition of another unit of labor increases cost just as much as it increases revenue. If there is a perfect market for labor, so the employment of another unit does not affect the wage paid, the addition to cost is the wage, the addition to revenue is the marginal value product of the work. From very plausible assumptions about the production function (the "law of diminishing returns") it can be shown that the marginal value product of a given kind of labor will fall with increased quantities of labor employed. It follows that increased quantities of labor can only be employed at a lower wage, or what is the same thing, that the higher the wage the less labor will be employed. It is this conclusion which labor economists have frequently rejected as either unpalatable or unrealistic. It is a conclusion of course which cannot be generalized without a serious fallacy of composition; just because a high money wage for bricklayers leads to less employment of bricklayers it does not necessarily follow that a general rise in money wages of all workers will either lead to an increase in their real wages or in a decline in employment. The feeling against the marginal analysis goes deeper, however, than the mere attempt to show that the demand for a particular kind of labor is very inelastic.

Another group of dissidents promotes the "full-cost pricing" theory of the firm, which is in turn closely related to the "markup" theory. This view supposes that the firm calculates some standard average cost for its product and then adds a percentage of this cost for "profit" in order to establish its price. The question whether the firm can sell enough (or any) of the product at this price to permit it to produce at the standard cost is somewhat glossed over!

Many of these criticisms of the marginal analysis have been ill-considered and have arisen out of a misunderstanding of its essentially tautological character: *given* the principle of maximization of something, the marginal conditions follow as simple mathematical tautologies. Even though some of these criticisms have attacked the wrong things, nevertheless the dissatisfaction which they represent is well grounded. As a theory which purports to represent actual behavior the maximization theory suffers from the almost fatal defect of failing to consider the *information* which is available to the decision maker. A theory which assumes knowledge of what cannot be known is clearly defective as a guide to actual behavior. What must be known, however, in order to maximize profits in a situation of imperfect markets and multivariable production functions is a whole set of functional relationships, such as demand and supply functions, which are *not* given by immediate experience, and often are not even given by the most refined analysis of past data. If a firm cannot know what its marginal costs and marginal revenues are it is useless to advise it to act so as to bring them to equality.

The failure of economists to recognize the crucial nature of the information problem arose, I suspect, because in the older and simpler theory of perfect competition the information problem is much less difficult. If a firm is faced with perfect markets all it has to know is the price at which it can buy and sell in these markets, for it can buy or sell unlimited quantities at this price. The price, however, is a piece of information which is readily available—the commodity comes, as it were, with a price tag tied to it, and all the decision-maker has to do is to look at the price tag. There may be something of an information problem in knowing his production function or cost curves, but in perfect competition he is likely to be operating in a region where the production function is homogeneous and average cost is constant, so that here again we do not need to know any functional properties; it is easy to find out how much input we need to produce the output, and even easier to calculate the cost of this input by multiplying each amount by its easily perceivable price.

The very laudable attempt to generalize this simple model to a condition of imperfect markets, nonconstant cost, and nonhomogeneous production functions (by Harrod, Joan Robinson, and Chamberlin) led to a failure to realize that the information problem, which could almost be neglected in the simple model, had now become of prime importance. It is one thing to look at a price tag and to know that any amount can be bought or sold at this price. It is quite another thing to discover a demand function, which is a set of *possible* prices and *possible* quantities, only one of which is given in present experience. Thus making what seems like a simple extension of the model from perfect markets to imperfect markets actually involves us in an information problem of first magnitude. We move from a situation where the information required for the making of a rational decision is a simple number such as a price, given by simple observation, to a situation where the information required is a set of functional relationships which are *not* given by simple observation, because what needs to be known is not what *is* but what *might be*. Of course, what needs to be known for rational decision is always what "might be." In the case of perfect competition, however, the happy situation prevails that what might be can be deduced immediately from what is at the moment. In the case of imperfect competition this is not so. In one case we are driving a straight road and can easily project our present direction for miles ahead; in the second case we are driving a twisting mountain track where we cannot see more than a few feet round the bend, and where the position of the moment tells us very little about where we might be next week.

This does not mean, of course, that there is *no* uncertainty or information problem under perfect markets, for there is always uncertainty about future prices, and there may be uncertainty, as in agriculture, about the production function. Under imperfect markets, however, there is a double uncertainty— we are not only uncertain as to the future, but we are uncertain even as to the present parameters of the market functions.

Thus the marginal analysis provides a rule of decision only under conditions of full knowledge which are unlikely to be realized in practice. The modern developments which lie beyond the marginal analysis can largely be interpreted in terms of attempts to solve the problem of decision-making under imperfect knowledge. Three such developments may be mentioned. The first is linear programming and the related techniques of operations research. This represents a breakdown of the larger problem of the optimum position or policy of the firm into smaller problems which are narrow enough so that information is available to solve them. The second is game theory, which formalizes the problem of decision-making under uncertain outcomes. The third is organization theory, an ill-defined but fruitful field which includes information and control mechanisms, role theory, team theory, and other attempts to formalize the processes of decision-making under hierarchical relationships. These developments do not represent a sharp break with the past; they can all be seen as extensions of the older theories of maximizing behavior, or what is much the same thing, the older theories can be seen as special cases of the new. Two basic concepts are common to them all; one, the concept of a limited field of choice of possible positions, and the other, the concept of a method of selecting the "best" position among those possible. In this volume only the first of these developments—linear programming and related topics—is treated in any detail. This is not because the other two are unimportant, but rather because these developments are not perhaps mature enough to be embodied in a volume of this kind.

## LINEAR PROGRAMMING

In the theory of linear programming the limits of the field of choice are set by an appropriate number of linear inequalities, a linear inequality being a special case of a boundary condition which divides the field of conceivable positions into a "possible" or "feasible" set consistent with the condition and an "impossible" or "unattainable" set inconsistent with the condition. Thus, suppose that our field of conceivable choice consisted of all possible ordered pairs of real numbers $(x, y)$ such as $(2, 10)$, $(8.56, 3.28)$, and so on. Let us now impose a condition that $2x - y$ must be less than 5. We can examine any pair of numbers to see whether it meets this condition; if it does (like the pair 5, 6, where $2 \cdot 5 - 6 = 4$) we put it into a box labeled "sheep" and if it does not, like the pair 5, 4, we put it into a box labeled "goats." We clearly have a rule here which enables us to divide the whole infinite set of ordered pairs into two boxes (called "half spaces"), and we can then throw away the goats as irrelevant to the problem. We still have an infinite number of pairs in the sheep box, owing to the delightful multitudinousness of infinite sets. We can make the box smaller by imposing more conditions: thus three inequalities are usually enough to enclose the box so that there are no infinite *numbers* in it, and if the box can be made small enough the field of choice can be restricted to a single point. This is illustrated in Figure 1. Any ordered pair of numbers can be represented by the co-ordinates of a point in a Cartesian plane. The line $LN$ is the line $2x - y = 5$. All points above and to the left of this are "sheep"; for these $2x - y < 5$. All points below and to the right are "goats": for these $2x - y \geqq 5$. We may note that as we have defined the condition as $2x - y$ *less than* 5, points *on* the line are "goats." Also in any case the figure illustrates how a single inequality divides the field into sheep and goats. Suppose now that we impose two further inequalities: say $x > 0$ and $y < 0$. Then everything above the $X$-axis becomes goats: everything to the left of the $Y$-axis becomes goats, and the only sheep left are those in the

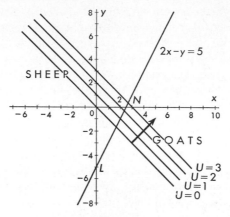

**Figure 1**

triangle $LON$. If the boundary lines which define the limiting inequalities all intersect at a point, and the signs of the inequalities are correct, the field of choice shrinks to a single point and the choice is made. Frequently one suspects decisions are made in this way: a field of choice is surveyed, and limiting conditions are noted which successively eliminate more and point elements of the field until only one position is left, which is the decision. In practice this may be a more important method of decision-making than "maximizing," if only because maximizing involves more trouble and judgment. A great deal of "socializing" of the educational process consists in deliberately limiting fields of choice, so that when, for instance, someone proffers a handshake we do not have to make the painful decision whether to shake his hand, rumple his hair, pull his nose, or kiss his cheek but habit automatically eliminates all but one of the conceivable alternatives and we shake hands.

Nevertheless "maximizing" does occur, and is peculiarly characteristic of the nonhabitual, nontraditional behavior which is supposed to be the peculiar glory of economic man. If, when we have eliminated all the impossible parts of the field something remains, as in the triangle $LON$—when, in our previous language, there is more than one "sheep," the problem of how to select one sheep and only one to go through the narrow gate of rational decision becomes a different kind of selective process from that which is involved in merely eliminating alternatives.

Thus in Figure 2 we show a typical "marginal analysis" situation, where the field of choice consists of points along the line $OX$, and the "maximand" such as profits or utility is measured along $OY$. $RMS$ is the limiting function—

nonlinear this time—which divides the $x$, $y$ field into the unattainable goats above it and the attainable sheep below it. A further condition is imposed that $y$ be a maximum; $M$ is the point finally selected. What this means is that within the set of sheep bounded by $RMS$ we move as far as we can in the direction of the vertical. Compare this now with a typical linear programming problem as in Figure 1, and we see the similarity immediately. Suppose in Figure 1 we wanted to maximize $U$, where $U = x + y$. The dotted lines are isomers $U = 0$, $U = 1$, $U = 2$, etc. The maximum $U$ within the "sheep" triangle is at the point $N$; this is the point which will be selected by linear programming techniques, and is as far "out" as we can go within the triangle in the direction of the arrow. The corresponding $U$-isomers in Figure 2 are the horizontal lines.

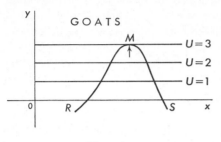

**Figure 2**

Although the basic principle behind linear programming and related techniques on the one hand and the marginal analysis is essentially the same, the greater value of the linear techniques lies in the fact that the basic limiting inequalities, as well as the utility or maximand function, may be more accessible to the information system. To some extent this simply follows from their being linear, a linear relationship being the next simplest to a plainly observable number. Thus if the theory requires moving from a simple condition of constant average cost describable in its entirety by a single number (dollars per bushel) to the more complex condition of cost varying with output, the next simplest relationship is a linear one with, say, cost as a linear function of output. In order to define a linear function we only need to know two numbers,[2] and while it is much harder to know two numbers than one (certainly more than twice as hard!) it is not as hard as it would be to know the still greater number of numbers which would be needed to define more general types of functional relationships. The success of linear programming, and, in general, of operations research, can be attributed mainly to its application to cases where the knowledge and information system permitted the discovery or assumption of that small set of numbers which define the parameters of the linear relation needed.

### GAME THEORY

If operations research runs in the direction of so limiting the conditions of the *problem* that the information is available to solve it, game theory and the related decision theory run in the direction of hedging against fatal solutions

---

[2] Any linear relationship between $x$ and $y$ can be expressed in the form $x + by + c = 0$: the whole relationship is defined if we know the parameters $b$ and $c$.

to insoluble problems. Although game theory arose quite properly out of a consideration of games, that is, situations involving the gainful interaction of two or more persons, its most basic concept—that of a payoff matrix—is as applicable to individual behavior as to the interaction of two or more individuals. A theory of interaction must also imply a theory of individual behavior, and where the actions of one actor cannot be known in advance to the other this involves a theory of behavior under uncertainty. This is illustrated in Figure 3. Let us suppose that $X$, $Y$, and $Z$ are three different circumstances or environments, and $A$, $B$, $C$, are three decisions or acts of the actor. It makes no difference at the moment whether we think of these as single acts or as whole sets of contingent acts (strategies). For each combination of an environment and an act there is a "payoff"—a number written in the appropriate cell of the matrix which represents the total net benefit or utility received by the actor as a result of the act. If now we can specify the circumstance—say $Y$—the problem reduces to one of simple maximizing behavior; we just look down the $Y$-column and pick out the largest net benefit, and this is the one corresponding to the appropriate rational act. Suppose now—and this is what makes the difference—we *cannot* specify which of the circumstances $X$, $Y$, or $Z$ will eventuate, what do we do then? This will be the case, for instance, if $X$, $Y$, and $Z$ represent an opponent's acts or strategies in a two-person game theory, but from the point of view of our particular decision-maker it does not matter whether $X$, $Y$, and $Z$ are acts of

|   | $X$ | $Y$ | $Z$ |
|---|-----|-----|-----|
| $A$ | $a_x$ | $a_y$ | $a_z$ |
| $B$ | $b_x$ | $b_y$ | $b_z$ |
| $C$ | $c_x$ | $c_y$ | $c_z$ |

Figure 3

another person or whether they are acts of "nature" over which he has no control—in which case the game is called a "game against nature."

If the probabilities of $X$, $Y$, and $Z$ are known as well as all the payoff figures we can compute an expected value for each of the acts $A$, $B$, and $C$, and assuming that a higher expected value will always be preferred to a lower (not necessarily a valid assumption!) the problem again reduces to simple maximization. Suppose now, however, that we do not even know the probabilities; that we have no idea whether either one of $X$, $Y$, or $Z$ is more probable than any other. The simple maximization principle breaks down; we cannot look over the whole field of the matrix and select the box with the highest payoff, for this box may not be open to us, and we do not know whether it will be open or not. All is not chaos, however; there may still be fragments of rational decision-making left. Suppose, for instance, that there are some payoffs that mean "disaster" that we cannot risk under any circumstances. Suppose, for instance, that payoffs $a_z$ and $b_z$ are "death." Then if circumstance Z enters our horizon at all, even if say $a_x$ and $b_x$ are very high and all the $c$'s are rather low we are likely to choose C, unless, of course, we are subtly guided by the Freudian death wish. In this type of case one suspects that in practice the method of decision-making is often that of successive elimination until only one alternative is left. For those who fear the worst more than they hope for the best this principle leads to the choice which will be the best protection against the worst happening: under some circumstances this is the classical "minimax" solution. On the other hand there may be hardy souls who fear regret more than they fear disaster, and who cannot bear the thought of missing a good thing. This is more likely to lead to choosing that alternative which yields the highest reward under the most favorable circumstance. The glittering prize attracts more than the bones of earlier aspirants repel. The truth seems to be that there is no one touchstone of "rational behavior" under uncertainty. A number of reasonably systematic patterns can be distinguished, and the choice among these is a further act of decision. All these, however, represent some kind of extension of the maximization principle to more general and complex situations, not a rejection of it.[3]

Game theory has something to contribute to the discussion of the inter-action of firms, especially in the case of oligopoly where the number of competing firms is small enough so that each is conscious of the effects of action on the part of any other. When there are more than two firms in competition the *n*-person game is relevant to the situation, for there is the possibility of coalitions and collusions. These aspects of the theory of interaction of firms have been developed in a recent work by Martin Shubik [149], and are not further considered in this volume.

**ORGANIZATION THEORY**

Another important line of theoretical development, somewhat different from the one we have been discussing, is organization theory. The traditional economic concept of the actor is that of the *person*—a single consumer or producer, directing his behavior toward this or that variable as the conditions which surround him change. We have been increasingly aware that most decisions are made in a framework of organization, even though it remains true that decisions are actually made by persons. A person acting in a role, however, is not the same thing as a person acting on his own behalf. The behavior of the President of the United States follows different principles in a

[3] Not wholly unrelated to the game theory approach is Shackle's lone-wolf attempt to reduce uncertainty to rationality: Shackle [148] postulates two "focus outcomes" as the center of the decision-makers' attention, and hence reduces the complex field of uncertain outcomes to a simple choice between two sets of outcomes such as X and Y in Figure 3, usually a "good" one and a "bad" one.

different field of choice from what the same person follows in his private life. The life of any individual therefore can be conceived as a series of intersecting roles, in each of which he plays a somewhat different part. An organization then comes to be visualized as a network of interacting roles, tied together by lines of communication, both formal and informal. These lines of communication may have several significant dimensions, involving not only the quantity and quality of the communications themselves, but also the degree of authority which they bear and the probable impact on the behavior of both sender and recipient. A role itself is created partly by the communications which have impinged on it in the past, partly by the idiosyncrasies of the present occupant. As each new occupant accepts a role a barrage of role-informing communications impinges on him, modifying his previous concept of the role; however, persons are not merely passive occupants of roles, but themselves actively change and even create roles. Thus the role of the presidency of the United States is in part a reflection of its past occupants and past history, in part what each present incumbent makes it.

One of the most interesting phenomena is that of the organizational entrepreneur who creates a whole set of new roles for others as well as himself to fill. Not much is really known about this process of "nucleation" of organizations—partly perhaps because it is a fairly rare phenomenon. It is not too difficult for the social scientist to study ongoing organizations, but the observer is rarely around in the crucial moment of organization formation. Of all organizations the firm is probably—after the family—the type most frequently initiated—but surprisingly little is known about the processes of initiation.

One development in the general field of theoretical systems which has had a considerable impact on behavior theory, and through this at least a potential impact on the theory of the firm, has been cybernetics [172], or the theory of control systems—sometimes described as servomechanisms. A control system is an apparatus designed to maintain some "state" of the system in the face of changes in its environment. Simple examples are the governor of an engine which maintains a steady speed, or a thermostat which maintains a steady temperature. The biological organism always has many such mechanisms in order to protect the sensitive processes of life from changes in temperature, chemical composition, etc., outside the narrow range within which these processes usually operate. The human body, for instance, operates (no doubt for reasons far back in evolutionary history) by means of physio-chemical processes which can only proceed satisfactorily within a very narrow range of temperature around $98.4°$ F., and the body therefore must have an elaborate system of devices to maintain this constancy of temperature. Similarly we can visualize a *role* as comprising, among other things, an image of a "normal" set of values of various variables descriptive of the organization. Messages received by the occupant of the role may change his image of the organization, and if the change carries the image of the value of these critical variables outside the range of tolerance, outgoing messages will be produced designed to bring the values back into the tolerable range again. Thus, suppose information is received that inventories of a certain item are above what is regarded as tolerable. Various steps may be initiated to reduced inventories: production may be cut back, sales effort expanded, prices cut, and so forth. These steps may be continued until information is received that inventories are back to tolerable amounts.

We thus visualize a firm as a "homeostatic" process, by which a certain structure of variables is maintained. At the simplest level we suppose that there is "homeostasis of the balance sheet"; on this assumption any change in balance sheet variables will evoke a counteracting behavior. If somebody buys product from the firm, this lowers its inventory and raises cash. In order to restore the previous balance sheet the firm must spend the cash to produce more product. Thus, on this theory any consumption is followed by production of the same things in the amount consumed, and total stocks of goods are always restored. This theory does not, of course, carry us very far, as we have to ask first what determines the balance sheet which is maintained, and secondly we have to account for changes in the balance sheet, both in over-all growth and in composition. The composition of the balance sheet is related to its changes and turnover—thus a balance sheet with an inventory of bustles is likely to turn over more slowly than one with an inventory of hula hoops—and hence is related to the rate of profit. We can suppose therefore either profit maximizing in the classic sense—we then choose to maintain that balance sheet which yields the highest rate of profit—or we suppose what H. A. Simon [112] calls profit "satisficing"—if there is some rate of profit which we regard as satisfactory we leave well alone, but if the rate falls below this level we change the composition of the balance sheet in the search for higher profits.

A problem of great interest is that of the relation of the "state of the market" to the information-image processes not only in the firm but in the economy as a whole. Consider for instance the problem of how changes in consumer taste are relayed to the people who make decisions to produce. With small firms, or at least many small independent producing units, many different kinds of products, and free entry, changes in consumer taste are very rapidly recorded in inventory and profit shifts. With giant firms and a restricted total line of products, changes in under-lying consumer preferences may not find easy expression, simply because there is no alternative line of products for the consumer to turn to, and dissatisfaction may build up to a point where sudden and drastic shifts in demand occur, or even riots and revolutions.[4] The problem is somewhat analogous to the difference between a responsible and a dictatorial government—the one sensitive to public approbation or dissatisfaction, and trimming its policies to quite small breezes of public

---

[4] I am indebted to P. S. Boarman for observations on this point.

opinion, so that dissatisfaction is released in small doses, and the other repressing even the news of dissatisfaction till the dictator is completely cut off from the world around him and pressure mounts to some violent explosion.

An interesting, but very difficult problem is that of the optimum degree of variety of product, or what is almost the same thing, of range of potential consumers' choice. This is not easy to measure but is clearly a meaningful concept. If there are "too few" products, not only are potential consumer satisfactions unfulfilled which could be fulfilled by the resources of the society, but there is a lack in the information system which may lead to the building up of repressed consumer dissatisfactions, sudden shifts in demand, and failure of producers to produce the "right things" even within the limited range of products. If there are "too many" products there is wasteful duplication, losses due to the production of "wrong things" which fail to find a market, and even perhaps losses due to consumer bewilderment! Somewhere, though where it is hard to say, is presumably a golden mean between these extremes. The position of this optimum may be affected by the efficacy of market research—the more direct inquiry can find out what consumers want, the less need there is for the trial and error processes of the market, and presumably fewer different kinds of product will be found at the optimum.

The problem of growth is more difficult, but even here we can suppose some "ideal" rate of growth which tends to be maintained—a slower rate is cause for alarm and increased activity designed to increase the growth rate, a faster rate produces a let-up in the pace of activity, with more golf and higher dividends to stockholders. We thus see the firm as an information-image process in which information received continually modifies the images of various role occupants, and produces a corresponding information output. Much interesting empirical work remains to be done in this area, especially in the field of the message-image relationship—we need to ask what kind of messages modify the prevailing image of the firm's situation, and what relates the image to the activity. One difficulty here is that one and the same image—for example, a surplus of inventory—may produce very diverse behavior, as we have suggested above. The question *under what circumstances* a surplus to inventory produces, say, a price cut, a sales effort, or a production cutback is very important for economics, and yet we know surprisingly little about it.

Another aspect of the theory of the firm which follows from the recognition of the firm as an organization is the political aspect of business decisions. By this I mean the view of the firm as involving an internal political process—a hierarchy of power and influence, and a process by which disputes within the organization are resolved. In the communication process it not infrequently happens that inconsistent messages—for example, diverse proposals—are received. Choice may have to be made among the views of different persons, or among competing images in the mind of a single person. Almost any decision involves a preliminary process by which a field is surveyed and various alternatives eliminated; this field is frequently represented by the views of different people within the organization, and the elimination of rejected alternatives is frequently a matter of the political process within the organization, by which the views of the more powerful elements prevail. One can even argue by analogy that decision within the individual takes place by a political process or power struggle among various aspects of the personality —the roundhead ancestor within us urging caution and probity, the cavalier urging us to live it up.

There is a wide field of research open in these political processes in firms: unfortunately it seems to be difficult to interest many political scientists in political processes outside those of government (which may not even be the most important) so perhaps a few amateurs will have to step in. In almost every aspect of the policy of a firm one can detect the pulling and hauling of various "parties" within the firm—the sales manager urging fancier products and lower prices, the production manager urging simpler products and higher prices, and so on. The hierarchical structure in the last analysis is the resolver of these conflicts—eventually an internal struggle reaches a level of the hierarchy at which a decision between competing points of view must be made. But it is naïve to suppose that hierarchical resolution of conflict is either absolute or arbitrary; if it is so the hierarchy itself tends to break down, for as Barnard has so well said, authority is granted from below, not imposed from above. Consequently, the democratic processes of compromise are necessary if an organization is to continue—that is to say, conflicts must either be resolved in a manner at least satisfactorily *enough* to all parties to persuade them to continue within the organization, or the parties who will not accept the solution must be removed from the organization and replaced by others who will accept it.

The theory of the *n*-person game has a significant, though rather abstract and formal contribution to this problem, in its theory of coalitions. Game theory, however, does not get us very far with this problem as long as we stay with the zero-sum game, in which what one person gains others must lose. Most social relations are positive-sum games in which all gain but the problem of the *sharing* of the gain arises. This leads us into a theory of bargaining, compromise, trust, threats, and so forth, as it has been developed by T. C. Schelling [144]. So far there has not been any attempt, as far as I know, to apply these concepts to the firm. This might well be a fruitful enterprise; it is clear, for instance, that prices are often set by a process of compromise among different proposals.

## THE LARGER ENVIRONMENT OF THE FIRM

As we move toward more "realistic" theories of business behavior we find ourselves increasingly aware of what might be called the "larger environment" of the firm, both external and internal. Externally the larger environment

consists of attitudes and opinions related to the firm on the part of government, other organizations, and the public at large. Internally the larger
environment consists of such factors as morale, self-confidence, and the
attitudes toward the firm of those most intimately connected with it. This
concern for the larger environment leads to "public relations" activity,
directed both toward outsiders and insiders. This has been perhaps the fastest
growing single item of business expenditures, yet it has received little attention
from the theorists. It may be distinguished roughly from selling expenditures
in that selling expenditures are designed to sell the product whereas public
relations expenditures are designed to sell the organization as such. Selling
persuades the customer that the product is a good thing: public relations
persuades various important publics that the firm itself is a good thing.
Public relations, that is, is concerned with the image of the firm in the minds
of those who might be important to it.

A somewhat related problem is that of the self-image of the managers. The
old theological problem of justification has an important psychological
counterpart: nobody can continue indefinitely in a pattern of behavior
which he cannot ultimately justify to himself. Justification, however, almost
inevitably implies some larger reference outside the immediate welfare of the
individual concerned: this larger reference is "ethics." Even in the theory of
the firm, therefore, there is no ultimate escape from ethics; the ethical
principles of the society will inevitably affect the behavior of businessmen.
Cybernetic theory demands that the businessman have some idea of a "good
performance" against which he can measure his perceived "actual performance." What is regarded as a good performance, however, depends on the
whole impact of social communications on the formation of the role. Thus,
even in the most capitalistic of societies there are limits on the quest for
profits which are imposed by the general ideals of the businessman's role, and
the "pure" profits maximizer, where he exists, pays for his profits heavily in
terms of social disapproval. The problem of defining the "ideal role", however, is a difficult one. This is the problem which lies behind much recent
concern with the "social responsibility" of the businessman. Here again,
however, it must be emphasized that the theory of socially responsible
behavior represents an extension rather than a contradiction of the "traditional" theory of the firm. Insofar, however, as we think of the businessman
as taking on a political role and reconciling the conflicting interests of
customers, labor, stockholders, government, and the larger public we are
getting into considerations which lead us a good way beyond the traditional
theory of profit maximization. Utility maximization, however, is always with
us, and it is perhaps the main concern of these extensions of theory to put
content into the otherwise purely formal propositions of utility maximization.

Here we face some of the most fundamental, and most puzzling problems in
the theory of behavior, where the old metaphysical demons of free will and
determinism lay in wait for the unwary theorist. By the constant moral

pressure which surrounds us from infancy constraints are not only imposed on behavior but on the preference or utility function itself. We start by finding a wall between us and our desires; we end by bringing our desires to our own side of the wall. We start by trying to get what we want; we end by wanting what we get. We are controlled at first by external constraints, such as the fear of punishment, and we end controlled by conscience well within the walls of our prison. What then is the constraint, and what is the maximand? In terms of linear programming, how do we identify in any particular problem what is the linear form to be maximized and what are the constraining inequalities? In more general terms do we maximize profit subject to the constraints of morality, or do we maximize virtue subject to the constraints of satisfactory profits? I am not sure that we have even got these questions to the point of clarity where empirical research can begin, and we may find a wide variety of different principles of behavior appropriate to different personalities.[5]

It may be that most of the extensions of the theory of the firm which I have outlined can be summed up in terms of the difference between the traditional "small firm" of classical theory and the "large firm" which has become so important a part of the modern economy. In the large firm, matters of organization, of politics, and of social responsibility which are present only in embryo in the small firm blossom into large and visible problems. General Motors is clearly a "political" organization both in its internal and external relations in the way that a small farming or retailing firm is not. Nevertheless, these problems are present in embryo even in the small firm, and it may be that as we study the problems of large-scale organization we will throw light even on the problem of the economic behavior of the person and the family, for every human being is in himself an organization of cells far more complex than General Motors! What we are witnessing, therefore, is not so much a revolution in the theory of the firm as a deepening and broadening, in which the broadening itself leads to a deepening, all of which we hope will lead to better understanding of the complex systems of human behavior in the framework of both small organizations and of large.

[5] I am indebted to Dr. H. S. Johnson for discussions on these points.

Chapter

2

# BASIC MATHEMATICAL CONCEPTS

*by* W. ALLEN SPIVEY

### Sets

We begin with a concept which is outwardly simple and which has an intuitive counterpart in everyday experience. This is the concept of a *set* of objects or elements. Although the mathematician in formally developing mathematical systems would prefer to consider the term "set" to be undefined, it is easy to suggest clearly both the meaning and the use of the term. A *set* is any well-defined collection of distinct objects, and it is synonymous with the terms aggregate, "batch," or class. Although this concept is quite general, we must be careful to observe two things: a set consists of distinct elements or objects, so that every element of a set is a separate object, and no two elements of a set are identical.

Sets will generally be indicated by capital letters such as $A$, $B$, $\cdots$, $T$, $X$, and elements or members of sets by lower-case letters, $a$, $b$, $c$, $\cdots$, $x$. Since we will consider objects as members of sets,[1] we define the inclusion symbol $\in$: $a \in A$ means that $a$ is an element (member) of the set $A$. We will need an exclusion symbol also, so when we write $a \notin A$ we mean that the element is not a member of the set $A$.

A set can be specified either by listing its elements between braces, as

$$B = \{1, 2, 3, 4, 5, 6, 7, 8, 9, 10\},$$

or by stating the property possessed by the elements comprising the set. For example, if we let $x$ be a symbol which can represent any element in the set $B$ above ($x$ in this case is said to be a *variable* over $B$), then we could identify the set $B$ by the following:

| $B$ | $=$ | $\{$ $x$ | $\mid$ | $x$ is an integer $1 \leq x \leq 10\}$. |
|---|---|---|---|---|
| the set | is | the set of | such | $x$ is an integer greater |
| $B$ | | all objects | that | than or equal to 1 and |
| | | $x$ | | less than or equal to 10. |

---

[1] We will always consider an element to be a member of some set; elements will not be permitted to exist without a parent set.

18

It will become evident in what follows that stating the property possessed by the elements of a set is the most meaningful way to specify a set.

The generality of the concept of set can be illustrated in several ways. For example, we are free to consider sets consisting of a finite number of elements, sets containing infinitely many elements, or even sets consisting of only one element, say the set $\{a\}$. Indeed, one-element sets are very important and they must be interpreted with care, for the set $\{a\}$ is not the same thing as the element $a$. The difference in categories here is easily illustrated. Suppose there is a Society for the Prevention of Cruelty to Economists with local chapters throughout the country, and that the chapter in your city has as its members two kind old ladies. If one of them resigns, then the chapter (set) consists of the one remaining member. However, this lady is surely different from the set (chapter) although she is the only member.

Furthermore, the elements of sets may be any definite objects whatever and they may themselves be sets (in which case we will call the set a collection of sets rather than a set of sets). We will also admit the "empty set" or the set which consists of no elements into our family sets. Although it may appear strange to admit the existence of the "null set"—as it is called—we will see that the convenience it affords in exposition is considerable and, furthermore, the concept is not as artificial as it might first appear to be. Returning to the example of the Society above, suppose now that the remaining lady were to resign from the local chapter. The chapter then becomes inactive (the set is empty), but this is not the same as having no chapter at all in the town. We will also make it part of our definition that the null set be a subset of every set, and we will indicate the null set by the symbol $\emptyset$.

### Operations with sets

Two elements are said to be equal, $x = y$, if $x$ and $y$ are the same element. Thus the word "equals" in mathematics means the same thing as "alias"; when we say that the elements $x$ and $y$ are equal we mean that these are two names for the same object. This leads to a definition for the equality of two sets: The sets $A$, $B$ are equal if they contain the same elements. Note that nothing is said about order in the definition of the equality of two sets. As long as $A$ and $B$ contain the same elements—regardless of order—they are said to be equal.

If we are given a set, it seems natural to think of subdividing the set and to consider parts of it. Parts of a set are called subsets, but we must be more specific about this definition:

The set $R$ is a subset of the set $T$ if every element of $R$ is an element of $T$.

We will indicate this by writing $R \subset T$, "$R$ is contained in $T$," or sometimes $T \supset R$, "$T$ contains the set $R$." It should be noted that the definition of subset does not necessarily mean that the set $R$ is a part of $T$ in the sense that $R$ is "smaller than" or contains fewer elements than does $T$.[2] A moment's reflection will indicate that the definition permits $R$ to be equal to $T$. If it should happen that $R$ is a subset of $T$ but that $T$ contains one or more elements not in $R$, then we say that $R$ is a *proper subset* of $T$, and we write $R \subsetneq T$.

Suppose now that we have two sets $A$ and $B$ before us.[3] Then several possible sets can be imagined. One rather obvious set is the one which would result if we combined the elements of $A$ and $B$:

The *union* of the sets $A$ and $B$, written $A \cup B$, is the set of all elements which belong either to $A$ or to $B$ or to both $A$ and $B$.

We can also use symbolism to state this definition:

$$A \cup B = \{x \mid x \in A \text{ or } x \in B\}.$$

For example, if $A = \{1, e^x, \text{dog, canary}, \bar{X}\}$, $B = \{1, \text{canary}, \bar{Y}\}$, then $A \cup B = \{1, e^x, \text{dog, canary}, \bar{X}, \bar{Y}\}$. Notice that although the element "canary" appears in both sets $A$ and $B$, it appears only once in the set $A \cup B$ (why?).

If $A$ and $B$ should have elements in common, then still other sets could be formed:

The *product* (or *intersection*) of the sets $A$ and $B$ is the set of elements which belong to both $A$ and $B$. This can be written

$$A \cap B = \{x \mid x \in A \text{ and } x \in B\}.$$

Furthermore, if $A$ and $B$ have elements in common, it is reasonable to expect that there would be occasions when we would want to consider those elements in $B$ which are not contained in $A$:

Let $A$ and $B$ be sets; then the *difference* $B - A$ is the subset of $B$ whose elements are not in $A$, or

$$B - A = \{x \mid x \in B \text{ and } x \notin A\}.$$

Finally, suppose that the elements that $A$ and $B$ have in common are such that all the elements of $B$ are contained in $A$. Then this would be a special case of the situation immediately above—a case of sufficient importance, however, to be given a special name:

Let $A$ and $B$ be sets and let $B \subset A$; then by the *complement of $B$ in $A$* we mean the set of elements in $A$ which are not in $B$, and we indicate this set by writing $\sim B$.

---

[2] However, if $A \subset B$ and $B \subset A$, then $A = B$ (why?).

[3] We will require that all sets under discussion be subsets of some given (or universal) set. This, together with the requirement mentioned earlier that an element must always be a member of some set, will assure that our work with sets will be free of paradoxes.

If a moment's reflection is given to these definitions, the great usefulness of the null set can be seen. For example, if we discover that $A \cap B = \emptyset$, we know that the sets $A$ and $B$ have no elements in common (or, as is sometimes stated, $A$ and $B$ are mutually exclusive sets). Similarly, the set $B - A$ might be empty, or we might have $\sim A = \emptyset$, where $A \subset B$, which must mean that $A = B$ (why?)[4]

These concepts can be conveniently illustrated by means of diagrams which are known as Venn diagrams.

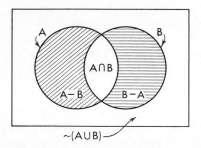
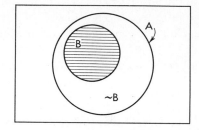

**Figure 1**

### The Number of Elements in a Set

Sometimes we can observe that two sets do not have the same number of elements without counting the elements in either set; if we arrive at a theater which is open and see a line of people waiting outside, we ordinarily conclude that the set of seats in the theater contains fewer elements than the set of individuals desiring to see the movie at that time, and in drawing this conclusion we do not know the number of elements in either set. So we determine whether two sets have the same number of elements by attempting to "pair off" elements in the two sets. If the pairing process or correspondence is complete—there are no elements "left over" in either set—we say they have the same number of elements. This pairing principle is the basis for an important concept in mathematics known as one-to-one correspondence:

The sets $S = \{a, b, c, \cdots\}$ and $T = \{x, y, z, \cdots\}$ are said to be in *one-to-one correspondence* if there is a pairing of the elements in the sets such that each element in $S$ corresponds to one and only one element in $T$ and each element in $T$ corresponds to one and only one element in $S$.

When two sets can be placed into a one-to-one correspondence, they are said to be *equivalent* (written $A \leftrightarrow B$). Unfortunately, the word "equivalent" is synonymous with the word "equal" in everyday usage, so this definition should be noted carefully. Two sets can be equivalent, of course, although

---

[4] Incidentally, it makes sense to say "the" null set rather than "a" null set, for there is only one such set. Suppose, for example, that there were two null sets, say $X$ and $Y$. By our understanding above that the null set is a subset of every set, we have $X \subset Y$ and also $Y \subset X$, which implies that $X = Y$.

their elements differ vastly; a set of fifteen elephants is equivalent to a set of fifteen football stadiums or to any other set containing fifteen elements.

The familiar operation of counting is intimately related to the concept of one-to-one correspondence. Let the set $A$ be a subset of the set of positive integers and the set $B$ be the set whose elements we desire to count. Then we count by pairing integers with elements in the set $B$ in a consecutive manner beginning with the integer 1, and the last integer paired off with a member of $B$ in this way is said to be the number of elements in $B$. We can also make use of the positive integers—or "natural numbers" as they are sometimes called— to introduce two new classes of sets: finite and infinite sets. A finite set is a set having the property that the process of counting its elements in this way can be terminated. This can be stated somewhat more carefully. Let $I$ be the set of all positive integers $\{1, 2, 3, \cdots, n, \cdots\}$ and let $I_n$ be the subset of $I$ defined by

$$I_n = \{x \mid x \in I \text{ and } 1 \leq x \leq n\}.$$

(That is, $I_n$ is that subset of $I$ consisting of the integers $1, 2, \cdots, n$.) Then a set $S$ is finite if $S \leftrightarrow I_n$. It should be noted that finite, as we have defined it, does not mean "small." The set of all electrons in the universe is a "large" set, but there is some $I_n$ which is equivalent to it.

It is a simple matter now to define an infinite set: a set is infinite if it is neither empty nor finite. Intuitively, an infinite set is a set which has so many elements that the process of counting them one by one would never come to an end. An example of a set which has no "last" element is the set $I$ of all positive integers. The natural number system, it will be recalled, has among its properties the following: if $x$ and $y$ are in $I$, then $x + y$ and $xy$ are in $I$ also. Suppose now there is an integer $x$ which is the last member in $I$. But $x + 5 \in I$; we have a contradiction—$x$ cannot be the last element in $I$.

Infinite sets have many interesting properties, besides having great importance in both pure and applied mathematics. One of the interesting features is that an infinite set can be placed into a one-to-one correspondence with a proper subset of itself.[5] Consider, for example, the set of all even integers $I_e = \{2, 4, 6, \cdots, 2n, \cdots\}$. This set is both infinite and a proper subset of $I$, yet one way of showing a one-to-one correspondence between $I$ and $I_e$ is the following:

$$
\begin{array}{ccccccc}
1 & 2 & 3 & 4 & \cdots & n & \cdots \\
\downarrow & \downarrow & \downarrow & \downarrow & & \downarrow & \\
2 & 4 & 6 & 8 & \cdots & 2n & \cdots
\end{array}
$$

A property of some sets is that although they are infinite, they cannot be placed into a one-to-one correspondence with $I$. That is, if the elements of one

---

[5] In more formal treatments of mathematics, an infinite set is defined to be a set which has this property (i.e., a set which is equivalent to a proper subset of itself). Then a finite set is defined as a set which cannot be placed into a one-to-one correspondence with a proper subset of itself.

of these sets are paired off with the elements of $I$, then all of $I$ will be exhausted and there will still be elements left in the set. An example of such a set is the set of all real numbers between 0 and 1. It can be shown that although this set is infinite, it is not equivalent to the set $I$—there are "more" real numbers in the set than integers in $I$. These two orders of infinity have led to the following definitions:

An infinite set which is equivalent to the set $I$ of all natural numbers is said to be *countably infinite*; otherwise it is said to be *uncountably infinite*.

The set of all real numbers between the numbers $x$ and $y$ $(x \neq y)$ and the set of all points in any interval on the real line are examples of uncountably infinite sets.

The reader may now have the impression that we have proliferated definitions merely for the sport of it, getting further and further away from possible applications in the process, but it turns out that these concepts are of fundamental importance to much of both pure and applied mathematics. The concept of uncountable infinity, for example, is widely used; the real number system is uncountable, as are the sets of points on straight lines and on portions of curves, and the notion is fundamental to both the continuity and differentiability of functions—concepts which lie at the heart of many applications. Indeed, countably and uncountably infinite sets have arisen out of real world demands placed upon the use of numbers, as is illustrated by the development of our number system. The operation of subtraction or "taking away from," for example, led out of the set of natural numbers to the set of all integers (positive, negative, and zero). The operation of division necessitated another extension so that numbers of the form $p/q$ could be considered, where $p$ and $q$ are integers, $q \neq 0$. The extraction of square roots brought about two more extensions of the system. The square roots of positive numbers such as $\sqrt{2}$, $\sqrt{3}$ could not be expressed as ordinary fractions; such numbers make up the set of irrational numbers (the rational and irrational numbers make up the set of all real numbers).[6] The square roots of negative numbers like $\sqrt{-2}$ make up the set of imaginary numbers (the unfortunate word imaginary is a holdover from an earlier century; an imaginary number has as firm an existence in mathematics as any other number).[7] The combined operations of addition of real numbers and extraction of the square root of

---

[6] Irrational numbers can be written as infinite decimal expansions such as $0.35291784392\cdots$. The decimal expansions of rational numbers are also infinite $(1/3 = 0.33333\cdots, \ 8/7 = 1.142857142857\cdots)$ but in each expansion the digits after a certain position repeat themselves in groups like (3) and (142857) above. It is a theorem, for example, that every periodic decimal is a rational number and conversely. It can also be shown that the irrational numbers do not have this property; no explicit formula is known for the successive digits in any irrational number.

[7] Since $\sqrt{-2} = \sqrt{2} \ \sqrt{-1}$, we can represent this imaginary number as $\sqrt{2}i$, that is, as a product of the root of a positive real number and $i$, where $i = \sqrt{-1}$. Hence any imaginary number of the form $\sqrt{-k}$ can be written as $\sqrt{k}i$.

negative real numbers yield the system of complex numbers which have the
form $a + bi$, where $a$ and $b$ are real numbers and $i = \sqrt{-1}$. The following
diagram summarizes these ideas.

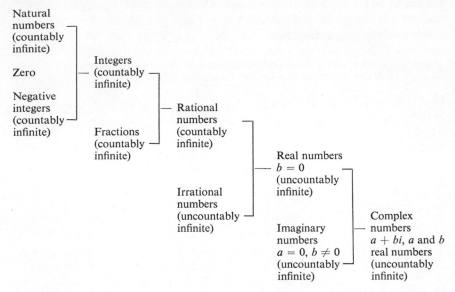

Many interesting features of infinite sets could be mentioned. There are,
for instance, higher "orders" of infinity which are dealt with in the theory of
cardinal numbers (see Breuer [25], Hausdorff [76], Kamke [89] for further
information), and there exist fascinating theorems about them (the union and
the product of two countably infinte sets are each countably infinite; the
union of countably many countably infinte sets is countably infinite; the
union of an uncountable set and a countable set is uncountable), but a
discussion of these is, unfortunately, beyond our scope (see Breuer [25],
pp. 17–54).

### Ordered Pairs and Functions

The concept of a function is used in a variety of ways in economics.
Sometimes it is used carefully, sometimes loosely, sometimes incorrectly;
occasionally an economist will use the word "function" to label loose associa-
tions between variables, thereby creating the possibility (perhaps inadvertently)
that others may think that the variables are related in a definite and more
clear-cut fashion than they really are. Not only is a careful definition of a
function indispensable to much of what is to follow, especially to the understanding of linear programming, but in view of the ambiguity created by the
variety of its uses in economics such a definition has merit in its own right.
We will consider initially some preliminary ideas. The first concept we introduce is that of a *pair* of elements. Let $A = \{a, b, c, \cdots\}$ be a set. Then a pair

from $A$ is a subset of $A$, $\{a, b\}$, consisting of two elements $a$, $b$ of $A$. Suppose that in addition to a pair from $A$ we consider an order for the elements, so that we specify which element comes first and which element is last, then the set consisting of $a$ and $b$, together with the specified order is called an *ordered pair*, and will be denoted by $(a, b)$.[8]

The ordered pairs $(a, b)$ and $(c, d)$ are said to be equal only in case $a = c$ and $b = d$. However, the pairs (sets) $\{a, b\}$ and $\{c, d\}$ are equal if either $a = c$ and $b = d$, or $a = d$ and $b = c$ (why?).

Now let $M = \{g, h, k, \cdots\}$ and $N = \{r, s, t, \cdots\}$ be sets. Then each selection of an element from $M$ and an element from $N$ can specify an ordered pair, say $(h, t)$. We will, for convenience, permit the concept of ordered pair to apply even if the two elements in the order pair are equal. In this case we have an ordered pair of the form say $(a, a)$, in which the order is of no significance. We add this understanding for when ordered pairs are formed from more than one set, the possibility that the sets may have elements in common arises quite naturally, and the selection of an element from one set and an element from the second set could yield an ordered pair of the form $(a, a)$. Such ordered pairs are quite important, as will be seen from some of the illustrations which appear below.

Let us return to the sets $M = \{g, h, k, \cdots\}$ and $N = \{r, s, t, \cdots\}$; let $x$ be a symbol which can represent any element in $M$ (i.e., $x$ is a variable over $M$) and let $y$ be a variable over $N$. Then each choice of an element $x \in M$ and $y \in N$ specifies an ordered pair $(x, y)$. Suppose we think of an ordered pair as a single object, and consider the set of *all* ordered pairs formed from the sets $M$ and $N$. This new set—each element of which is an ordered pair—is called the Cartesian product set of $M$ and $N$, or more briefly, the product set, and is denoted by $M \times N$, read "$M$ cross $N$." Using set notation, this set can be defined as

$$M \times N = \{(x, y) \mid x \in M \text{ and } y \in N\}.$$

The real plane of analytic geometry provides perhaps the most familiar example of a product set. Each point in the plane is represented by an ordered pair of real numbers $(x, y)$, and in this illustration the importance of order is easily seen, for the point $(2, 5)$ is not the same as the point $(5, 2)$. Alternatively, let $P = \{p_1, p_2, p_3\}$ and $Q = \{q_1, q_2\}$. Then $P \times Q$ is the set $\{(p_1, q_1), (p_1, q_2), (p_2, q_1), (p_2, q_2), (p_3, q_1), (p_3, q_2)\}$. (Note that the concept of ordered pair requires neither that the sets $M$ and $N$ be equivalent nor that they be different sets.)

We are now ready to define the concept of a function. Consider the equation

---

[8] The concept of ordered pair does not involve ideas outside set theory such as "to the left of," or "preceding." An ordered pair is specified by stating which two elements are members of the pair and which of them is the first element. This specification can be made clearly by indicating the set composed of two elements and then the set consisting of the first element alone:

$$\{\{a, b\}, \{a\}\}.$$

$x + y = 5$.[9] When graphed in the plane this will yield a straight line, and every point on this line (set) can be represented by an ordered pair $(x, y)$ which has the property that the sum of the entries in the ordered pair is 5.

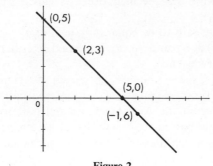

**Figure 2**

The set of ordered pairs $(x, y)$ such that $x + y = 5$ is a subset of the set of all points in the $x, y$ plane, and the set of all points in the plane is the product set $X \times Y$, where $X$ is the set of all real numbers paired off with points on the $x$-axis and $Y$ is the set of all real numbers paired off with points on the $y$-axis. Therefore the equation $x + y = 5$ directs attention to a subset of the product set— a subset, it should be noted, with the feature that a given number $x$ does not appear as the first entry of an ordered pair more than once. This example leads to the general definition of a function:

Let $S$ and $T$ be sets, and suppose that to each $x \in S$ a rule or correspondence assigns a uniquely specified element $y \in T$. Then this rule specifies a set $f$ of ordered pairs, and this set $f$ is called a function from $S$ into $T$.

A function is then a set—a set of ordered pairs—and it is a subset of the product set, $S \times T$. The rule or correspondence is the property which specifies the set, or which specifies which of those elements in $S \times T$ are to be placed in a subset called the function set.

The set $S$ is called the domain of definition of the function $f$ and the set of all elements $y \in T$ which appear as second entries of the ordered pairs in $f$ is called the *range* of the function. The symbol $y$ is called the value of the function $f$ at $x$ and is sometimes written $f(x)$. The range of the function—which is a subset of $T$—is called the set of values of the function $f$. Also if $x$ is a variable over $S$, then $x$ is called the *independent variable* of the function; if $y$ is a variable over the range of the function, then $y$ is said to be the *dependent variable*. The examples below will facilitate the understanding of the definition of a function.

Example (1) meets the requirements of the definition of a function. In this instance, the range of the function is a proper subset of $T$. Example (2) is also a function and the ordered pairs in this function set are $\{(p, a), (q, a), (r, a), (s, b)\}$. No two ordered pairs have the same first element—as is required—

---

[9] The use of an equality sign in equations differs from its use between elements and sets. In an equation such as $x + y = 5$, the equality sign indicates a conditional equality; the equation is satisfied only for those values of $x$ and $y$ whose sum is 5—not for all values of $x$ and $y$. In equations which are satisfied for *all* values of the variables, the equality sign is usually written with three bars $\equiv$ and the equation is called an *identity* for all values of the variables.

but some ordered pairs have the same second element—which is permitted. Example (3) is a more conventional representation of a function. Here the set of ordered pairs is the set $(x, y = x^2)$, $x \geq 0$. This function has a property not shared by the others: each element $y \in Y$ has a "mate" in $X$. When the range of the function is all of $Y$ we say that we have a function from $X$ onto $Y$. An onto function is then a special case of an into function: if a function is onto, then it is into, but the converse is not necessarily true, as we have seen above in Examples (1) and (2).

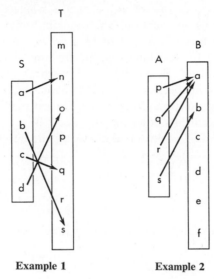

Example 1                    Example 2

It should be noted that a function is not fully defined until three specifications are made: the domain set, the set $Y$, and the rule of association. Strictly speaking, the equation $y = x^2$ does not define a function unless the domain and range sets are indicated. For example, if we let $X$ be the set of all real numbers and $Y$ be the set of all nonnegative real numbers, then the graph of $y = x^2$ is different from that in Example (3) in that the function is now defined for $x < 0$. Thus defining the domain set differently can yield a different function set even if the same pairing rule is used.

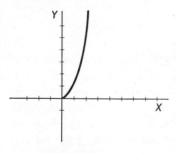

Example 3

Let $X$ be the set of all nonnegative real numbers, let $Y$ be the set of all nonnegative real numbers, and let $f$ be the set of ordered pairs $(x, y)$, where $y = f(x) = x^2$.

There are other notations for a function which emphasize the importance of the underlying sets. The function discussed immediately above can be indicated as $f : X \to Y$, where $X$ is the set of all real numbers, $Y$ is the set of all nonnegative reals, and where the values of the function are given by

$y = f(x) = x^2$. We sometimes say that $X$ is mapped into $Y$ by $f$, or that $X$ is transformed into $Y$, so that we will consider the words mapping or transformation to be synonymous with the word function. The function above, for example, can be considered to be a mapping of the real numbers (or $x$-axis) into the nonnegative real numbers (nonnegative part of the $y$-axis). Still another notation for a function is $f : (x, y)$. This has the advantage of emphasizing that the function is a set of ordered pairs, where $x \in X$ and $y \in Y$.

This definition of function or transformation is, of course, quite general. The sets $X$ and $Y$ may consist of any elements whatever, and the rule of association need not be an equation. The domain $X$ may be a collection of sets; in this case the function is said to be a *set function*. If the range of a *function* is a subset of the real numbers, the function is called a *real valued function*. Also, the pairing rule can be stated in words, indicated by a table, illustrated by a graph, or specified by a mathematical equation or formula.

A few more illustrations may help to emphasize the variety of relations which meet the requirements of a function. Let $X$ be the set of all real numbers, let $Y$ be the set of all positive real numbers, and let the pairing rule be

$$f(x) = \tfrac{1}{2} \text{ when } \quad x \leq 0,$$
$$f(x) = 1 \text{ when } 0 < x \leq 1,$$
$$f(x) = 2 \text{ when } 1 < x \leq 2,$$
$$f(x) = 3 \text{ when } 2 < x \quad .$$

Then the graph of this function (called a step function) is (Figure 3):

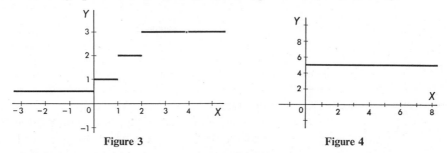

Figure 3                                     Figure 4

Alternatively, let $X$ be the set of all nonnegative real numbers, $Y$ be the set of all real numbers greater than 2, and let the rule of association be $f(x) = 5$. The graph of the function is shown in Figure 4. In this case, each element $x \in X$ is mapped into one element of $Y$, the element 5, so that the nonnegative reals are mapped into the real number 5. A function which has the property that each element in the domain is mapped into one element of the set $Y$ is called a *constant function* or, briefly, a *constant*.

It should be clear that an essential property of a function set is that no two ordered pairs in the set have the same first element (although more than one ordered pair may have the same second element). In some books on mathematics this is called a single-valued function and the concept of function is broadened to include multiple-valued functions as well, in which more than one element in the range is paired off with a given element in the domain. We will restrict the term to apply only to single-valued functions, however, and other subsets of the product set will be called *relations*. A relation, then, is merely a set of ordered pairs, and it is not required that no two ordered pairs have the same first element. As an example of a relation, consider the graph of the equation of a circle with center at the origin and radius $r$, $x^2 + y^2 = r^2$:

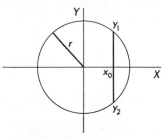

**Figure 5**

Here the element $x_0$ is paired off with two values, $y_1$, and $y_2$, so the equation $x^2 + y^2 = r^2$ does not define a function by our definition; it is an example of a relation.

### Equalities and Inequalities in Two-space

Suppose we now consider a (linear) function set in the plane (two-space) whose rule is $y = 5 - x$. Then the function set is $f = \{(x, y) \mid y = 5 - x\}$.[10] This set is sometimes called the solution set of the equation $y = 5 - x$. The points $(x, y)$ will lie on a straight line when graphed, hence the name linear function.

The straight line can be used as a basis for defining other point sets in the plane. Consider the set of points $(x, y)$ defined by

$$A = \{(x, y) \mid y < 5 - x\}$$

where for each $x$, $y$ satisfies the (strict) linear inequality $y < 5 - x$ (or, as we will write it, $x + y - 5 < 0$). The set of points specified by means of a linear inequality is called a *half space* or a solution space of the inequality. Still another half space is the set of points

$$B = \{(x, y) \mid x + y - 5 > 0\}.$$

The sets $f$, $A$, and $B$ appear below.[11]

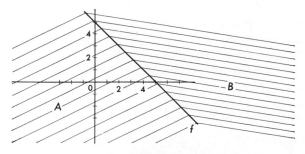

**Figure 6**

[10] Unless otherwise specified, we will understand that the domain and range sets of the functions under consideration are the maximal subsets of the set of all real numbers.

[11] Since the sets $f$, $A$, and $B$ are infinite sets, this, like all the others in this chapter, is an incomplete graph; a complete graph would extend to infinity in all directions in the plane.

Intuitively we see that a straight line separates the plane into three non-overlapping or mutually exclusive subsets whose union is the plane: the set of points below the line, on the line, and above the line. The set of points on the line is the *boundary* of the set $A$ and of the set $B$. When a set is defined so as to include its boundary, as for example,

$$C = \{(x, y) \mid x + y - 5 \leqq 0\},$$

which in this case is the half space together with points on the line, it is said to be a *closed set* (and the inequality is said to be a weak inequality). For this reason the set $C$ is called a *closed half space* as is the set

$$D = \{(x, y) \mid x + y - 5 \geqq 0\}.$$

A set which does not contain its boundary is called an *open set*, and half spaces defined by strict or strong linear inequalities (the sets $A$ and $B$ for example) are called open half spaces.[12] These concepts may be summarized as follows:

an open half space is the set of points satisfying a strong linear inequality $ax + by + c < 0$ or $ax + by + c > 0$; a closed half space is the set of points satisfying a weak inequality $ax + by + c \leqq 0$ or $ax + by + c \geqq 0$ (where $a$, $b$, $c$, are real numbers and $a$, $b$ are not both 0).[13]

Suppose we consider two linear equations whose graphs are not colinear,

(1)                                    $x + y - 5 = 0$

(2)                                    $-x + y + 2 = 0.$

Then there is an ordered pair $(x, y)$ which will simultaneously satisfy the two equations, and from the graph of these equations below it can be seen that the ordered pair is the point of intersection $(\frac{7}{2}, \frac{3}{2})$. If $f$ and $g$ are the sets of ordered pairs satisfying (1) and (2) respectively, then the set $f \cap g$ is the simultaneous solution set of the two equations, which in this case consists of only one point $(\frac{7}{2}, \frac{3}{2})$. When $f \cap g$ consists of only one point, the linear equations are *independent*. If the graphs of the two linear equations are parallel lines, then the intersection is the empty set; there is no simultaneous solution and the equations are *inconsistent*. If the graphs of two

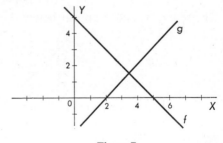

**Figure 7**

---

[12] It can be seen from the graph immediately above that the closed set $D$ is the complement of the open set $A$, and that the open set $A$ is the complement of the closed set $D$. This is a special case of a theorem (the complement of an open set is closed and conversely) which is proved in Topology, a branch of mathematics in which general properties of sets and transformations are studied.

[13] These definitions refer to a two-dimensional space; they can be generalized to spaces of higher dimension.

equations are the same straight line (the lines are colinear), then there are infinitely many solutions (the intersection has an uncountable infinity of points) and the equations are *dependent*. For an example of this case consider equation (1) and

$$10x + 10y - 50 = 0.$$

The graph of (3) is the same straight line as that of (1); this equation is merely (1) multiplied by 10. More generally, if two linear equations are dependent, then one is a constant multiple of the other.

If we are given two straight lines we can also consider the set of points which simultaneously satisfy the corresponding linear inequalities. The solution sets, like those for equalities and inequalities, are intersections of sets, but since the sets involved are half spaces, there is never a unique solution—the intersection is either uncountably infinite or empty. This is an important distinction between pairs of equalities and inequalities and it should be clearly understood. For example, consider two intersecting straight lines in the plane. The simultaneous solution of the equalities is the point of inter-section of the lines, but the simultaneous solution set of the corresponding inequalities is a wedge-shaped region in the plane which is uncountably infinite. The following are illustrations of this case.

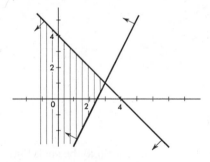
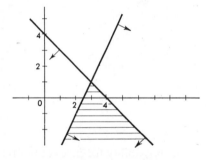

| Figure 8A | Figure 8B |
|:---:|:---:|
| Solution set for | Solution set for |
| $x + y - 4 < 0$ | $x + y - 4 < 0$ |
| $2x - y - 5 < 0$ | $2x - y - 5 > 0$ |

If, however, the straight lines are parallel (but not colinear), there are three possibilities: the inequalities have the same sense (the inequality symbols point in the same direction) and the intersection of the half spaces is a half space; the inequalities do not have the same sense and the intersection of the half spaces is an infinte "strip" in the plane; the inequalities do not have the same sense and the intersection of the half spaces is empty. Some examples may make these statements clear. Let the equations of the straight lines be $x + 2y - 6 = 0$ and $x + 2y - 10 = 0$.

Case 1: the inequalities have the same sense. Consider the inequalities

(4) $$x + 2y - 6 \leqq 0$$

(5) $$x + 2y - 10 \leqq 0.$$

The set of points simultaneously satisfying these two inequalities is the set of points satisfying the first inequality alone—it is the half space defined by (4). Hence we say that the inequality (5) is *redundant* (see Figure 9A below).

Case 2: the inequalities do not have the same sense and the intersection of the corresponding half spaces is the infinite set of points between the two straight lines. Consider $x + 2y - 6 \geqq 0$ and $x + 2y - 10 \leqq 0$. The simultaneous solution set is the strip shown in 9B below, which extends to infinity upward to the left and downward to the right.

Case 3: the inequalities do not have the same sense and the simultaneous solution set is empty. Let the inequalities be $x + 2y - 6 \leqq 0$ and $x + 2y - 10 \geqq 0$. Clearly, there are no points which simultaneously satisfy these requirements. The solution set is empty (see 9C) and the inequalities are said to be *inconsistent*.

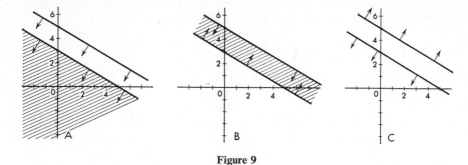

**Figure 9**

One possibility for inequalities remains. Two inequalities may be such that one is a constant multiple of the other. The reader will find it instructive to enumerate the possible outcomes for this case; they depend upon whether the inequalities are weak or strong as well as upon the sense of the inequalities (in what case would the simultaneous solution set be a straight line?).

A discussion of the simultaneous solution set of three or more inequalities is largely an extension of the preceding remarks; in every case, the simultaneous solution set is the intersection of the half spaces defined by the inequalities.

Consider

(6) $$x \geqq 0$$

(7) $$y \geqq 0$$

(8) $$x + 2y - 5 \geqq 0.$$

The intersection $M$ is shown below. This is an example of an unbounded set. A point set in the plane is said to be *bounded* if it lies inside a circle with

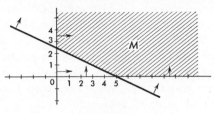

center at the origin and finite radius $k$, otherwise it is *unbounded*. Sometimes it is useful to specify the direction in which a set is unbounded. The set $M$ above is bounded on the left or from below and it is unbounded to the right or from above.

**Figure 10**

Still another set of inequalities is

(9) $$x \geqq 0$$
(10) $$y \geqq 0$$
(11) $$x + y - 5 \geqq 0$$
(12) $$x + 3y - 18 \leqq 0.$$

The intersection $N$ is both a bounded and a closed set.

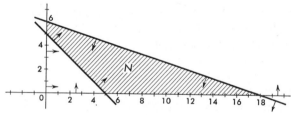

**Figure 11**

### Co-ordinate Systems

Since in our approach to linear programming in the next chapter we will be concerned with its underlying geometry, some comments on the relation between geometry and algebra will be helpful. As might be expected, the concept of one-to-one correspondence provides the link between geometry and algebra, so we will consider a sketch of the process of establishing such a correspondence for the real line and the plane.

Suppose that we have a fixed straight line and that we specify two distinct points $O$ and $U$ on the line. The point $O$ is called

the origin and the point $U$ the unit point. The point $O$ divides the line into two rays (straight lines which extend to infinity in one direction only). The ray on which $U$ lies is the positive ray, or $U$ is in a positive direction from $O$; the point $Q$ is on the negative ray, or $Q$ is in a negative direction from $O$. The line segment $OU$ is used as a unit of measurement in measuring lengths on the line; to each point $P$ on the positive ray we assign the number which measures the length of the line segment $OP$, the length being the ratio of the length of $OP$ to that of $OU$. To each point $Q$ on the negative ray we assign the negative of the number measuring the length $OQ$. This means that the origin will be assigned the number zero and that $U$ will be assigned the number 1. It can be shown that this method pairs off each point on the line with a real number and that no real number is paired off with a point more than once; when a one-to-one correspondence between the points on the line and the set of all real numbers is established by this method we say that a (one-dimensional) co-ordinate system has been introduced on the line.

A two-dimensional space can be constructed by taking any two intersecting lines, called the $x_1$-axis and $x_2$-axis, choosing a positive direction on each axis, and setting up a one-dimensional co-ordinate system on each axis by means of the chosen unit of length. Specifically, let $O$ be the point of intersection of the lines, let $U_1$ and $U_2$ be points on the $x_1$- and $x_2$-axis respectively, each different from $O$, and let $U_1$ and $U_2$ each be in a positive direction from $O$. Then a co-ordinate system can be introduced on the $x_1$-axis with $O$ as origin and $U_1$ as unit point, and on the $x_2$-axis with $O$ and $U_2$ as origin and unit point respectively. It should be clear that the intersecting lines need not be perpendicular and that the

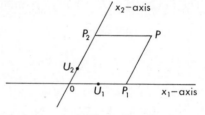

**Figure 12**

line segments $OU_1$ and $OU_2$ need not have the same length.

To each point $P$ in the two-dimensional space or plane an ordered pair of real numbers, called the co-ordinates of the point, can be assigned. Draw two line-segments through the point $P$, one parallel to the $x_1$-axis, the other parallel to the $x_2$-axis, and label the points of intersection of these line segments with the $x_1$- and $x_2$-axes $P_1$ and $P_2$ respectively. The number attached to the point $P_1$ on the $x_1$-axis is called the $x_1$-co-ordinate or *abscissa* of the point $P$, and the number attached to the point $P_2$ on the $x_2$-axis is called the $x_2$-co-ordinate or *ordinate* of $P$. These two numbers, $x_1$ and $x_2$, are then assigned to the point $P$ as its co-ordinates and the point is denoted by the symbol $(x_1, x_2)$. This method then assigns an ordered pair of real numbers to each point $P$ in the plane, and it is intuitively clear that given a point $P$, the method will lead to only one pair of real numbers $x_1$ and $x_2$. Conversely, given any two real numbers $x_1$ and $x_2$ it can be shown that there is one and only one point $P$ which has $x_1$ and $x_2$ for its first and second co-ordinates. For by the one-dimensional co-ordinate systems introduced on the straight lines which form the axes, if we are given $x_1$ and $x_2$, there will be unique points

$P_1$ and $P_2$ which have these numbers as abscissa and ordinate respectively. The line segments through $P_1$ and $P_2$ parallel to the axes will then meet in the point $P$, and the point will have $x_1$ and $x_2$ as its first and second co-ordinates, and we see intuitively that there is only one such point $P$. A one-to-one correspondence between the points in the plane and the set of all ordered pairs of real numbers can be established in this manner, and when this is done we say that a linear co-ordinate system has been introduced in the plane or two-space.

A three-dimensional space can be constructed similarly. We take any three intersecting lines which do not all lie in the same plane, called the $x_1$-, $x_2$-, $x_3$-axes, choose a positive direction on each axis, and set up a one-dimensional co-ordinate system on each axis. Then an ordered triple of real numbers is associated with a point, and it can be further shown that given any ordered triple of real numbers the method will lead to one and only one associated point. This establishes a one-to-one correspondence between points and ordered triples of real numbers, and in this way a linear co-ordinate system can be established in three-space.[14]

The association between a point and an ordered collection of real numbers suggests that we can associate a point with a collection of seven real numbers, or even more generally, with an ordered collection of $n$ real numbers where $n$ is any positive integer. Then we can define an $n$-dimensional space $R_n$ to be the set of all ordered $n$-tuples $(x_1, x_2, \cdots, x_n)$ of real numbers; each $n$-tuple is called a point in the space, and the numbers $x_1, x_2, \cdots, x_n$ are called the first, second, $\cdots$, $n$th co-ordinates of the point. Although there is no corresponding geometrical interpretation for $n \geq 4$, the usefulness of the generalization will be obvious in much of the material that is to follow.

### Distance

Suppose we consider a given one-dimensional co-ordinate system in which the distance between the origin and unit point is taken as the unit of length. Then the distance from the origin to the point paired off with the number 5 is 5 units, and since we understand that distance is a nonnegative number, the distance from the origin to the point whose co-ordinate is $-5$ is also 5 units. The distance from the origin to the point whose co-ordinate is $x$, called the absolute value of the real number $x$ and denoted by $|x|$, is the number $x$ if $x$ is positive or it is the positive number $-x$ if $x$ is negative. Also it can be shown that if $P$ and $T$ are any two points having co-ordinates $x_1$ and $y_1$ respectively, then the distance between the points is $|y_1 - x_1|$. If we recall that when we write $b = \sqrt{a}, a \geq 0$, we mean the number

---

[14] Since there is such an intimate association between a point and its corresponding numerical representation, the two can be used interchangeably without ambiguity, and we will sometimes refer to one-dimensional space as the set of all real numbers, to two-dimensional space as the set of all ordered pairs of real numbers, and to three-dimensional space as the set of all ordered triples of real numbers.

$b \geqq 0$ such that $b^2 = a$, then another way to indicate the distance $|\, y_1 - x_1 \,|$ between two points is $\sqrt{(y_1 - x_1)^2}$. We will frequently use the square root notation for the distance between two points in a one-dimensional space.

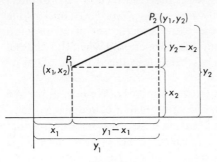

**Figure 13**

Suppose we now consider a two-dimensional space with a given rectangular co-ordinate system having the same unit length on the axes. Then the distance between two points $P_1 = (x_1, x_2)$ and $P_2 = (y_1, y_2)$ can be specified by means of the Pythagorean theorem, since the distance in this case is the hypotenuse of a right triangle. The length of the line segment $P_1 P_2$, or the distance from $P_1$ to $P_2$, is then

$$d = \sqrt{(y_1 - x_1)^2 + (y_2 - x_2)^2}.$$

This suggests the following general definition. Let $(x_1, x_2, \cdots, x_n)$ and $(y_1, y_2, \cdots, y_n)$ be points in $n$-space. Then the distance between the points is

$$d = \sqrt{(y_1 - x_1)^2 + (y_2 - x_2)^2 + \cdots + (y_n - x_n)^2}. \text{ [15]}$$

Two aspects of the general definition should be noted. When $n = 1$ and $n = 2$, our previous definitions of distance in one-dimensional and two-dimensional spaces emerge as special cases, and the definition holds only for spaces having rectangular co-ordinate systems with the same unit of length on each axis.

## Vectors

The need to give a mathematical representation to certain physical quantities such as forces and velocities—quantities having both magnitude and direction so that representation by a single number is inadequate—gave rise to the mathematical concept of a vector, and mathematical definitions relating to vectors are often motivated by physical or geometrical considerations. We define a vector in $n$-space to be an ordered pair of points in the space (i.e., an ordered pair of $n$-tuples). The first point is called the *initial* point and the second point is called the *end point*. We give a direction to a vector by specifying which is the initial point and which is the end point. The physical concept of magnitude is represented by the length of the vector. A

[15] It should be noted that this is not the only way to define distance. In more advanced books on mathematics both the co-ordinate system and the unit of length on the axes are arbitrary, and the concept of distance is generalized to that of a function having certain properties. See for example Munroe [127], pp. 24 ff.

vector in $R_n$ $(n \leq 3)$ can be represented geometrically by a directed line segment or "arrow" connecting the ordered pair of points.

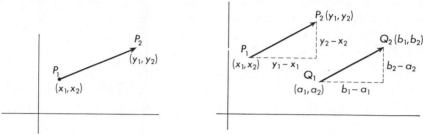

| Figure 14 | Figure 15 |

Two vectors are said to be equal if they are parallel, have the same direction and the same length. Since two vectors may be equal even if they occupy different positions in space, a vector does not have a definite position (the initial point can be chosen arbitrarily) although it has both a definite direction and length. The implications of the definition of vector equality should be clearly understood. Let $P_1$, $P_2$ and $Q_1$, $Q_2$ be equal vectors in $R_2$, and consider the right triangles formed as shown above. The lengths of the sides of the triangles, are $y_1 - x_1$, $y_2 - x_2$, $b_1 - a_1$, $b_2 - a_2$. Since the vectors are equal, the triangles have the same hypotenuse and acute angle, so they are congruent. This means that the sides are also equal,

$$y_1 - x_1 = b_1 - a_1, \; y_2 - x_2 = b_2 - a_2.$$

This leads to the general definition of the equality of vectors. Let $(x_1, x_2, \cdots, x_n)$, $(y_1, y_2, \cdots, y_n)$ and $(a_1, a_2, \cdots, a_n)$, $(b_1, b_2, \cdots, b_n)$ be two vectors in $R_n$ relative to a fixed co-ordinate system. Then the vectors are equal if $y_1 - x_1 = b_1 - a_1$, $y_2 - x_2 = b_2 - a_2$, $\cdots$, $y_n - x_n = b_n - a_n$.

Since the choice of the initial point of a vector is arbitrary, the numbers $k_i = y_i - x_i$ determine a vector up to equality. For given any initial point $(x_1, \cdots, x_n)$, the co-ordinates of the end point are $y_1 = x_1 + k_1$, $y_2 = x_2 + k_2$, $\cdots$, $y_n = x_n + k_n$. This is easily seen in $R_2$. Suppose we have a vector $(x_1, x_2)$, $(y_1, y_2)$ and that we displace this vector parallel to itself into the vector $(x_1', x_2')$, $(y_1', y_2')$. The co-ordinates of the initial and end points are changed, but the change in the $x_1$ and $x_2$ co-ordinates is exactly the same as in the $y_1$ and $y_2$ co-ordinates. Therefore the differences $y_i - x_i = k_i$ are unchanged, and the numbers $k_i$ can be used to identify either vector given the initial point.[16] Hence we are led to call the numbers $k_i$ the *components* of the vector $(x_1, x_2, \cdots, x_n)$, $(y_1, y_2, \cdots, y_n)$ in $R_n$ (or of any vector equal to it) and if we let

---

[16] The reader should satisfy himself that this is true. Draw a rectangular co-ordinate system in $R_2$ and plot the vectors $(3, 2)$, $(10, 6)$ and $(-2, 4)$, $(5, 8)$. The numbers $k_i$ are the same for the two vectors. Suppose three vectors having initial points of $(0, 5)$, $(6, -1)$, $(-3, -7)$ are equal to the vector having $(3, 2)$, $(10, 6)$ as initial and end points respectively. Then what are the end points of the three vectors?

$P_1$ and $P_2$ denote the points respectively we can write

$$P_1P_2 = [k_1, k_2, \cdots, k_n].$$

It should be noted that the vector $P_2P_1$—the vector with initial point $P_2$ and end point $P_1$—has as its components the numbers $x_1 - y_1$, $x_2 - y_2$, $\cdots$, $x_n - y_n$. Since $k_i = y_i - x_i$, we have $x_i - y_i = -k_i$, so the components of $P_2P_1$ are $-k_1, -k_2, \cdots, -k_n$, and we write

$$P_2P_1 = [-k_1, -k_2, \cdots, -k_n].$$

The length of a located vector in $n$-space is defined to be the distance between its initial and end points. Specifically, let $(x_1, x_2, \cdots, x_n)$, $(y_1, y_2, \cdots, y_n)$ be the initial and end points of a vector. Then $y_1 = x_1 + k_1$, $y_2 = x_2 + k_2$, $\cdots$, $y_n = x_n + k_n$; using our definition of distance in $n$-space, the length of the vector is therefore

$$l = \sqrt{(y_1 - x_1)^2 + (y_2 - x_2)^2 + \cdots + (y_n - x_n)^2}.$$

But since $k_i = y_i - x_i$

$$l = \sqrt{k_1^2 + k_2^2 + \cdots + k_n^2}.$$

The length of a vector is therefore determined by its components, so the choice of initial point of a vector does not affect its length. An example is provided by the lengths of the vectors $P_1P_2$ and $P_2P_1$ above. They are, of course, equal for $(-k_i^2) = k_i^2$.

We now have two kinds of ordered $n$-tuples of real numbers, the vector $[k_1, k_2, \cdots, k_n]$ and the point in $n$-space $(x_1, x_2, \cdots, x_n)$. Although the concepts are different, it is a simple matter to identify the two and to thereby eliminate the possibility of confusion. Given a point $(x_1, x_2, \cdots, x_n)$, we merely consider the vector with initial point $O = (0, 0, \cdots, 0)$ and end point $P = (x_1, x_2, \cdots, x_n)$. The components of the vector $OP$ are then $x_1 - 0$, $x_2 - 0$, $\cdots$, $x_n - 0$, or $OP = [x_1, x_2, \cdots, x_n]$. If we discard the bracket notation and agree to use parentheses to enclose the co-ordinates of vectors whose initial points are the origin, then the ordered $n$-tuple $(x_1, x_2, \cdots, x_n)$ can be considered either as a point in $n$-space or as a vector with initial point at the origin and this point as end point.[17] Also it should be clear that the words "component" and "co-ordinate" can be used synonymously without confusion for any vector with initial point at the origin, and that such a vector is uniquely determined by the co-ordinates of the end point. Furthermore, two vectors are said to be equal if their corresponding co-ordinates—relative to a given co-ordinate system—are equal. Finally, we will agree to consider the point $(0, 0, \cdots, 0)$ to be a vector; it is called the zero or null vector.[18]

---

[17] It should be noted that the length of a vector having the origin for initial point is

$$l = \sqrt{(x_1 - 0)^2 + (x_2 - 0)^2 + \cdots + (x_n - 0)^2} = \sqrt{x_1^2 + x_2^2 + \cdots x_n^2}.$$

[18] Vectors with arbitrary initial points will be called *free vectors*, and we will use the term "vector" only for those vectors with initial points at the origin. Also, the bracket notation will be retained for free vectors. Finally, a given vector with initial point other than the origin will be called a *located vector*.

Let $P$ be a point in $R_2$. We have indicated that the directed line segment $OP$ is called the geometric representation of the vector (we will usually indicate vectors by Greek letters). If the co-ordinates of $P$ are $(x_1, x_2)$, then we can say that the algebraic representation of the vector relative to a chosen co-ordinate system is the right-hand side of the expression

$$\alpha = (x_1, x_2).$$

All vectors in $R_n$, $n \le 3$, have a dual identity: algebraic and geometric, and it is useful to emphasize both, for although the algebraic representation can be generalized to spaces of higher dimension and consequently has greater analytical power, the geometric representation provides both motivation for many abstract concepts and intuitively meaningful illustrations of them.

### Operations with Vectors and the Concept of a Vector Space

The operation of addition of vectors is motivated by the parallelogram of forces in physics. Given two vectors $\alpha = (x_1, x_2)$ and $\beta = (y_1, y_2)$ in $R_2$, the sum $\alpha + \beta$ is the vector shown in Figure 16, and its algebraic representation is

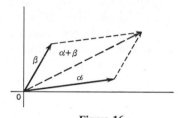

**Figure 16**

$$\alpha + \beta = (x_1 + y_1, x_2 + y_2).$$

Since vectors are added by adding their corresponding co-ordinates, and since the co-ordinates are real numbers, the properties of vector addition are derived from the properties of the operation of addition in the system of real numbers. The addition of vectors is therefore commutative and associative,

$$\alpha + \beta = \beta + \alpha,$$

$$\alpha + (\beta + \delta) = (\alpha + \beta) + \delta$$

and the set of all vectors in $R_2$ is closed under vector addition, for if $\alpha$ and $\beta$ are vectors in $R_2$, then $\alpha + \beta \in R_2$.[19]

[19] Among the postulates or axioms assumed to hold in the real number system are the following, where $a, b, c$ are real numbers:

Closure: if $a, b \in R$, then $a + b \in R$ and $ab \in R$;
Commutative laws: $a + b = b + a$, $ab = ba$;
Associative laws: $a + (b + c) = (a + b) + c$, $a(bc) = (ab)c$;
Distributive law: $a(b + c) = ab + ac$;
Zero and unity elements: $R$ contains elements $0$ and $1$ ($\ne 0$) such that $a + 0 = a$ and $1a = a$, for all $a \in R$.

Hence in showing that $\alpha + (\beta + \delta) = (\alpha + \beta) + \delta$, one shows that the vectors are equal co-ordinate by co-ordinate by going back to the properties of the underlying system of real numbers. The system of real numbers is an example of a more general algebraic system called a *field*. In more advanced treatments of vector spaces, vectors are defined over a field, meaning that the elements of the field—called *scalars*—are the basic building units of the vector space. All vectors considered here will be defined over the field of real numbers.

We have seen above that $-\alpha$ is the vector equal in length but opposite in direction to $\alpha$ (we know that if $\alpha$ is any vector in $R_2$, $-\alpha$ is in $R_2$ because the negative real numbers which are the co-ordinates of $-\alpha$ are in the real number system).

Suppose $\alpha, -\alpha$, and $\beta$ are as shown in Figure 17. If we rotate $\beta$ about zero until it coincides with $-\alpha$, then the length of $\alpha + \beta$ must approach zero. In this case $\beta = -\alpha$, and we have $\alpha + \beta = \alpha + (-\alpha) = 0$. Hence if $\alpha$ is any vector in $R_2$, then there is a vector $\beta \in R_2$ such that $\alpha + \beta = 0$. The vector $\beta$ is, of course, $-\alpha$. We also con-clude that if $\alpha$ and $\delta$ are any two vectors in

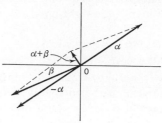

**Figure 17**

$R_2$, then the vector $\alpha + (-\delta)$ is the same as the vector $\alpha - \delta$. This means that we can define the difference $\alpha - \delta$ of two vectors in terms of the operation of addition; $\alpha - \delta$ is the vector which when added to the vector $\delta$ yields the vector $\alpha$. In the figure below, $\alpha - \delta$ is the directed line segment forming one side of a parallel-ogram which has $\delta$ for one side and $\alpha$ for a diagonal, and if $\alpha = (x_1, x_2)$ and $\delta = (y_1, y_2)$, we write $\alpha - \delta = (x_1 - y_1, x_2 - y_2)$. Note that the zero vector has the property that $\alpha + 0 = 0 + \alpha = \alpha$ for every vector $\alpha \in R_2$.[20]

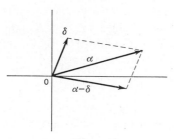

**Figure 18**

Let $k$ be a positive real number. Then by the notation $k\alpha$ we mean the vector whose direction is the same as that of $\alpha$ and whose length is $k$ times the length of $\alpha$. If $k$ is a negative real number, then by $k\alpha$ we mean $|k|(-\alpha)$ or $-(|k|\alpha)$, the vector having a direction opposite to that of $\alpha$ and length $|k|\alpha$. If $k = 0$, then $k\alpha$ is the zero vector. Now let $k$ be any real number. Then we define the vector $k\alpha$ to be a *scalar product* or *scalar multiple* of $\alpha$. The real number $k$ is called a scalar and it should be contrasted with the concept of a vector which has both length and direction. Geometrical con-siderations again lead to the algebraic representation, for it can be shown by the use of similar triangles that the co-ordinates of $k\alpha$ are the co-ordinates of $\alpha$ each multiplied by $k$,

$$k\alpha = k(x_1, x_2) = (kx_1, kx_2).$$

For example, choose $\alpha = (6, 2)$. If $k$ is any real number greater than or equal to zero, then the set of all scalar multiples $k\alpha$ "fills out" the ray or half line from the origin in the direction of $\alpha$. If $0 \leq k \leq 1$, we have all the vectors whose directions are the same as that of $\alpha$ and whose lengths vary from 0 to

[20] We use the symbol 0 to indicate both the zero vector and the scalar 0; which of these is indicated will be clear from the context.

that of $\alpha$; the scalar product in these cases fills out all points on the line segment *OP*. If $k > 1$, the scalar product fills out all points on the half line above and to the right of *P*. If $k$ varies over the set of all nonpositive real numbers, then $k\alpha$ is the ray extending from the origin in the direction opposite to that of

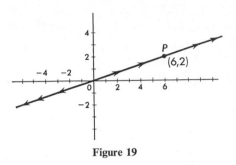

**Figure 19**

$\alpha$. Thus we see that although there is a difference between a vector and a straight line—the former being an ordered $n$-tuple and hence an element of a set whereas the latter is a set and hence is of the same category as $R_n$—there is an intimate relationship between the set of all scalar multiples of a given nonzero vector and a straight line through the origin. Indeed, this is merely a special case of the statement in plane geometry that two distinct points serve to determine a straight line, for given the origin and a nonzero vector $\alpha$, the set of all scalar multiples $k\alpha$ determines the straight line containing the origin and the end point of $\alpha$.

It is a simple matter to generalize these comments and to show by using both the operation of scalar multiplication and addition of vectors that if we are given two distinct points neither of which is the origin we can also fill out the straight line containing the points. Consider the located vector $P_1P_2$; we can call this the vector $\delta$ having $P_1$ and $P_2$ as initial and end points respectively. Then $\alpha$ is the diagonal of a parallelogram and the side opposite to $\delta$ is formed by the vector $\xi$ having the origin for initial point as shown below. Then $\delta = \xi$, and since $\beta + \xi = \alpha$, we have $\beta + \delta = \alpha$ or $\delta = \alpha - \beta$. Now let $P_3$ be a point between $P_1$ and $P_2$. Then the located vector $P_1P_3$ is

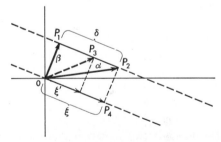

**Figure 20**

equal to the vector $\xi'$, where $\xi' = k\xi$, $0 \leq k \leq 1$. Therefore $P_1P_3 = k\xi = k\delta$. Also $OP_3$ is the diagonal of a new parallelogram, and we have $OP_3 = \beta + k\xi = \beta + k\delta$. But we have seen that $\delta = \alpha - \beta$, so we have upon substitution,

$$OP_3 = \beta + k(\alpha - \beta) = k\alpha + (1 - k)\beta, \quad 0 \leq k \leq 1.$$

Therefore we can obtain any point on the line segment $P_1P_2$ merely by a choice of $k$, where $0 \leq k \leq 1$, and for all such $k$ we fill out the line segment $P_1P_2$ (or $OP_4$). Also, if $k > 1$ we fill out the points on the line to the right of $P_2$ (or the points to the right of $P_4$ on the line segment $OP_4$) and if $k < 0$ we fill out all points on the line to the left of $P_1$. Some illustrations will make these statements clear. Let $\alpha = (8, 2)$, $\beta = (2, 6)$, and let $k = \frac{1}{4}$. Then

$$k\alpha + (1 - k)\beta = \tfrac{1}{4}(8, 2) + \tfrac{3}{4}(2, 6) = (3\tfrac{1}{2}, 5).$$

If $k = \frac{1}{2}$, then $k\alpha + (1 - k)\beta = \frac{1}{2}(8, 2) + \frac{1}{2}(2, 6) = (5, 4)$, the midpoint on the line segment $P_1 P_2$. For $k = \frac{2}{3}$, $k\alpha + (1 - k)\beta = (6, 3\frac{1}{3})$. We see both that a selection of $k$, $0 \leq k \leq 1$, divides the segment $P_1 P_2$ in the ratio $k :$ $1 - k$, and that as $k$ varies from 0 to 1, the end point of the vector $k\alpha + (1 - k)\beta$ moves from $P_1$ to $P_2$. For $k = -\frac{1}{4}$ and $k = 2$ we have respectively the points $(\frac{1}{2}, 7)$ and $(14, -2)$. To summarize: given any two distinct points $(x_1, x_2)$ and $(y_1, y_2)$, the straight line containing them is determined by the set of all sums of scalar multiples of the

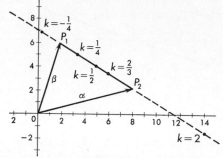

**Figure 21**

vectors $\alpha = (x_1, x_2)$, $\beta = (y_1, y_2)$ of the form $k\alpha + (1 - k)\beta$, where $k$ varies over the set of all real numbers.[21]

Other properties of the operation of scalar multiplication can be derived from those of operations in the underlying system of real numbers. If $\alpha \in R_2$ then $k\alpha \in R_2$—we have closure of $R_2$ with respect to scalar multiplication. The following can also be verified: $k(\alpha + \beta) = k\alpha + k\beta$, $(c + k)\alpha = c\alpha + k\alpha$, $(ck)\alpha = c(k\alpha)$, and $1\alpha = \alpha$.

Still another operation of considerable importance, that of *inner multiplication*, is suggested by geometry. Let $\alpha = (x_1, x_2)$ and $\beta = (y_1, y_2)$ be two vectors relative to a fixed rectangular co-ordinate system; then the *inner product* $\alpha \cdot \beta$ is defined to be

$$\alpha \cdot \beta = x_1 y_1 + x_2 y_2.$$

The inner product of two vectors is thus a number or scalar and is not a vector. It can be shown by the use of the law of cosines that if $\theta$ is the angle between two vectors, $0° \leq \theta \leq 180°$, then

$$\cos \theta = \frac{x_1 y_1 + x_2 y_2}{\sqrt{x_1^2 + x_2^2} \ \sqrt{y_1^2 + y_2^2}}.$$

The denominator of this expression is the product of the length $l_1$ of the vector $\alpha$ and the length $l_2$ of the vector $\beta$. Hence

$$\alpha \cdot \beta = x_1 y_1 + x_2 y_2 = l_1 l_2 \cos \theta;$$

---

[21] It will be seen below that these simple geometrical considerations are of fundamental importance in the geometry of convex sets.

the inner product of two vectors is the product of the length of two vectors multiplied by the cosine of the angle between them. An important feature of the inner product is that although the algebraic representations of the vectors $\alpha$ and $\beta$ depend upon the choice of co-ordinate axes, the inner product does not, for the length of a vector, we have seen, is independent of the choice of initial point, and the angle between two vectors is also independent of the co-ordinate system.[22] Note that the inner product is positive, zero, or negative according as $\theta$ is an acute angle, a right angle, or an obtuse angle respectively. We also have the inner product of a vector with itself,

$$\alpha \cdot \alpha = x_1^2 + x_2^2,$$

which is the square of the length of the vector $\alpha$. We will indicate the length or absolute value of a vector $\alpha$ by $|\alpha|$, so we have $\alpha \cdot \alpha = |\alpha|^2$. It is a simple matter to verify, using the properties of real numbers, that $\alpha \cdot \alpha \geq 0$ and that the equality holds only for the zero vector, that $\alpha \cdot \beta = \beta \cdot \alpha$, $\alpha \cdot (k\beta) = k(\alpha \cdot \beta)$, and that $\alpha \cdot (\beta + \delta) = \alpha \cdot \beta + \alpha \cdot \delta$.

We now generalize the definitions of addition of vectors and scalar multiplication to $n$-space. If $\alpha = (x_1, x_2, \cdots, x_n)$ and $\beta = (y_1, y_2, \cdots, y_n)$ are two vectors in $n$-space and if $k$ is a real number, then we define the sum of the vectors $\alpha$ and $\beta$ to be

$$\alpha + \beta = (x_1 + y_1, x_2 + y_2, \cdots, x_n + y_n),$$

and the scalar product to be

$$k\alpha = (kx_1, kx_2, \cdots, kx_n).$$

It is useful exercise to show that the following laws, which are generalizations of relationships holding in two- and three-space, hold also for vectors in $n$-space.

### ADDITION OF VECTORS

(A 1) Closure: if $\alpha$ and $\beta$ are in the space, then there is a vector $\alpha + \beta$ in the space called the sum of $\alpha$ and $\beta$.

(A 2) Commutative law: $\alpha + \beta = \beta + \alpha$.

(A 3) Associative law: $\alpha + (\beta + \delta) = (\alpha + \beta) + \delta$.

(A 4) Zero vector: there is a vector 0 in the space such that $\alpha + 0 = 0 + \alpha = \alpha$.

(A 5) Negative of a vector: for every $\alpha$, there is a vector $\beta$ such that $\alpha + \beta = \beta + \alpha = 0$. The vector $\beta$ is usually written $-\alpha$.

---

[22] This statement is true only for rectangular co-ordinate systems having the same unit of length on each axis. For arbitrary co-ordinate systems the definition of inner product must be modified.

SCALAR MULTIPLICATION

($S$ 1) If $\alpha$ is in the space and $k$ is a scalar, then $k\alpha$ is in the space.
($S$ 2) $(ck)\alpha = c(k\alpha)$.
($S$ 3) $k(\alpha + \beta) = k\alpha + k\beta$.
($S$ 4) $(c + k)\alpha = c\alpha + k\alpha$.
($S$ 5) If $\alpha$ is in the space, then $0\alpha = 0$, $1\alpha = \alpha$, $(-1)\alpha = -\alpha$.

These operations, which can be proved in $n$-space given the definitions of addition of vectors and scalar multiplication, are taken to be *axioms* for a mathematical system more general than $n$-space, that of a *vector space*. A vector space $V$ over the real numbers is defined to be a nonempty set of elements called vectors together with two operations, addition of vectors and scalar multiplication, which satisfy ($A$ 1) through ($A$ 5) and ($S$ 1) through ($S$ 5) above (where for this definition it is understood that $\alpha$, $\beta$ are any vectors in $V$ and $c$, $k$ are scalars). Then $n$-space becomes a special case of a vector space and we will henceforth denote it by $V_n$.

The concept of inner product can also be generalized to $n$-space. If $\alpha = (x_1, x_2, \cdots, x_n)$ and $\beta = (y_1, y_2, \cdots, y_n)$ are two vectors in $n$-space (where the space is assumed to have a rectangular co-ordinate system with the same unit of length on each axis), then the inner product is defined to be $x_1 y_1 + x_2 y_2 + \cdots + x_n y_n$, and the following rules, which again are generalizations of geometrical relationships in two- and three-space, can be verified in $n$-space.

INNER MULTIPLICATION

($I$ 1) $\alpha \cdot \alpha \geqq 0$ for every vector $\alpha$ and the equality is satisfied only for the zero vector,
($I$ 2) $\alpha \cdot \beta = \beta \cdot \alpha$,
($I$ 3) $\alpha \cdot (k\beta) = k(\alpha \cdot \beta)$,
($I$ 4) $\alpha \cdot (\beta + \delta) = \alpha \cdot \beta + \alpha \cdot \beta$.

If a vector space is assumed to satisfy ($I$ 1) through ($I$ 4), then it is called a Euclidean vector space, or more briefly a *Euclidean space*. It should be noted that the concept of a vector space is more general than that of a Euclidean space, for a vector space need not be a Euclidean space. When we wish to use subsequently the concept of inner product in a vector space, we will explicitly indicate that the vector space is a Euclidean space; otherwise the vector spaces considered will be the more general ones satisfying ($A$ 1) through ($A$ 5) and ($S$ 1) through ($S$ 5) only.

Returning now to a consideration of vector spaces, it can be seen that among the axioms of a vector space are those of closure under the operations of vector addition and scalar multiplication. This means that the operations do not result in a vector "outside" the space. It is a useful exercise to show that if a set of vectors over the reals is closed with respect to vector addition and scalar multiplication then it is a vector space, i.e., $(A\ 1)$–$(A\ 5)$ and $(S\ 1)$–$(S\ 5)$ are satisfied for the set of vectors. We have as a consequence the following:

Any set of vectors over the reals that is closed with respect to addition of vectors and scalar multiplication is called a vector space over the reals.

Also, by a *subspace* of $V$ we mean a subset of vectors of $V$ which is itself a vector space; or, using the result immediately above, we can say that a subset of vectors is a subspace if it is closed under vector addition and scalar multiplication. Thus three-space, which we will now call $V_3$, is a subspace of $V$, as is two-space, $V_2$ (why?).

Now let $\alpha_1$, $\alpha_2 \cdots$, $\alpha_k$ be a set of vectors in $V$. Then the *vector* $c_1\alpha_1 + c_2\alpha_2 + \cdots + c_k\alpha_k$, which results when we combine the operations of vector addition and scalar multiplication, is called a *linear combination* of the vectors $\alpha_1$, $\alpha_2$, $\cdots$, $\alpha_k$.[23] It is easy to show that the set of all linear combinations of a given set of vectors is a vector space. For suppose that $\beta_1$ and $\beta_2$ are two vectors in the set of linear combinations,

$$\beta_1 = a_1\alpha_1 + a_2\alpha_2 + \cdots + a_k\alpha_k$$

$$\beta_2 = c_1\alpha_1 + c_2\alpha_2 + \cdots + c_k\alpha_k,$$

then

$$\beta_1 + \beta_2 = (a_1 + c_1)\alpha_1 + (a_2 + c_2)\alpha_2 + \cdots + (a_k + c_k)\alpha_k$$

and

$$b\beta_1 = (ba_1)\alpha_1 + (ba_2)\alpha_2 + \cdots + (ba_k)\alpha_k,$$

are also linear combinations of the vectors $\alpha_1$, $\alpha_2$, $\cdots$, $\alpha_k$. The set (space) of all linear combinations of a given set of vectors is called the space *spanned* or *generated* by the given set of vectors, and the set of vectors is called a *spanning set* for the space.

If the vectors $\alpha_1$, $\alpha_2$, $\cdots$, $\alpha_r$ satisfy an equation of the form

(1) $$c_1\alpha_1 + c_2\alpha_2 + \cdots + c_r\alpha_r = 0,$$

and the scalars $c_i$ are not all zero, then the set of vectors $\alpha_1$, $\cdots$, $\alpha_r$ is said to be *linearly dependent* (we sometimes say also that the vectors in the set are linearly dependent).[24] The equation (1) is, of course, satisfied for any set of $r$ vectors when $c_1 = c_2 = \cdots = c_r = 0$; if the set of vectors has the property that (1) is satisfied *only* for $c_i = 0$, $i = 1, \cdots, r$, then the set of vectors is said

---

[23] Although addition has been defined only for pairs of vectors, it is a consequence of the generalized associative law of addition of real numbers that the sum of $c_1\alpha_1 + c_2\alpha_2 + \cdots + c_k\alpha_k$ is unambiguous.

[24] We also say that a vector $\beta$ is dependent on the nonempty set of vectors $S$ if there are vectors $\alpha_1, \cdots, \alpha_k$ in $S$ such that

$$\beta = a_1\alpha_1 + \cdots + a_k\alpha_k,$$

and that the set $T$ is dependent on $S$ if every vector in $T$ is dependent on $S$.

to be *linearly independent*, and we sometimes say the vectors themselves are linearly independent.

EXAMPLES. The vectors $\alpha_1 = (2, 1, 0)$, $\alpha_2 = (0, 1, 1)$, $\alpha_3 = (4, 5, 3)$ are linearly dependent since $2\alpha_1 + 3\alpha_2 - \alpha_3 = 0$. The vectors $\beta_1 = (1, 0, 0)$, $\beta_2 = (0, 12, 0)$, and $\beta_3 = (0, 0, 72)$ are linearly independent, for consider the vector equation $c_1\beta_1 + c_2\beta_2 + c_3\beta_3 = 0$. Then $c_1 (1, 0, 0) + c_2 (0, 12, 0) + c_3 (0, 0, 72) = (c_1, 12c_2, 72c_3)$, which is the zero vector only in case $c_1 = c_2 = c_3 = 0$.

The general definition of the basis and dimension of a vector space also coincide with intuitive notions suggested by two-space:

Let $V$ be a vector space containing the vectors $\alpha_1, \alpha_2, \cdots, \alpha_k$. Then the set of vectors $\alpha_1, \cdots, \alpha_k$ is a *basis* (essentially a co-ordinate system) for $V$ if and only if

1. the vectors $\alpha_i$ span $V$,
2. the vectors $\alpha_i$ are linearly independent.

Thus a basis for a space is an "economical" or "smallest" spanning set for the space. The *dimension* of a vector space is the maximal number of linearly independent vectors contained in the space.

It is instructive to reconsider the discussion on co-ordinate systems above in the light of the definitions of basis and dimension. The selection of unit lengths and the construction of co-ordinate systems in one-, two-, and three-dimensional space can be thought of as the process of selecting a *basis* for the space and then forming the set of all linear combinations of the basis vectors, getting as a consequence the given space. For example, consider the two-dimensional space, $V_2$. We began earlier by selecting two axes which were not colinear, and then we indicated that a one-to-one correspondence between points and ordered pairs of real numbers could be established. An equivalent procedure is the following. Suppose we select two linearly independent vectors in $V_2$, say $\alpha_1 = (1, 0)$ and $\alpha_2 = (0, 1)$. Then $V_2$ is the set of all linear combinations $c_1\alpha_1 + c_2\alpha_2$ of these basis vectors. For let $(x_1, x_2)$ be any point or vector in the space. Then $x_1\alpha_1 + x_2\alpha_2 = x_1(1, 0) + x_2(0, 1) = (x_1, x_2)$ and the vector is expressed in terms of $\alpha_1$ and $\alpha_2$. In particular, we obtain the $x_1$-axis by letting $x_2 = 0$ and $x_1$ vary over $R$, the set of all real numbers, and the $x_2$-axis by letting $x_1 = 0$ and $x_2$ vary over $R$. Points or vectors not on the axes are obtained, of course, by letting $x_1$ and $x_2$ vary over the nonzero real numbers. We again see that the basis vectors need not be perpendicular; any two linearly independent vectors in $V_2$ will span the space.

Intuitively we expect that the dimension of two-space should be two, and the general definition states that the dimension is two if that is the maximal number of linearly independent vectors in the space. Obviously one vector will not span $V_2$. Consider the three vectors $\alpha_1$, $\alpha_2$ (as defined above), and $\alpha_3 = (x_1, x_2)$, where $\alpha_3$ is any nonzero vector in $V_2$. Then

$$(2) \qquad\qquad x_1\alpha_1 + x_2\alpha_2 - \alpha_3 = 0,$$

and since the coefficients of the vectors are nonzero, $\{\alpha_1, \alpha_2, \alpha_3\}$ is linearly dependent (note also that if (2) is solved for $\alpha_3$, we will have $\alpha_3$ expressed as a linear combination of the basis vectors $\alpha_1$ and $\alpha_2$). Another way of stating this is to say that the vector $\alpha_3$ adds nothing to the spanning power of $\alpha_1$ and $\alpha_2$. The concept of dependence is essentially that of redundance; a vector is dependent on a set of vectors if it lies in the space spanned by the given set of vectors.

We have shown that the three vectors $\alpha_1$, $\alpha_2$, and $\alpha_3$ in $V_2$ are dependent, but how do we know that *any* set of three, four, five, $\cdots$, $n$ vectors in $V_2$ will also be linearly dependent (or to put it another way, that two is the maximum number of linearly independent vectors in $V_2$)? The following are two theorems in linear algebra which are relevant to our discussion (the latter is a general statement which was illustrated above):

Any set of $k$ vectors in $V_n$ is linearly dependent if $k > n$.

If $\{\alpha_1, \cdots, \alpha_k\}$ is a linearly dependent set, then at least one vector in the set is a linear combination of the remaining vectors and conversely.[25]

Similar comments hold for three-space, $V_3$. The dimension is three, and a basis can be taken to be any three linearly independent vectors (any three vectors which do not all lie in the same plane). Suppose we choose the unit vectors as our basis, $\alpha_1 = (1, 0, 0)$, $\alpha_3 = (0, 1, 0)$, and $\alpha_3 = (0, 0, 1)$. Then $V_3$ is the set of all linear combinations of the form

$$x_1\alpha_1 + x_2\alpha_2 + x_3\alpha_3 = (x_1, x_2, x_3).$$

An interesting (and powerful) feature of a basis of a space is that not only is every vector in the space expressible in terms of the basis vectors, but that the representation is unique—a given vector can be expressed in one and only one way in terms of a given basis (the reader should try to prove this). However, it should be clear from our comments that a basis is *not* unique; it is a theorem that if $V$ is a vector space of finite dimension $n$, then any set of $n$ linearly independent vectors is a basis for $V$. The arbitrariness in the selection of a basis for a space should be contrasted with the uniqueness of representation of a vector in the space once a given basis has been chosen.

### Dependence and Nontrivial Solutions
### to Homogeneous Linear Equation Systems

We have seen in a preceding example that the vectors $\beta_1 = (1, 0, 0)$, $\beta_2 = (0, 12, 0)$, $\beta_3 = (0, 0, 73)$ are linearly independent (i.e., that $c_1\beta_1$

---

[25] The reader should be able to prove the second of these. For a discussion of the first theorem, see Murdoch [128], pp. 13–19, Schreier and Sperner [145], pp. 19–27.

$+ c_2\beta_2 + c_3\beta_3 = 0$ is satisfied only for $c_1 = c_2 = c_3 = 0$). Suppose we write the vectors as column vectors rather than as row vectors,

$$\beta_1 = \begin{pmatrix} 1 \\ 0 \\ 0 \end{pmatrix}, \beta_2 = \begin{pmatrix} 0 \\ 12 \\ 0 \end{pmatrix}, \beta_3 = \begin{pmatrix} 0 \\ 0 \\ 73 \end{pmatrix}.$$

Then the vector equation

(1) $$c_1\beta_1 + c_2\beta_2 + c_3\beta_3 = 0$$

can be written as

(2) $$c_1 \begin{pmatrix} 1 \\ 0 \\ 0 \end{pmatrix} + c_2 \begin{pmatrix} 0 \\ 12 \\ 0 \end{pmatrix} + c_3 \begin{pmatrix} 0 \\ 0 \\ 73 \end{pmatrix} = \begin{pmatrix} 0 \\ 0 \\ 0 \end{pmatrix},$$

or as

(3) $$\begin{pmatrix} c_1 \\ 0 \\ 0 \end{pmatrix} + \begin{pmatrix} 0 \\ 12c_2 \\ 0 \end{pmatrix} + \begin{pmatrix} 0 \\ 0 \\ 73c_3 \end{pmatrix} = \begin{pmatrix} 0 \\ 0 \\ 0 \end{pmatrix}.$$

Since vectors are added component by component, (1) or (3) is equivalent to the system of scalar equations

$$c_1 + \quad 0 \quad + \quad 0 \quad = 0$$
$$0 + 12c_2 + \quad 0 \quad = 0$$
$$0 + \quad 0 \quad + 73c_3 = 0.$$

Now let us consider a more general situation. We have the vector equation

(4) $$x_1\alpha_1 + x_2\alpha_2 + \cdots + x_r\alpha_r = 0,$$

where the $\alpha_i$ are column vectors denoted

$$\alpha_1 = \begin{pmatrix} a_{11} \\ a_{21} \\ \cdot \\ \cdot \\ \cdot \\ a_{k1} \end{pmatrix}, \quad \cdots \quad, \alpha_r = \begin{pmatrix} a_{1r} \\ a_{2r} \\ \cdot \\ \cdot \\ \cdot \\ a_{kr} \end{pmatrix}.$$

Then (4) can be written

(5) $$x_1 \begin{pmatrix} a_{11} \\ a_{21} \\ \cdot \\ \cdot \\ \cdot \\ a_{k1} \end{pmatrix} + x_2 \begin{pmatrix} a_{12} \\ a_{22} \\ \cdot \\ \cdot \\ \cdot \\ a_{k2} \end{pmatrix} + \cdots + x_r \begin{pmatrix} a_{1r} \\ a_{2r} \\ \cdot \\ \cdot \\ \cdot \\ a_{kr} \end{pmatrix} = \begin{pmatrix} 0 \\ 0 \\ \cdot \\ \cdot \\ \cdot \\ 0 \end{pmatrix}.$$

Using scalar multiplication this becomes

$$(6) \quad \begin{pmatrix} a_{11}x_1 \\ a_{21}x_1 \\ \cdot \\ \cdot \\ \cdot \\ a_{k1}x_1 \end{pmatrix} + \begin{pmatrix} a_{12}x_2 \\ a_{22}x_2 \\ \cdot \\ \cdot \\ \cdot \\ a_{k2}x_2 \end{pmatrix} + \cdots + \begin{pmatrix} a_{1r}x_r \\ a_{2r}x_r \\ \cdot \\ \cdot \\ \cdot \\ a_{kr}x_r \end{pmatrix} = \begin{pmatrix} 0 \\ 0 \\ \cdot \\ \cdot \\ \cdot \\ 0 \end{pmatrix}.$$

If the vector which is sum of the vectors on the left of the equality sign is to be the zero vector, each component in the sum of the vectors must be zero, so (6) is equivalent to the system of $k$ scalar equations in $r$ unknowns,

$$a_{11}x_1 + a_{12}x_2 + \cdots + a_{1r}x_r = 0$$

$$(7) \qquad a_{21}x_1 + a_{22}x_2 + \cdots + a_{2r}x_r = 0$$

$$\cdots \cdots \cdots \cdots \cdots \cdots$$

$$a_{k1}x_1 + a_{k2}x_2 + \cdots + a_{kr}x_r = 0.$$

Such a system of equations, where the $a_{ij}$ are known constants, is called a homogeneous system of linear equations. Also if $x_1 = c_1$, $x_2 = c_2$, $\cdots$, $x_r = c_r$ is a solution to system (7), then the vector $(c_1, c_2, \cdots, c_r)$ is called a *solution vector* to (7). If $c_i = 0$, $i = 1, \cdots, r$, is the only solution to (7), the solution vector in this case is called a trivial solution and (7) is said to be trivially satisfied. If some $c_i$ is nonzero in the solution vector, then (7) is said to have a nontrivial solution.

The intimate relationship between the existence of nontrivial solutions to (7) and linear dependence of the set of vectors $\alpha_1, \cdots, \alpha_r$ can now be made clear. If there are nontrivial solutions to (7) then the vector equation (4), $x_1\alpha_1 + \cdots + x_r\alpha_r = 0$, is satisfied for some $x_i$ not all zero. This means that the vectors $\alpha_1, \cdots, \alpha_r$ are linearly dependent, and the converse is also true: if the vectors $\alpha_1, \cdots, \alpha_r$ are dependent, then the corresponding equation system (7) must have a nontrivial solution. On the other hand, if (7) has only the trivial solution, then (4) is satisfied only for coefficients all zero; the vectors $\alpha_1, \cdots, \alpha_r$ are in this case linearly independent (the converse of this is also true, of course). It is a theorem that any set of $k$ homogeneous linear equations in $r$ unknowns has nontrivial solutions if $k < r$, i.e., if there are fewer equations than unknowns (see Murdoch [128], pp. 13–16).

Another important feature of the system (7) is that the set of all solution vectors forms a vector space. The proof of this theorem is both simple and instructuve, so we will now consider it. First we observe that the set of solution vectors is not empty, for (7) always has at least one solution, $x_1 = x_2 = \cdots = x_r = 0$.

Now let $\alpha = (x_1, \cdots, x_r)$ be a solution vector; then

$$k\alpha = (kx_1, \cdots, kx_r)$$

is a solution since

$$(kx_1)\alpha_1 + (kx_2)\alpha_2 + \cdots + (kx_r)\alpha_r = 0$$

is satisfied. Also if $\beta = (y_1, \cdots, y_r)$ is another solution vector, then

(8)                                        $y_1\alpha_1 + \cdots + y_r\alpha_r = 0.$

The sum of (8) and (4) satisfies

(9)                              $(x_1 + y_1)\alpha_1 + \cdots + (x_r + y_r)\alpha_r = 0,$

and is therefore a solution. This shows that the set of solution vectors is closed under scalar multiplication and vector addition and it is therefore a vector space.

### Convexity

We have seen that the set of all linear combinations of the form $k_1\alpha_1 + k_2\alpha_2$ of two linearly independent vectors in $V_2$ fills out the two-dimensional space. The coefficients in these combinations, of course, can be any real numbers, positive, negative, or zero. Suppose we consider the combinations having nonnegative coefficients only, the combinations $k_1\alpha_1 + k_2\alpha_2$, $k_1$, $k_2 \geqq 0$; then the subset spanned by these vectors is a set of points called a *cone*. For example, let $\alpha_1 = (8, 2)$, $\alpha_2 = (2, 6)$. If $k_1 = 0$ and $k_2$ varies over the set of all nonnegative real numbers, we get the ray from the origin through the point $(2, 6)$ part of which is indicated by a line segment in the figure. If $k_1$ varies over the nonnegative real numbers and $k_2 = 0$, we fill out the ray from the origin through the end point of the vector $\alpha_1$. For all other permissible values of $k_1$ and $k_2$ the vectors will lie in the cone bounded by the two rays. For additional examples, suppose we have the set of vectors consisting of $\alpha_1$ and $\alpha_2$ as above and $\alpha_3 = (5, -4)$.

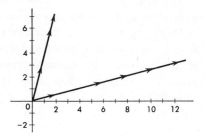

**Figure 22**

Then the set of all nonnegative linear combinations of these vectors also forms a cone as is shown in graph A, Figure 23 (note that the vectors in this case are linearly dependent; the cone spanned by the three vectors is the same as that spanned by the vectors $\alpha_1$ and $\alpha_3$). Alternatively, suppose the vectors are the unit vectors, $\beta_1 = (1, 0)$, $\beta_2 = (0, 1)$. The cone in this case is the first quadrant (graph B, Figure 23).

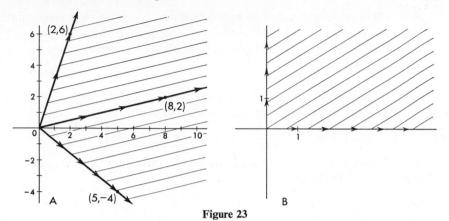

**Figure 23**

Suppose that in addition to being nonnegative, we further restrict the coefficients in the linear combinations by requiring that they sum to 1, i.e., if $\alpha_1$, and $\alpha_2$ are as defined above, we have

$$k_1\alpha_1 + k_2\alpha_2 \qquad k_1, k_2 \geqq 0, \qquad k_1 + k_2 = 1.$$

Since if $k_1 + k_2 = 1$, $k_2 = 1 - k_1$, this can be written as

$$k_1\alpha_1 + (1 - k_1)\alpha_2 \qquad 0 \leqq k_1 \leqq 1.$$

This is called a *convex linear combination,* and the set of all convex combinations of the vectors $\alpha_1$ and $\alpha_2$ is the straight-line segment containing the end points of the vectors shown below (graph A). If $\beta_1 = (5, 2)$, $\beta_2 = (2, 3)$, $\beta_3 = (4, 5)$, then the set of all convex combinations $k_1\beta_1 + k_2\beta_2 + k_3\beta_3$ of these vectors is the triangle shown in graph B. If $k_3 = 0$, then the convex combinations of the form $k_1\beta_1 + k_2\beta_2$ fill out the line segment containing the points $(2, 3)$ and $(5, 2)$; if $k_2 = 0$, the convex combinations of $k_1\beta_1$ and $k_3\beta_3$ fill out the side of the triangle containing the end points of $\beta_1$ and $\beta_3$; and if $k_1 = 0$, the convex combinations $k_2\beta_2 + k_3\beta_3$ fill out the side of the triangle. Points in the interior of the triangle are obtained by letting the permissible $k_i$, $i = 1, 2, 3$, assume nonzero values.

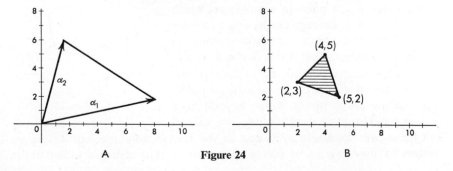

**Figure 24**

Since nonnegative and convex combinations of vectors are very important in linear programming and since much of the remainder of this chapter will be concerned with them, we will need the generalized concepts suggested by the geometrical considerations above.

Let $\alpha_1, \cdots, \alpha_r$ be a set of vectors, and let $k_1, \cdots, k_r$ be scalars. Then a *nonnegative linear combination* of these vectors is the vector

$$k_1\alpha_1 + k_2\alpha_2 + \cdots + k_r\alpha_r, \qquad k_i \geqq 0, i = 1, \cdots, r.$$

Also, a *convex linear combination* (or briefly, a convex combination) of these vectors is the vector

$$k_1\alpha_1 + \cdots + k_r\alpha_r,$$

where $k_i \geqq 0$, $i = 1, \cdots, r$, and $k_1 + k_2 + \cdots + k_r = 1$.

It can be shown that any point on the line segment joining two points in $V_n$ is a convex combination of the points (vectors) and that if any point can be expressed as a convex combination of two points in $V_n$ then it lies on the line segment connecting the two points (the proof of this is suggested by the geometrical discussion appearing above on pages 41 and 42). These results enable us to give a precise statement of the geometrical notion of a *convex set*. Geometrically, a set is convex if, given any two points in the set, the straight line joining the points lies entirely within the set. More precisely:

A set $S$ is *convex* if $\alpha$ and $\beta$ are vectors (points) in $S$, then $k\alpha + (1 - k)\beta \in S$ for every $k$ such that $0 \leqq k \leqq 1$.

Examples of convex sets are the set of all points on the circumference and in the interior of a circle, of a square, of a triangle; the entire space; the set of all points on a line segment. The set of all points on the circumference of a circle is not a convex set, nor is the set of three points which are the vertices of a triangle.

Suppose we consider a given convex set in the plane. The points which comprise the corners of the set are called *extreme points*, i.e., a point in a convex set which does not lie on a line segment joining two *other* points in the set is said to be an extreme point (or a point is an extreme point if it is not a convex combination of two other points in the set). The set of points consisting of the six extreme points alone in the graph above is not, of course, a convex set. However, we know that we can fill out the convex set above by taking all the convex combinations of the six vectors having the extreme points as end points. The convex set filled out in

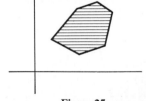

**Figure 25**

this way has a special name; it is called the *convex hull* of the given set of points:

Let *A* be a set of points. Then the set of all convex combinations of the points of *A* is called the *convex hull* of the set *A*.

The convex hull of any two points in $V_n$ is the line segment joining the points, the convex hull of any three distinct points in the plane is a triangle, and the convex hull of the set of points on the circumference of a circle is the solid disk having the circumference as the boundary (note that each point on the circumference of the circle is an extreme point of the convex set). The convex hull of a given set can also be defined as the smallest convex set containing the given set (why?).

The convex set in the diagram above is an example of a *convex polyhedron*, a set which is defined as follows: if *M* is a finite set of points, then the set of all convex linear combinations of the points of *M* is called a *convex polyhedron* (or, to put it another way, a convex polyhedron is the convex hull of a finite set of points).

We can now also define the concept of a cone carefully. A set of vectors *T* is called a cone if, for every vector $\alpha \in T$ the vector $k\alpha \in T$ for all $k \geq 0$. Thus the sets in Figure 23(A) and (B) above are cones as is the entire space. It should be noted that a cone contains the origin since *k* can be equal to zero.

A cone which is also a convex set is called a convex cone (the cones in Figure 23 (A) and (B) are convex cones); a convex cone can also be defined as the set of all nonnegative linear combinations of a finite set of vectors.

It is a theorem that the intersection of any collection of convex sets is a convex set, although the union of two convex sets is not necessarily convex as the following example shows.[26] It can also be shown that a half space is a convex set.[27]

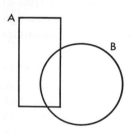

**Figure 26**
The sets A, B are convex;
A ∪ B is not convex.

This, together with the theorem on the convexity of the intersection of convex sets, assures us that the intersection of any number of half spaces is a convex set. This means that the simultaneous solution set of a system of linear inequalities is a convex set—a result which is of fundamental significance in linear programming.

---

[26] We prove this for two convex sets *S* and *T*. If $S \cap T$ is the null set or a set containing one element then it is convex (in these cases, the mathematician would say that the definition of convexity is satisfied "vacuously"). Suppose $S \cap T$ contains at least two points $\alpha$ and $\beta$. By definition of set intersection this implies that $\alpha, \beta \in S$ and $\alpha, \beta \in T$. If $\alpha, \beta \in S$, then $k\alpha + (1 - k) \beta \in S$, $0 \leq k \leq 1$, since *S* is convex. Also, if $\alpha, \beta \in T$, then $k\alpha + (1 - k) \beta \in T$, for *T* is convex. This implies that $k\alpha + (1 - k) \beta \in (S \cap T)$. We have shown that $\alpha, \beta \in (S \cap T)$ and $k\alpha + (1 - k) \beta \in (S \cap T)$, $0 \leq k \leq 1$, so $S \cap T$ is a convex set.

[27] The proof of this theorem forms a good exercise.

Turning now to matrix algebra, we define a matrix to be a rectangular array of real numbers of the form

$$A = \begin{pmatrix} a_{11} & a_{12} & \cdots & a_{1n} \\ a_{21} & a_{22} & \cdots & a_{2n} \\ \cdots\cdots\cdots\cdots \\ a_{m1} & a_{m2} & \cdots & a_{mn} \end{pmatrix}.$$

The matrix $A$ has $m$ rows and $n$ columns (where $m$ and $n$ are positive integers) and for this reason the matrix is said to be of order $m$ by $n$. The numbers $a_{ij}$ which appear in the array are called elements of the matrix, and the elements $a_{11}, a_{22}, \cdots, a_{mn}$ are its principal diagonal elements. If the number of rows and columns is clear from the context, a matrix can be written in abbreviated form $(a_{ij})$, the $a_{ij}$ indicating the element in the $i^{\text{th}}$ row and $j^{\text{th}}$ column of the matrix $A$.

Since a rectangle can be square, "thin," or "flat," the definition includes square matrices $(m = n)$, matrices having one row and $n$ columns (1 by $n$ matrices),

(5) $$(a_{11} \ a_{12} \ \cdots \ a_{1n}),$$

and matrices having $m$ rows and one column ($m$ by 1 matrices),

(6) $$\begin{pmatrix} a_{11} \\ a_{21} \\ \cdot \\ \cdot \\ \cdot \\ a_{m1} \end{pmatrix}.$$

Matrices of the form (5) and (6) are called row and column vectors respectively, and the rows and columns of the matrix $A$ above are also referred to as row and column vectors. Since we can have $m = n = 1$, there is also a 1 by 1 matrix which is merely a real number or scalar.

The definition of equality of matrices is analogous to that of equality for vectors: the matrices $A$ and $B$ are said to be equal if they have the same order and each element of $A$ is equal to the corresponding element of $B$.

If $A$ is an $m$ by $n$ matrix, then the $n$ by $m$ matrix obtained from $A$ by making the rows into columns and the columns into rows is called the *transpose* of $A$ and is denoted by $A^T$. For example, if

$$A = \begin{pmatrix} a_{11} & a_{12} & a_{13} & a_{14} \\ a_{21} & a_{22} & a_{23} & a_{24} \\ a_{31} & a_{32} & a_{33} & a_{34} \end{pmatrix},$$

then

$$A^T = \begin{pmatrix} a_{11} & a_{21} & a_{31} \\ a_{12} & a_{22} & a_{32} \\ a_{13} & a_{23} & a_{33} \\ a_{14} & a_{24} & a_{34} \end{pmatrix}.$$

Note also that the transpose of a row vector is a column vector and that the transpose of a column vector is a row vector.

We defined earlier three operations on vectors: addition (and consequently subtraction), scalar multiplication, and inner multiplication. Since row and column vectors are matrices, we wish now to define corresponding operations on matrices in such a way that the operations on vectors will still hold.

Vectors having the same number of components are added by summing their corresponding components, so we define matrix addition as follows. Let $A = (a_{ij})$ and $B = (b_{ij})$ be matrices of order $m$ by $n$. Then the *sum* $A + B$ is the matrix $(a_{ij} + b_{ij})$ obtained by adding corresponding elements of $A$ and $B$. It should be observed that addition is defined only for matrices having the same order. The operation of multiplication of a vector by a scalar leads to the definition of the product of a scalar $k$ and the matrix $A = (a_{ij})$: $kA$ is defined to be the matrix obtained from $A$ by multiplying each element of the matrix $A$ by the scalar $k$,

$$kA = \begin{pmatrix} ka_{11} & ka_{12} \cdots ka_{1n} \\ ka_{21} & ka_{22} \cdots ka_{2n} \\ \cdots\cdots\cdots\cdots \\ ka_{m1} & ka_{m2}\cdots ka_{mn} \end{pmatrix}.$$

The operation of matrix multiplication is slightly more complicated but it is based upon the operation of "multiplication" of vectors. Vectors are "multiplied" by forming their inner product, so we will make use of this operation in defining matrix multiplication. For a particular example of matrix multiplication, let $A$ be a 2 by 3 matrix and $B$ be a 3 by 2 matrix. Then the product matrix $AB$ is the matrix

$$AB = \begin{pmatrix} a_{11} & a_{12} & a_{13} \\ a_{21} & a_{22} & a_{23} \end{pmatrix} \begin{pmatrix} b_{11} & b_{12} \\ b_{21} & b_{22} \\ b_{31} & b_{32} \end{pmatrix}$$

$$= \begin{pmatrix} a_{11}b_{11} + a_{12}b_{21} + a_{13}b_{31} & a_{11}b_{12} + a_{12}b_{22} + a_{13}b_{32} \\ a_{21}b_{11} + a_{22}b_{21} + a_{23}b_{31} & a_{21}b_{12} + a_{22}b_{22} + a_{23}b_{32} \end{pmatrix}.$$

The product matrix is of order 2 by 2, and each element in $AB$ is the *inner product* of one of the rows of $A$ with one of the columns of $B$. If $AB$ is denoted by $(c_{ij})$, then the element in the first row and column of $AB$, $c_{11}$, is the *number* $a_{11}b_{11} + a_{12}b_{21} + a_{13}b_{31}$, which is the inner product of the first row of $A$ and the first column of $B$. The element in the first row and second column of the matrix $AB$, $c_{12}$, is the number $a_{11}b_{12} + a_{12}b_{22} + a_{13}b_{32}$, or the inner product of the first row of $A$ and the second column of $B$. In other words, the element in the $i^{th}$ row and $j^{th}$ column of $AB$ is the inner product of the $i^{th}$ row of $A$ and the $j^{th}$ column of $B$ (the reader should check this for each element of the matrix $AB$).

These observations are all we need to give a general definition of matrix multiplication. Let $A = (a_{ij})$ be an $m$ by $n$ matrix, and let $B = (b_{ij})$ be an $n$ by

$q$ matrix. Then the matrix $AB$ (in the given order) is the matrix $(c_{ij})$ of order $m$ by $q$ whose elements are

$$c_{ij} = (a_{i1}\ a_{i2} \cdots a_{in}) \begin{pmatrix} b_{1j} \\ b_{2j} \\ \cdot \\ \cdot \\ \cdot \\ b_{nj} \end{pmatrix} = a_{i1}b_{1j} + a_{i2}b_{2j} + \cdots + a_{in}b_{nj}.$$

Three features of this definition should be noted carefully. First, the orders of $A$ and $B$ are respectively $m$ by $n$ and $n$ by $q$. This means that in order to multiply matrices the number of columns of $A$ must be equal to the number of rows of $B$. The numbers $m$ and $q$, however, the number of rows of $A$ and the number of columns of $B$ respectively, can be any positive integers. Secondly, the matrix $AB$ is of order $m$ by $q$; it has the same number of rows as $A$ and the same number of columns as $B$. Finally, the element in the $i^{\text{th}}$ row and $j^{\text{th}}$ column of $AB$ is the inner product of the $i^{\text{th}}$ row of $A$ and the $j^{\text{th}}$ column of $B$.

The following are illustrations of the three operations defined for matrices:

$$\begin{pmatrix} 1 & 0 & 2 \\ 0 & 1 & 1 \\ 0 & 4 & -1 \end{pmatrix} + \begin{pmatrix} 1 & 5 & -2 \\ 6 & 7 & 4 \\ -9 & 3 & 1 \end{pmatrix} = \begin{pmatrix} 2 & 5 & 0 \\ 6 & 8 & 5 \\ -9 & 7 & 0 \end{pmatrix};$$

$$5\begin{pmatrix} 3 & 3 & 2 \\ 4 & -7 & -1 \end{pmatrix} = \begin{pmatrix} 15 & 15 & 10 \\ 20 & -35 & -5 \end{pmatrix};$$

$$\begin{pmatrix} 2 & 4 & 3 \\ 1 & 0 & 1 \end{pmatrix} \begin{pmatrix} 1 & -7 \\ 5 & 2 \\ 9 & -1 \end{pmatrix} = \begin{pmatrix} 49 & -9 \\ 10 & -8 \end{pmatrix}.$$

Although it is not our intention to present an extensive treatment of matrix algebra here, it will be useful to mention several properties of the matrix operations we have defined together with a few of their implications. It can be proved, for example, that matrix addition is commutative and associative, and that matrix multiplication is distributive with respect to addition,

$$A + B = B + A,$$
$$A + (B + C) = (A + B) + C,$$
$$A(B + C) = AB + AC,$$

for matrices of suitable order. Also if $A = (a_{ij})$ is of order $m$ by $n$ and if $k = -1$, then by scalar multiplication of matrices we have

$$kA = (-1)A = \begin{pmatrix} -a_{11} & -a_{12} & \cdots & -a_{1n} \\ -a_{21} & -a_{22} & \cdots & -a_{2n} \\ \cdots\cdots\cdots\cdots\cdots \\ -a_{m1} & -a_{m2} & \cdots & -a_{mn} \end{pmatrix}$$

so for every matrix $A$ there is a negative matrix $-A$ with the property that $A + (-A) = A - A = 0$, where the symbol 0 indicates the zero matrix— a matrix every element of which is zero (we also have $A + 0 = 0 + A = A$ for every matrix $A$). Again, following our earlier work with vectors, matrix subtraction is defined in terms of addition. The matrix $A - B$ is defined to be the matrix which when added to the matrix $B$ yields $A$, so we have $A - B = A + (-B)$.

Concerning multiplication it can be proved that if $A$ is $m$ by $n$, $B$ is $n$ by $q$, and $C$ is $q$ by $r$, then

$$ABC = A(BC) = (AB)C;$$

the associative law holds for matrix multiplication, as might have been anticipated, but the commutative law for multiplication does not hold in general,

$$AB \neq BA$$

for all suitable matrices $A$, $B$. For example, let

$$A = \begin{pmatrix} 0 & 0 \\ 1 & 1 \end{pmatrix} \text{ and } B = \begin{pmatrix} 2 & 3 \\ 4 & 5 \end{pmatrix}$$

Then

$$AB = \begin{pmatrix} 0 & 0 \\ 1 & 1 \end{pmatrix} \begin{pmatrix} 2 & 3 \\ 4 & 5 \end{pmatrix} = \begin{pmatrix} 0 & 0 \\ 6 & 8 \end{pmatrix}$$

and

$$BA = \begin{pmatrix} 2 & 3 \\ 4 & 5 \end{pmatrix} \begin{pmatrix} 0 & 0 \\ 1 & 1 \end{pmatrix} = \begin{pmatrix} 3 & 3 \\ 5 & 5 \end{pmatrix}.$$

Indeed, it is possible for the product $XY$ to be defined and for $YX$ to be undefined.

If

$$X = \begin{pmatrix} 2 & 1 \\ -1 & 0 \end{pmatrix}, \quad Y = \begin{pmatrix} 2 & 0 & -1 \\ 2 & 1 & -3 \end{pmatrix},$$

then

$$XY = \begin{pmatrix} 6 & 1 & -5 \\ -2 & 0 & 1 \end{pmatrix},$$

but $YX$ is not defined because the orders of the matrices do not permit multiplication.

The $n$ by $n$ matrix

$$I = \begin{pmatrix} 1 & 0 & \cdots & 0 \\ 0 & 1 & \cdots & 0 \\ & & \cdots \cdots \\ 0 & 0 & \cdots & 1 \end{pmatrix},$$

having the number 1 for its principal diagonal elements, is called the *unit* or *identity* matrix, for it plays the same role in matrix multiplication that the number 1 plays in the multiplication of real numbers. If $A$ is any matrix we have

$$AI = IA = A.$$

The operation of matrix multiplication is also useful in writing systems of linear equations in abbreviated form. For example the linear equation system

$$2x_1 + 8x_2 + 6x_3 = 2$$

$$2x_1 + 5x_2 + 4x_3 = 4$$

$$-x_1 + 3x_2 + 2x_3 = -5$$

can be written

$$\begin{pmatrix} 2 & 8 & 6 \\ 2 & 5 & 4 \\ -1 & 3 & 2 \end{pmatrix} \begin{pmatrix} x_1 \\ x_2 \\ x_3 \end{pmatrix} = \begin{pmatrix} 2 \\ 4 \\ -5 \end{pmatrix}$$

This, of course, can be generalized; the system of $m$ nonhomogeneous linear equations in $n$ unknowns

$$a_{11}x_1 + a_{12}x_2 + \cdots + a_{1n}x_n = b_1$$

$$a_{21}x_1 + a_{22}x_2 + \cdots + a_{2n}x_n = b_2$$

$$\cdots\cdots\cdots\cdots\cdots\cdots\cdots\cdots$$

$$a_{m1}x_1 + a_{m2}x_2 + \cdots + a_{mn}x_n = b_n$$

can be written as

$$\begin{pmatrix} a_{11} & a_{12} & \cdots & a_{1n} \\ a_{21} & a_{22} & \cdots & a_{2n} \\ \cdots & \cdots & \cdots \\ a_{m1} & a_{m2} & \cdots & a_{mn} \end{pmatrix} \begin{pmatrix} x_1 \\ x_2 \\ \vdots \\ x_n \end{pmatrix} = \begin{pmatrix} b_1 \\ b_2 \\ \vdots \\ b_m \end{pmatrix},$$

or still more briefly

$$AX = B,$$

where $A = (a_{ij})$ is the $m$ by $n$ matrix of coefficients of the variables in the equations, $X$ is the $n$ by 1 column vector of unknowns, and $B$ is the $m$ by 1 column vector of constant terms.

# Chapter 3

## AN INTRODUCTION TO LINEAR PROGRAMMING*

*by* W. ALLEN SPIVEY

### Linear Programming in Two-space

Since many of the fundamental concepts of linear programming can be clearly illustrated in two-dimensional space, we will first consider a linear programming problem in two-space before giving a general statement of both the geometry and algebra. We will assume that all the spaces under discussion are Euclidean—the axes are perpendicular and each axis has the same unit of length (see pp. 43–44).

Consider now the following problem: find an $x$ and $y$ which will make the value of the function whose rule is $f(x, y) = x + 5y$ as large as possible, where $x$ and $y$ are not unrestricted but are subject to the following restraints:

(1) $$5x + 6y \leq 30$$

(2) $$3x + 2y \leq 12$$

(3) $$x \geq 0$$

(4) $$y \geq 0.$$

Suppose we experiment by choosing several values for $x$ and $y$ and observe how large we can make the value $f(x, y) = x + 5y$.[1] We select first $x = 2$ and $y = 2$. Upon substituting each of these in (1) – (4) it is seen that each restraint is satisfied [for example, substitution in (1) gives $5(2) + 6(2) = 22 \leq 30$]. Next we compute $f(x, y) = x + 5y = 2 + 5(2) = 12$. If we select

---

*The author wishes to express his appreciation to Professor J. E. Bishop, Graduate School of Business Administration, Harvard University, for helpful conversations and suggestions concerning some of the material in this chapter.

[1] The equation $f(x, y) = x + 5y$ specifies a family of straight lines in two-space, each member of which is obtained by setting $f(x, y)$ equal to some real number. For example, $x + 5y = -10$, $x + 5y = 2$, $x + 5y = 47$ are three equations whose graphs are parallel lines belonging to the family.

61

another pair of values, say $x = 1$ and $y = 3$ (restraints (3) and (4) prevent the selection of negative values for $x$ and $y$), then upon substituting these in (1) – (4) we again find that each is satisfied. For this pair of values $f(x, y) = 1 + 5(3) = 16$; the ordered pair (1, 3) yields a larger value for $f(x, y)$ than does (2, 2). Suppose we select still another pair of values, $x = 2$ and $y = 4$. Substitution in (1) shows that the restraint is not satisfied, so we are not permitted to select the ordered pair (2, 4). Suppose we let $x = 0$ and $y = 5$. The restraints are satisfied and we have $f(x, y) = 0 + 5(5) = 25$, the largest value assumed by the function so far.

One might now ask how long this process is to continue. Theoretically there is an uncountable infinity of ordered pairs $(x, y)$ satisfying the restraints, so we need methods other than that of trial and error substitution to solve the problem. Fortunately there are several theorems which simplify the process of solving linear programming problems considerably and in discussing the geometry underlying them we will use many of the geometrical concepts presented in Chapter 2.

Turning now to the geometry of the problem above, each of the inequality restraints (1) – (4) specifies a half space and the set of points $(x, y)$ which simultaneously satisfy the inequalities is the intersection of the corresponding half spaces. By earlier results we know that a half space is a convex set and that the intersection of any collection of half spaces is a convex set, so the set of points satisfying (1) – (4) is a (closed) convex set. The convex set of solutions

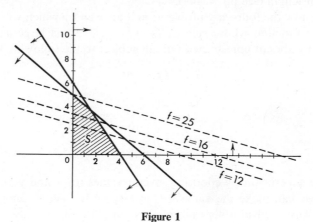

**Figure 1**

$S$ is the shaded polygon. The graphs of $x + 5y = 12$, $x + 5y = 16$, and $x + 5y = 25$ are the dashed straight lines appearing in the figure, where 12, 16, and 25 are the values of the function for the ordered pairs (2, 2), (1, 3), (0, 5) respectively. Geometrically, maximizing $f(x, y) = x + 5y$ subject to restraints (1) – (4) can be thought of as moving the straight line specified by $f(x, y) = x + 5y$ across the convex set $S$ until we reach a point of $S$ lying on the line which is most distant from the origin. The co-ordinates of this point will then yield a maximum value for $f(x, y)$. It can be seen that the point $(0, 5)$—which is an extreme point of $S$—is such a point. The value of the function can be made larger than 25 only by moving the line upward, and this would take us out of the set $S$. If, on the other hand, we were interested in the minimum value of the function subject to $(1) - (4)$ we would seek that point of $S$ lying on the line $f(x, y) = x + 5y$ which is closest to the origin. In this problem the point is obviously the origin (which is also an extreme point of $S$) and the minimum value of the function subject to the restraints is $f(x, y) = 0 + 5(0) = 0$.

The convex set $S$ is called the set of *feasible solutions* of the given linear programming problem and the feasible solutions which maximize or minimize the linear function are called *optimal feasible solutions*.

The figure above appears to suggest that a linear function will assume maximum and minimum values at an extreme point of the convex set of feasible solutions. This does not hold in general, however, for the linear function can have neither a maximum nor a minimum, or it can have one and not the other. Some examples will make this point clear. Suppose the problem is as follows:

maximize $\qquad\qquad f(x, y) = 3x + 2y$

subject to: $\qquad\qquad -2x + 3y \leq 9$

$$- x + 5y \leq 20$$

$$x \geq 0$$

$$y \geq 0.$$

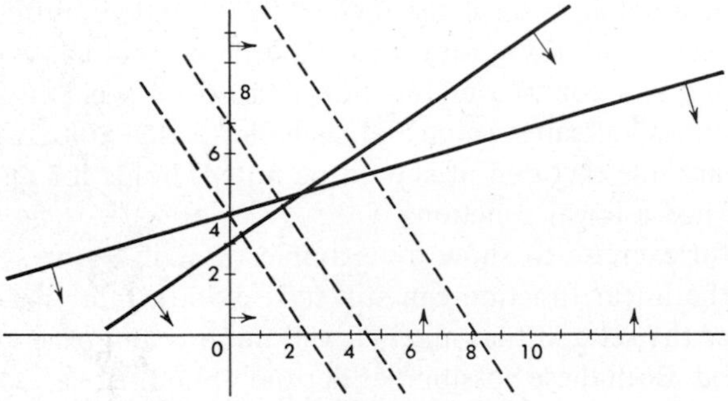

**Figure 2**

As can be seen from the figure, the convex set of solutions is unbounded and $f(x, y)$ has no finite maximum, although it has a minimum value at the origin. Alternatively, a problem in which the function has a maximum value but no minimum is the following:

minimize $\qquad\qquad f(x, y) = 2x + 9y$

subject to:

$$-x + y \leq 5$$
$$2x + 3y \leq 24$$
$$x > 0$$
$$y > 0.$$

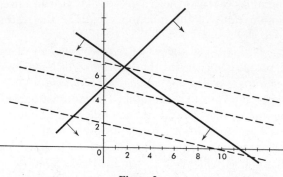

**Figure 3**

In this case the solution set $S$ is bounded but it is not closed; the function assumes values closer and closer to zero as $x$ and $y$ approach zero but there is no smallest value of the function for $(x, y) \in S$. There is, however, a maximum value for the function over the set. If $S$ were closed (i.e., if the restraints were $x \geq 0, y \geq 0$ instead of the corresponding strict inequalities) then the function would have a minimum at the origin.

These examples suggest that a linear function will have a maximum and a minimum over a solution set if the set is both bounded and closed. This is actually a special case of a general theorem on continuous functions due to Weierstrass: if $f$ is a continuous function defined on a closed and bounded set, then $f$ assumes a greatest value and a smallest value at least once over the set. This remarkable theorem, it should be noted, holds for any continuous function, not just a linear function.

It is a useful exercise to show by examples that if $S$, the solution set, is unbounded, the linear function can still have both a finite maximum and a minimum over the set and that maxima and minima can exist even when the set is not closed. Both these possibilities depend upon the relationship between the slope of the straight lines specified by $f(x, y)$ and the slopes of the straight lines forming the boundaries of the relevant half spaces.

The Weierstrass theorem contains no information as to where the maximum or minimum is reached over a closed and bounded set, nor does it tell us how many times the function assumes a maximum or a minimum (maxima and minima can occur over an interior point or over a point on the boundary, and they can occur over infinitely many points of the set). It is a theorem in linear programming—which will be proved below—that if the function is linear and if the restraints are (weak) linear inequalities, then the maximum and minimum values will be reached at an extreme point of the bounded convex set of feasible solutions. This greatly simplifies the problem of solving a linear programming problem for we now need to examine only the extreme points to find the optimal solutions and there are only a finite number of these since there are a finite number of restraints (the number of extreme points, however, may be quite large).

### The General Linear Programming Problem

The problem of linear programming is as follows:

maximize the linear function

(1) $$f = c_1 x_1 + c_2 x_2 + \cdots + c_n x_n,$$

subject to

(2)
$$a_{11} x_1 + a_{12} x_2 + \cdots + a_{1n} x_n \leqq b_1$$
$$a_{21} x_1 + a_{22} x_2 + \cdots + a_{2n} x_n \leqq b_2$$
$$\cdots\cdots\cdots\cdots\cdots\cdots\cdots\cdots$$
$$a_{m1} x_1 + a_{m2} x_2 + \cdots + a_{mn} x_n \leqq b_m$$

(3) $$x_i \geqq 0, \ (i = 1, \cdots, n),$$

where the $a_{ij}$, $b_i$ and $c_j$ are known constants. This is a more general formulation than it might appear to be, for if any (weak) inequality does not have the same sense as those in (2), then multiplication of the inequality by $-1$ will convert it into this form. The formulation permits equality to hold, so a restraint can be an equality, and it describes a minimization problem as well, for minimizing $-f$ is the same as maximizing $f$. The inequalities (2) and (3) specify a closed set; if it turns out that this set is also bounded, then by the Weierstrass theorem the function assumes both a maximum and a minimum over the set and optimal feasible solutions to the problem will exist. Furthermore, since the setting of the problem is linear, we know that the optimal feasible solutions will be extreme points of the convex set of solutions.

Although the notation of the general formulation is somewhat forbidding, we can use the geometry of the preceding section to see the problem more clearly. Analogous to the simpler problem, each inequality in (2) and (3) specifies a closed half space in $n$-dimensional space. The simultaneous solution set is a convex set in $n$-space and the equality corresponding to each inequality defines a hyperplane in $n$-space. A hyperplane is essentially a generalization of the concept of a straight line; a hyperplane in two-space is a straight line as is a plane in three-space (the concept of a hyperplane will be discussed more fully below). The equation $f = c_1 x_1 + c_2 x_2 + \cdots + c_n x_n$ specifies a family of hyperplanes in $n$-space, and the maximizing of $f$ subject to (2) and (3) can be thought of as moving the hyperplane defined by the equation (1) across the convex set $S$ of feasible solutions until the point in $S$ most distant from the origin and lying on the hyperplane is reached. This point will yield a maximum for $f$, and the theorem on extreme points assures us that $f$ will be maximized over an extreme point of $S$ if $S$ is bounded. Similar remarks can be made regarding the minimizing of $f$.

Alternative formulations of the general problem make use of the summation sign and matrix algebra. We can write down the problem in the abbreviated form,

maximize
$$f = \sum_{j=1}^{n} c_j x_j,$$

subject to

$$\sum_{j=1}^{n} a_{ij} x_j \leq b_i \qquad (i = 1, \cdots, m)$$

$$x_j \geq 0 \qquad (j = 1, \cdots, n),$$

and if we write vectors as column vectors and denote row vectors as transposes of column vectors, then the problem can be written in the following way: find a vector $X$ which will maximize $f = C^T X$ subject to

$$AX \leq B$$

$$X \geq 0,$$

where by $X \geq 0$ we mean $x_i \geq 0$ for $i = 1, \cdots, n$, and the matrices $A$ and $B$ are the matrix of coefficients and column vector of constant terms, respectively, in (2).

### Systems of Linear Inequalities and Related Systems of Linear Equalities

Theorems and solution techniques for general linear programming problems are usually stated in terms of a related system of linear equalities rather than in terms of inequalities. Each inequality in (2) is converted into an equality by the use of a "slack" variable. Consider for example the first inequality in system (2),

(4)                     $$a_{11}x_1 + a_{12}x_2 + \cdots + a_{1n}x_n \leq b_1.$$

This states that the sum of the terms on the left of the inequality sign is less than or equal to the number $b_1$. Stated another way, (4) means that there is a number $x_{n+1} \geq 0$ which, when added to the sum on the left, will convert it into an equality,

$$a_{11}x_1 + a_{12}x_2 + \cdots + a_{1n}x_n + x_{n+1} = b_1.$$

Similar remarks hold for the other inequalities in (2). Since there are $m$

inequalities in (2), $m$ slack variables are introduced (if a restraint is an equality, no slack variable is introduced), and the resulting linear equation system is

(5)
$$a_{11}x_1 + a_{12}x_2 + \cdots + a_{1n}x_n + x_{n+1} \qquad\qquad = b_1$$
$$a_{21}x_1 + a_{22}x_2 + \cdots + a_{2n}x_n \qquad + x_{n+2} \qquad = b_2$$
$$\cdots\cdots\cdots\cdots\cdots\cdots\cdots\cdots\cdots\cdots\cdots\cdots\cdots\cdots$$
$$a_{m1}x_1 + a_{m2}x_2 + \cdots + a_{mn}x_n \qquad\qquad + x_{n+m} = b_m,$$

(6)
$$x_i \geq 0 \qquad\qquad (i = 1, \cdots, n+m).$$

We can think of each equation in (5) as containing $n+m$ variables. In the first equation the variables $x_{n+2}, \cdots, x_{n+m}$ have zero coefficients, in the second equation the variables $x_{n+1}, x_{n+3}, \cdots, x_{n+m}$ have zero coefficients, etc., so (5) can be interpreted as a system of $m$ nonhomogeneous linear equations in $n+m$ unknowns. Then the linear programming problem involving equalities corresponding to (1) – (3) can be written as follows:

maximize

(7)
$$f = c_1x_1 + c_2x_2 + \cdots + c_nx_n + 0x_{n+1} + \cdots + 0x_{n+m},$$

subject to

(8)
$$a_{11}x_1 + a_{12}x_2 + \cdots + a_{1n+m}\, x_{n+m} = b_1$$
$$a_{21}x_1 + a_{22}x_2 + \cdots + a_{2n+m}\, x_{n+m} = b_2$$
$$\cdots\cdots\cdots\cdots\cdots\cdots\cdots\cdots\cdots\cdots\cdots\cdots$$
$$a_{m1}x_1 + a_{m2}x_2 + \cdots + a_{mn+m}\, x_{n+m} = b_m$$

(9)
$$x_i \geq 0 \qquad\qquad (i = 1, \cdots, n+m).$$

Note that although the slack variables may constitute an important part of the final solution they cannot by (7) make a contribution to $f$ and hence they will not appear in the optimal solution.

Although it may appear at first sight that the two problems are different in that (8) refers to an intersection of hyperplanes in $n+m$-space whereas the system of inequalities (2) and (3) refers to an intersection of half spaces in $n$-space, the formulations are algebraically equivalent because a feasible solution to one of the problems is a feasible solution to the other. In order to understand this equivalence fully we will first consider the geometrical conditions under which the solution set of (8) and (9) is the same set as the convex set defined by (2) and (3) and then we will consider some further geometry relating to the optimal solutions in the two formulations.

Suppose we begin by considering the inequality

(10)                                    $x_1 \leqq 5,$

which specifies a set in one-space which is both closed and convex:

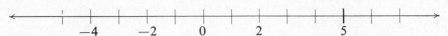

The inequality $x_1 \leqq 5$ means there is some number $x_2$, itself nonnegative, which when added to $x_1$ will equal 5 (if $x_1$ is $-12$, for example, $x_2$ would be 17; since $x_1$ is a variable, $x_2$ is also a variable). Therefore the inequality (10) can be interpreted as

(11)                                    $x_1 + x_2 = 5$

(12)                                    $x_2 \geqq 0.$

Now the question is, under what conditions do (11) and (12) specify the same set as (10)? Graphing (11) we see that the set of all ordered pairs $(x_1, x_2)$ satisfying (11) and (12) is the set of all points on the line to the left and above the point of intersection with the $x_1$-axis. This set, of course, is not the same set as that defined by the inequality $x_1 \leqq 5$. However, (11) and (12) will specify the same set as (10) if they are interpreted in the following way. Consider all the values of $x_1$ alone in the ordered pairs satisfying (11) and (12). This set can be thought

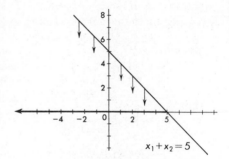

**Figure 4**

of as the "projection" on the $x_1$-axis of the values of $x_1$ in the ordered pairs $(x_1, x_2)$ satisfying (11) and (12); it is the set of all ordered pairs of the form $(x_1, 0)$. Since this set of points in two-space is not, strictly speaking, the same set as specified by $x_1 \leqq 5$ in a one-space, we further associate each point in two-space having co-ordinates $(x_1, 0)$, $x_1 \leqq 5$, with a point in one-space having co-ordinate $x_1 \leqq 5$. Then the set of all $x_1$ values in the ordered pairs satisfying (11) and (12), given this understanding, is the same set as specified by (10). Diagramatically we have

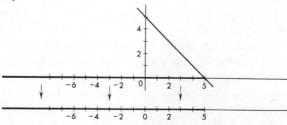

**Figure 5**

For still another example, consider the inequalities

(13) $$a_1x_1 + a_2x_2 \leq b$$

(14) $$x_1, x_2 \geq 0,$$

where we will also assume that $a_1$ and $a_2$ are positive numbers. Then the line specified by the equation $a_1x_1 + a_2x_2 = b$ will have a negative slope,

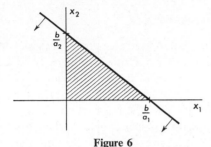

and the intersection of the half spaces defined by the inequalities (13) and (14) is the convex set shown below. Again, $a_1x_1 + a_2x_2 \leq b$ means there is a number $x_3 \geq 0$ such that

(15) $$a_1x_1 + a_2x_2 + x_3 = b$$

(16) $$x_1, x_2, x_3 \geq 0.$$

**Figure 6**

The graph of (15) is a plane in three-space and the inequalities (16) restrict the ordered triples satisfying (15) to be in the first octant. The graph of (15) and (16) appears below. We again see that the set of all ordered triples $(x_1, x_2, x_3)$ satisfying (15) and (16) is not the same set as that specified by (13) and (14).

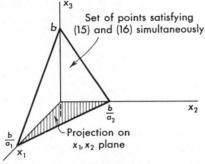

**Figure 7**

However, the projection on the $x_1$-, $x_2$-plane, or those ordered triples $(x_1, x_2, 0)$, where $(x_1, x_2, x_3)$ satisfy (15) and (16), can be associated with the set in two-space whose points satisfy (13) and (14) in a manner analogous to that in the preceding example. We merely associate the points $(x_1, x_2, 0)$ in the $x_1$-, $x_2$-plane in three-space with the corresponding points $(x_1, x_2)$ in two-space. With this understanding (15) and (16) specify the same set as (13) and (14). It can be seen from Figures 6 and 7 that the correspondence $(x_1, x_2, 0) \rightarrow (x_1, x_2)$ will associate points in the solution set shown in Figure 7 with those in the solution set appearing in Figure 6.

A similar projection must be used to associate the set formed by the intersection of hyperplanes in the general formulation (8) and (9) above with the set formed by the intersection of half spaces in (2) and (3). Each equation in (8), we have noted, specifies a hyperplane in $n + m$-space. A hyperplane in an $r$-space is defined to be a *linear space* of dimension $r - 1$, and by a linear space we mean a space having all the properties of a vector space except that the origin is not required to be in the space. The definition is as follows. Let $L$ be a subset of the vector space $V_n$. Then $L$ is a linear space if

1. for any two *points a, b* $\in L$, $a + b \in L$;

2. if $a \in L$, then $ka \in L$, where $k$ is a real number.

Note the word "points" in the definition; if we had used the word "vectors" instead this would have lead to the definition of a vector space (why?). In two-space a linear space is any straight line specified by the equation $a_1x_1 + a_2x_2 = b$. If $b = 0$, then the straight line or linear space contains the origin.

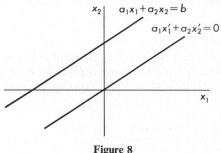

**Figure 8**

In this case the linear space is also a vector space. If $b \neq 0$, then the linear space does not contain the origin and hence it is not a vector space. Corresponding comments hold in three-space. The equation $a_1x_1 + a_2x_2 + a_3x_3 = b$ defines a plane or linear space in three-space, and the dimension of the linear space is $r - 1 = 3 - 1 = 2$. Again, if $b = 0$, the plane contains the origin and the linear space is a vector space; if $b \neq 0$, the origin is not contained in the space and the linear space is not a vector space.

The intersection of two hyperplanes, each having dimension $r - 1$ in $r$-space, is a linear space of dimension $r - 2$, providing that the equation of one hyperplane is not a linear combination of the other. For a special case of this consider two intersecting planes in three-space. The intersection is a straight line in three-space, or a one-dimensional linear space. These comments can be generalized. If we have $k$ intersecting hyperplanes in $r$-space and if the equation of each hyperplane is not a linear combination of the others, then two of the hyperplanes intersect in a linear space of dimension $r - 2$, three hyperplanes intersect in a linear space of dimension $r - 3$, and the intersection of $k$ hyperplanes is linear space having dimension $r - k$.

Returning to the general linear programming formulations, let us look at (2) and (3) and at (8) and (9) in the light of the comments above on linear spaces. Each of the hyperplanes in (8) is a linear space of dimension $n + m - 1$; the intersection of $m$ of these hyperplanes is a linear space of dimension $n + m - m = n.$[2] The convex set specified by (2) is also in $n$-space, and since in both formulations we are restricted to nonnegative values of the variables, it appears that the intersections specify the same set. This is true if we follow

[2] We assume that no equation in (8) is a linear combination of the others.

the procedure discussed above concerning association by means of a suitable projection.

A simple example will help to clarify these comments. Suppose we wish to maximize the linear function $f = c_1 x_1 + c_2 x_2$ subject to

(17) $$a_{11} x_1 + a_{12} x_2 = b_1$$

(18) $$a_{21} x_1 + a_{22} x_2 \leqq b_2$$

(19) $$x_1, x_2 \geqq 0,$$

where for simplicity we further assume that each $a_{ij} > 0$. The graph of (17) is the straight line (1) in the figure below and the boundary of the half space (18) is the line (2). The set of feasible solutions to the problem is the line segment indicated.

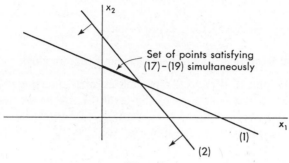

**Figure 9**

Using slack variables we get the linear equation system

(20) $$a_{11} x_1 + a_{12} x_2 + 0 x_3 = b_1$$

(21) $$a_{21} x_1 + a_{22} x_2 + x_3 = b_2$$

(22) $$x_i \geqq 0 \qquad (i = 1, 2, 3),$$

in which the equations define hyperplanes in three-space. Graphs of the equations appear below, where for simplicity only those values of the variables satisfying (20) and (21) which are also nonnegative are shown. The plane (1) is the graph of (20); since (20) has a zero coefficient for $x_3$, any value of $x_3$

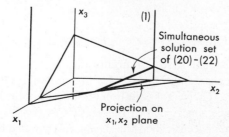

**Figure 10**

will satisfy the equation so we have the plane (1) part of which is indicated in the figure. The set of points whose co-ordinates satisfy (21) lie in the plane a triangular "slice" of which also appears in the figure. The set of points simultaneously satisfying (20) – (22) is the line segment indicated. If we project this set on the $x_1$, $x_2$ plane, that is, if we consider those points ($x_1$, $x_2$, 0) where ($x_1$, $x_2$, $x_3$) satisfy (20) – (22), and then associate these points with the corresponding points ($x_1$, $x_2$) in two-space, we will get the set appearing in Figure 9.

The general case can be considered analogously. The set of feasible solutions to the inequalities (2) and (3) is a convex set in $n$-space and the set of feasible solutions to (8) and (9) is also a set in $(n + m) - m = n$-space. The two feasible solution sets will be the same if we project the set of points ($x_1$, $\cdots$, $x_n$, $\cdots$, $x_{n + m}$) whose co-ordinates satisfy (8) and (9) on the linear subspace of points ($x_1$, $\cdots$, $x_n$, 0, $\cdots$, 0) and then associate these points with corresponding points ($x_1$, $x_2$, $\cdots$, $x_n$) in $n$-space.

### Solution and Requirements Spaces in Linear Programming

The formulation (7), (8) and (9) has still another interpretation. We have seen earlier that scalar equations of the form (8) can be written as a single vector equation by regarding the coefficients $a_{ij}$ of each variable as a column vector. The vector equation corresponding to (8) is

$$\begin{pmatrix} a_{11} \\ a_{21} \\ \cdot \\ \cdot \\ \cdot \\ a_{m1} \end{pmatrix} x_1 + \begin{pmatrix} a_{12} \\ a_{22} \\ \cdot \\ \cdot \\ \cdot \\ a_{m2} \end{pmatrix} x_2 + \cdots + \begin{pmatrix} a_{1\,n+m} \\ a_{2\,n+m} \\ \cdot \\ \cdot \\ \cdot \\ a_{m\,n+m} \end{pmatrix} x_{n+m} = \begin{pmatrix} b_1 \\ b_2 \\ \cdot \\ \cdot \\ \cdot \\ b_m \end{pmatrix}.$$

which can be written, if $P_i = \begin{pmatrix} a_{1i} \\ a_{2i} \\ \cdot \\ \cdot \\ \cdot \\ a_{mi} \end{pmatrix}$ and $P_0$ represents the column vector

of constants $b_i$, as

$$(23) \qquad P_1 x_1 + P_2 x_2 + \cdots + P_{n+m} x_{n+m} = P_0.$$

The $m + n$-dimensional space of points ($x_1$, $x_2$, $\cdots$, $x_{n+m}$) is called the *solution space* because solutions to the linear programming problem are points in this space. The vector equation (23), on the other hand, refers to an $m$-dimensional space, since each of the vectors $P_i$ consist of $m$ components. The $m$-dimensional space is called the *requirements space* because some of its points come from the restraint equations which state the requirements of the problem. Note that although the numbers $(x_1, x_2, \cdots, x_{n+m})$ are the co-ordinates of a point in solution space, in requirements space they do not represent a point but are a collection of numbers which appear as coefficients of vectors in requirements space.

If $P_0$ can be expressed as a nonnegative linear combination of the vectors $P_i$, then the coefficients $x_i$ in the linear combination will satisfy both (8) and (9), and this means that the coefficients will be the co-ordinates of a point in the feasible solution set in $n + m$-space (the solution space).[3] Conversely, any point $(x_1, x_2, \cdots, x_{n+m})$ in the feasible solution set can be interpreted in requirements space as a way of expressing $P_0$ as a nonnegative linear combination of the vectors $P_1, \cdots, P_{n+m}$. Finally, if $P_0$ is a nonnegative linear combination of $P_1, \cdots, P_{n+m}$, then $P_0$ lies in the cone spanned by the $P_i$; on the other hand, if $P_0$ is not in the cone, then no nonnegative linear combination of the $P_i$ will yield $P_0$ and the linear programming problem does not have a feasible solution.

A simple example will be useful at this point. Suppose the linear programming problem is to maximize $f(x_1, x_2) = 2x_1 + 5x_2$ subject to

(24) $$x_1 + 4x_2 \leq 24$$

(25) $$3x_1 + x_2 \leq 21$$

(26) $$x_1 + x_2 \leq 9$$

(27) $$x_1, x_2 \geq 0.$$

The inequalities define a convex set $S$ in two-space. The straight lines forming the boundaries of the relevant half spaces in the graph below have the same numbers as do the corresponding inequalities above. The linear function is

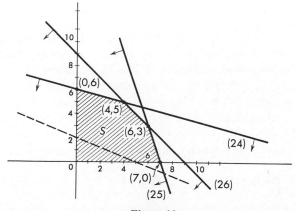

**Figure 11**

[3] In order to simplify the discussion, when we speak of the solution set it will be understood that a suitable projection of the points $(x_1, \cdots, x_{n+m})$ on the linear subspace of points $(x_1, \cdots, x_n, 0, \cdots, 0)$ has been made.

also shown and the point of $S$ for which $f(x_1, x_2)$ reaches a maximum value is the point $(4, 5)$ for which $f(x_1, x_2) = 2x_1 + 5x_2 = 2(4) + 5(5) = 33$. The space containing the intersection of the half spaces defined by the inequalities in the original statement of the problem will be called the *initial space*. In this example, the initial space is two-space.

Slack variables are now introduced, one for each of the inequalities (24)–(26), and the equivalent statement of the linear programming problem is to maximize $f(x_1, x_2) = 2x_1 + 5x_2 + 0x_3 + 0x_4 + 0x_5$ subject to

$$(28) \qquad x_1 + 4x_2 + x_3 + 0x_4 + 0x_5 = 24$$

$$(29) \qquad 3x_1 + x_2 + 0x_3 + x_4 + 0x_5 = 21$$

$$(30) \qquad x_1 + x_2 + 0x_3 + 0x_4 + x_5 = 9$$

$$(31) \qquad\qquad\qquad\qquad x_i \geq 0 \qquad (i = 1, \cdots, 5).$$

Each of these equations specifies a four-dimensional hyperplane in five-space. The intersection of the three hyperplanes is a linear space of dimension $5 - 3 = 2$. If we project the set of solutions $(x_1, x_2, x_3, x_4, x_5)$ to (28) – (31) on the linear subspace $(x_1, x_2, 0, 0, 0)$ and identify these points with the corresponding points $(x_1, x_2)$ in two-space, then the set of feasible solutions to (28) – (31) can be considered to be the same set as the convex set $S$ shown in Figure 11 above.

Suppose we now write the system (28) – (31) in the vector form.

$$(32) \quad \begin{pmatrix} 1 \\ 3 \\ 1 \end{pmatrix} x_1 + \begin{pmatrix} 4 \\ 1 \\ 1 \end{pmatrix} x_2 + \begin{pmatrix} 1 \\ 0 \\ 0 \end{pmatrix} x_3 + \begin{pmatrix} 0 \\ 1 \\ 0 \end{pmatrix} x_4 + \begin{pmatrix} 0 \\ 0 \\ 1 \end{pmatrix} x_5 = \begin{pmatrix} 24 \\ 21 \\ 9 \end{pmatrix}$$

$$(33) \qquad\qquad x_i \geq 0 \qquad (i = 1, \cdots, 5).$$

For this problem solution space is a five-space and feasible solutions to the problem are points of the form $(x_1, x_2, x_3, x_4, x_5)$. Incidentally, merely writing the equation in this form indicates a feasible solution: $x_1 = 0$, $x_2 = 0$, $x_3 = 24$, $x_4 = 21$, $x_5 = 9$. This is not an optimal solution, however, because for this point $f(x_1, x_2) = 2x_1 + 5x_2 = 2(0) + 5(0) = 0$.

The requirements space is three-dimensional, as a glance at the column vectors in (32) shows. If we plot the requirements vectors as points in requirements space the geometry that will result is shown in Figure 12. The point $\begin{pmatrix} 24 \\ 21 \\ 9 \end{pmatrix}$ is not shown in the figure but it lies in the cone spanned by the vectors $P_1, \cdots, P_5$. In order to solve the linear programming problem, however, we want not only an expression for $P_0$ as a nonnegative linear combination of the $P_i$, but we want a nonnegative combination which will make $f$ as large as possible. Since we know that $f$ will be maximized over an extreme point we need a means of experimenting with nonnegative linear combinations of $P_i$ which will give not merely points in solution space but extreme points in solution space. Fortunately a theorem, which will be stated more carefully and proved below, comes to our rescue. It turns out that if $P_0$ is expressed

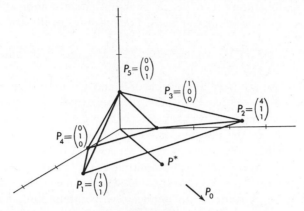

**Figure 12**

as a nonnegative linear combination of a set of independent vectors in requirements space, then the coefficients in this combination are the co-ordinates of an extreme point of the convex set of feasible solutions. Since requirements space in the example is a three-space, no set containing more than three vectors can be linearly independent, so the linear combinations which will result in extreme points in solution space can have at most three positive coefficients. The point $(0, 0, 24, 21, 9)$ given by the solution we saw above is an extreme point of the set of feasible solutions.

Furthermore, given an extreme point of the convex set, there is a way of moving to an adjacent extreme point which makes the value $f(x_1, x_2)$ at least as large. Since we can get an extreme point solution from the vector equation (32), once we have this technique we will have a means of solving the problem.

The set of all *convex* combinations of the points $P_1, \cdots, P_5$ is the convex polygon in three-space shown in Figure 12 above. The point $P_0$ is not, of course, in this set. However, the line segment $OP_0$ from the origin to the point $P_0$ does contain points in the convex polygon. This means that the points on $OP_0$ which are in the set must be positive scalar multiples of the vector $P_0$ of the form $kP_0$, where (in this case) $0 < k < 1$. Thus if we have an equation giving $P_0$ as a nonnegative linear combination of $P_1, \cdots, P_5$, then we can multiply it through by some $k$, $0 < k < 1$, getting an equation which gives a scalar multiple of $P_0$ as a *convex* combination of $P_1, \cdots, P_5$. It is also true that if we have a scalar multiple of $P_0$ expressed as a convex combination of the $P_i$, then multiplication of the equation by an appropriate positive number will yield $P_0$ as a nonnegative combination of $P_1, \cdots, P_5$. Therefore, in seeking an optimal solution we can, if we wish, work with convex combinations of the

$P_i$, for we can always convert the convex combination into a corresponding nonnegative combination which will give points in solution space.

If we think of the line segment $OP_0$ passing through the convex polygon in Figure 12, then we see that we can express positive scalar multiples of $OP_0$ as convex combinations (and hence as nonnegative combinations) of the vectors $P_1, \cdots, P_5$ in a number of ways. For purposes of illustration consider the point $P^* = \begin{pmatrix} 4 \\ 3\frac{1}{2} \\ 1\frac{1}{2} \end{pmatrix}$ shown in Figure 12. This point is obtained by multiplying $P_0$ by $1/6$, so it is a scalar multiple of $P_0$ and lies on the line segment $OP_0$. As the line segment $OP^*$ passes through the convex polygon it passes through the triangular face spanned by $P_3$, $P_4$, $P_5$. These and other triangles (which can be either interior to the polygon or comprise faces of it) are convex combinations of the three relevant vectors, so when we say that $OP^*$ passes through a triangle, we are saying that a scalar multiple of $OP^*$ (and of $OP_0$) is a convex combination of the three vectors spanning the triangle. Since convex combinations can be converted into nonnegative combinations, and since the triangles are each spanned by *three* vectors, there are extreme points in solution space corresponding to expressions of $P_0$ as positive combinations of the three vectors spanning each triangle. Of course, since the line segment passes through the entire set, there are also combinations of $OP^*$ (and of $OP_0$) in terms of four and five of the vectors $P_i$. These combinations, however, would not give extreme points in solution space and so would not be of interest to us.

It will be useful to keep these comments in mind as we develop a means of moving from one extreme point to an adjacent extreme point which gives at least as large a value to the linear function $f$. We begin with the solution computed above for which $f(x_1, x_2) = 0$,

$$(34) \qquad\qquad P_0 = OP_1 + OP_2 + 24P_3 + 21P_4 + 9P_5.$$

Since we want to find another extreme point, and since there can be no more than three among the five vectors having positive coefficients, we must take one of the vectors $P_3$, $P_4$, $P_5$ out of the combination (in the sense that it will have a zero coefficient) if we are to give one of the vectors $P_1$, $P_2$ a nonzero coefficient. By giving a positive coefficient to one or both $P_1$ and $P_2$ we can make $f(x_1, x_2)$ larger than it is for the solution above. Suppose we choose $P_1$ as the vector to receive the nonzero coefficient (we could just as easily choose $P_2$ as the initial vector). Then $P_3$, $P_4$, or $P_5$, must be given a zero coefficient. First we observe that $P_1$ can be expressed as a nonnegative linear combination of $P_3$, $P_4$, $P_5$, since the latter vectors are a basis for three-space. Furthermore, the representation of $P_1$ in terms of $P_3$, $P_4$, $P_5$ is unique, as we saw earlier in Chapter 2. Since $P_1 = \begin{pmatrix} 1 \\ 3 \\ 1 \end{pmatrix}$, we have

$$P_1 = 1P_3 + 3P_4 + 1P_5.$$

Multiplying both sides of this equation by $t > 0$, we get

(35) $$tP_1 = tP_3 + 3tP_4 + tP_5.$$

This holds for any $t$, but we restrict $t$ to be positive for we wish the vector $P_1$ to have a positive coefficient. We now add $tP_1$ to the right-hand side of (34), and to preserve the equality we subtract the right-hand side of (35) from the right-hand side of (34),

$$P_0 = OP_1 + OP_2 + 24P_3 + 21P_4 + 9P_5 + tP_1 - tP_3 - 3tP_4 - tP_5.$$

Collecting terms,

(36) $$P_0 = tP_1 + OP_2 + (24 - t)P_3 + (21 - 3t)P_4 + (9 - t)P_5.$$

We want $t$ to be as large as possible but not so large that some vector in the equation above will have a negative coefficient. A consideration of the equation will show that $t = 7$ is as large as $t$ can become, for if $t > 7$, the coefficient of $P_4$ becomes a negative number. Substituting $t = 7$ in (36) we get

(37) $$P_0 = 7P_1 + OP_2 + 17P_3 + OP_4 + 2P_5.$$

The corresponding point in solution space is (7, 0, 17, 0, 2) which is an extreme point of the feasible solution set in five-space. For this solution,

(38) $$f = 2x_1 + 5x_2 + 0x_3 + 0x_4 + 0x_5,$$
$$f = 2(7) + 5(0) = 14,$$

which is an improvement in the value of $f$ over the preceding solution, and under the correspondence $(7, 0, 17, 0, 2) \rightarrow (7, 0, 0, 0, 0) \rightarrow (7, 0)$, we get an extreme point of the convex set $S$ in two-space (see Figure 11). Note that the correspondence $(7, 0, 17, 0, 2) \rightarrow (7, 0, 0, 0, 0)$ is established by the zero coefficients of the slack variables in (38).

We apply the technique again, this time giving a nonzero coefficient to $P_2$. We first express $P_2$ as a linear combination of the vectors having nonzero coefficients in (37). These vectors are a basis for three-space, and by solving an appropriate system of simultaneous linear equations, we get

$$P_2 = \tfrac{1}{3}P_1 + \tfrac{11}{3}P_2 + \tfrac{2}{3}P_5.$$

Multiplying both sides of this equation by $k > 0$ and repeating the procedure above, we get

(39) $$P_0 = (7 - \tfrac{1}{3}k)P_1 + kP_2 + (17 - \tfrac{11}{3}k)P_3 + OP_4 + (2 - \tfrac{2}{3}k)P_5.$$

The largest value that $k$ can assume if all coefficients are to be nonnegative is 3. Substituting $k = 3$ in (39) we have

(40) $$P_0 = 6P_1 + 3P_2 + 6P_3 + OP_4 + OP_5.$$

The point in solution space is (6, 3, 6, 0, 0) which gives the point (6, 3) in two-space. This point is the extreme point adjacent to the extreme point obtained in the preceding step (see Figure 11), and for it we have

$$f = 2(6) + 5(3) = 27,$$

which is a still larger value for $f$.

To complete the example, we repeat the procedure. We desire to increase the coefficient of one of the vectors $P_1$, $P_2$, so we will let one of the vectors $P_4$, $P_5$ have a nonzero coefficient. We select $P_4$ and express it as a combination of the vectors in (40) which have nonzero coefficients, namely $P_1$, $P_2$, and $P_3$. It can be shown that

$$P_4 = \tfrac{1}{2}P_1 - \tfrac{1}{2}P_2 + \tfrac{3}{2}P_3.$$

If $a > 0$, then

$$aP_4 = \tfrac{1}{2}aP_1 - \tfrac{1}{2}aP_2 + \tfrac{3}{2}aP_3.$$

Adding to and subtracting from (40), we have upon grouping terms,

$$P_0 = (6 - \tfrac{1}{2}a)P_1 + (3 + \tfrac{1}{2}a)P_2 + (6 - \tfrac{3}{2}a)P_3 + aP_4 + 0P_5.$$

The largest permissible value for $a$ is 4. Substituting,

$$P_0 = 4P_1 + 5P_2 + 0P_3 + 4P_4 + 0P_5.$$

The corresponding point in solution space is (4, 5, 0, 4, 0). The linear function projects this on the point (4, 5, 0, 0, 0) and we have

$$f = 2(4) + 5(5) + 0x_3 + 0x_4 + 0x_5 = 34.$$

Returning to Figure 11 we see that this is the largest value for $f$ and we see also that our solution technique began with an extreme point and moved to an adjacent extreme point which made $f$ at least as large.

This technique is essentially that of the Simplex method for solving a linear programming problem. The Simplex technique is a refined method of performing these manipulations and it will be discussed in detail in the Appendix.

This completes our discussion of the geometry of linear programming. In conclusion it should be noted that there are *three* spaces of relevance to a linear programming problem. First, the space in which the intersection of the inequalities in the original statement of the problem defines a convex set. Called the initial space, this was a two-space in our example. Then after the introduction of appropriate slack variables, we have the solution space (a five-space in our example). Then requirements space is the space containing the column vectors of constant terms (a three-space in the example). Note that although the requirements and solution spaces can have the same dimension, they should be thought of as separate spaces in considering linear programming problems.

An important feature of the optimal solution should also be noted. The optimal solution is the point (4, 5, 0, 4, 0), in which one slack vector, $P_4$, has a nonzero coefficient. This affords no complication, for the form of the linear function in the linear equation statement of the problem,

$$f = 4x_1 + 5x_2 + 0x_3 + 0x_4 + 0x_5,$$

assures us that the point in five-space will be projected on the point (4, 5, 0, 0, 0). Making the further association $(4, 5, 0, 0, 0) \rightarrow (4, 5)$ we get the point in Figure 11 which we saw graphically gave rise to the optimal solution in the original statement of the problem.

### Basic Theorems in Linear Programming

In order to prove that a linear function having a maximum over a closed and bounded set assumes a maximum value over an extreme point of the set, we need a precise definition of linear function. A function $f(x_1, x_2)$ is said to be a linear function if

$$f(kx_1, kx_2) = kf(x_1, x_2)$$

and

$$f[(x_1, x_2) + (x_1^*, x_2^*)] = f(x_1, x_2) + f(x_1^*, x_2^*)$$

are satisfied. This definition is generalized by using vectors and by combining the two conditions into one condition as follows. Let $X_1, \cdots, X_n$ be vectors having $n$ components each, and let $k_1, \cdots, k_n$ be scalars; then $f$ is a *linear function* if

$$f(k_1 X_1 + k_2 X_2 + \cdots + k_n X_n) = k_1 f(X_1) + k_2 f(X_2) + \cdots + k_n f(X_n).$$

We noted earlier in simple geometrical examples that any point in a convex set is a convex combination of the extreme points of the set. This is a theorem, and although it is geometrically obvious in two-space we wish now to prove it.

THEOREM 1.   Let $S$ be a (bounded) convex polygon. Then every point $X$ that is a convex combination of the extreme points of $S$ belongs to $S$.

PROOF.   Since $S$ is a bounded convex polygon, $S$ has a finite number of extreme points, say $X_1, \cdots, X_p$, and $S$ is also the intersection of a finite number of half spaces. Therefore, for any point $Y = \begin{pmatrix} y_1 \\ \cdot \\ \cdot \\ \cdot \\ y_n \end{pmatrix}$ in $S$ we have

$$a_{11}y_1 + \cdots + a_{1n}y_n \leqq b_1$$
$$a_{21}y_1 + \cdots + a_{2n}y_n \leqq b_2$$
$$\cdots \cdots \cdots \cdots \cdots \cdots \cdots$$
$$a_{m1}y_1 + \cdots + a_{mn}y_n \leqq b_m,$$

or

$$AY \leqq B.$$

Also, the extreme points $X_i$ are in $S$ and we have

$$AX_i \leqq B, \qquad (i = 1, \cdots, p).$$

Suppose $X^*$ is a convex combination of the extreme points,

$$X^* = k_1 X_1 + \cdots + k_p X_p,$$

where $k_i \geqq 0$, $\sum_{i=1}^{p} k_i = 1$. We want to show that $X^* \in S$. If we multiply both sides of the equation immediately above by the matrix $A$, we get

$$AX^* = A(k_1 X_1 + \cdots + k_p X_p),$$

or

$$AX^* = k_1 AX_1 + \cdots + k_p AX_p.$$

Now $AX_i \leqq B$, so $k_i AX_i \leqq k_i B$, for $i = 1, \cdots, p$ since $k_i \geqq 0$. Therefore,

$$AX^* = k_1 AX_1 + \cdots + k_p AX_p \leqq k_1 B + \cdots + k_p B = B,$$

since $\sum_{i=1}^{p} k_i = 1$. Therefore $AX^* \leqq B$ and $X^* \in S$.

We have seen that any linear programming problem can be converted by the use of slack variables to a problem involving linear equations in non-negative variables. We now state a linear programming problem in converted form and in subsequent theorems on linear programming we will understand —unless it is indicated otherwise—that we are referring to the problem formulated as follows:

maximize $f = c_1 x_1 + \cdots + c_n x_n$

subject to $a_{11} x_1 + \cdots + a_{1n} x_n = b_1$

$\qquad\qquad a_{21} x_1 + \cdots + a_{2n} x_n = b_2$

(41) $\qquad \cdots\cdots\cdots\cdots\cdots\cdots\cdots$

$\qquad\qquad a_{m1} x_1 + \cdots + a_{mn} x_n = b_m$

(42) $\qquad\qquad\qquad\qquad x_i \geqq 0 \qquad (i = 1, \cdots, n),$

where $a_{ij}$, $b_i$, and $c_j$ are known constants and $m < n$.

THEOREM 2.   If the convex set $S$ of feasible solutions to the linear programming problem is a (bounded) convex polygon, then $f$ assumes a maximum at an extreme point of $S$.

PROOF.   Since $S$ is a convex polygon, there is a finite number of extreme points, $X_1, \cdots, X_n$. Let $X^*$ be a point of $S$ such that $f(X^*) = m$ is a maximum (i.e., $X^*$ is an optimal feasible solution). Then $f(X^*) \geqq f(X)$ for all $X \in S$.

If $X^*$ is an extreme point then the theorem is true. Suppose $X^*$ is not an extreme point. If $X^* \in S$, then by Theorem 1, $X^*$ is a convex combination of the extreme points of $S$, so

$$X^* = k_1 X_1 + \cdots + k_n X_n, \quad \sum_{i=1}^{n} k_i = 1, \; k_i \geq 0 \; (i = 1, \cdots, n).$$

Also, $f$ is a linear function, so

$$f(X^*) = f(k_1 X_1 + \cdots + k_n X_n) = k_1 f(X_1) + \cdots + k_n f(X_n) = m,$$

where $m$ is the maximum of $f(X)$ for all $X \in S$. Now choose the largest of the values ($f(X_i)$ and substitute it for each $f(X_i)$ in the equation above. Call this largest value $f(X_p)$; then

$$k_1 f(X_p) + \cdots + k_n f(X_p) \geq k_1 f(X_1) + \cdots + k_n f(X_n) = f(X^*),$$

since the $k_i$ are nonnegative. Also $\sum_{i=1}^{n} k_i = 1$, therefore

and
$$k_1 f(X_p) + \cdots + k_n f(X_p) = (k_1 + \cdots + k_n) f(X_p) = f(X_p),$$

$$f(X_p) \geq f(X^*) = m.$$

Since we have assumed $f(X^*) \geq f(X)$ for all $X \in S$, only the equality can hold,

$$f(X_p) = f(X^*) = m,$$

and since $X_p$ is an extreme point, we have shown that $f$ assumes a maximum over an extreme point of $S$.

We can further show that if $f(X)$ assumes a maximum value over more than one extreme point, then it assumes the same maximum value for every convex combination of these points. Let $X_1, \cdots, X_k$ be the extreme points for which $f(X_1) = f(X_2) = \cdots = f(X_k) = m = $ maximum. Now if $X^*$ is a convex combination of the $X_i$, then

and
$$f(X^*) = f(r_1 X_1 + \cdots + r_k X_k) = r_1 f(X_1) + \cdots + r_k f(X_k),$$

$$f(X^*) = r_1 m_1 + \cdots + r_k m = m,$$

since $\sum_{i=1}^{k} r_i = 1$. This completes the proof.

The system (41) and (42) can be written in the following vector equation form,

(43) $$x_1 P_1 + x_2 P_2 + \cdots + x_n P_n = P_0$$

(44) $$x_i \geq 0 \qquad (i = 1, \cdots, n),$$

where $P_i = \begin{pmatrix} a_{1i} \\ \cdot \\ \cdot \\ \cdot \\ a_{mi} \end{pmatrix}$ and $P_0 = \begin{pmatrix} b_1 \\ \cdot \\ \cdot \\ \cdot \\ b_m \end{pmatrix}$. A feasible solution to the linear programming problem is a vector $X = (x_1, \cdots, x_n)$ satisfying (43) and (44). We have the following theorems concerning extreme points of the set of feasible solutions.

THEOREM 3. If there exists a set of $k \leqq m$ linearly independent vectors $P_1, \cdots, P_k$ such that

$$x_1 P_1 + \cdots + x_k P_k = P_0$$

$$x_i > 0 \qquad (i = 1, \cdots, k),$$

then the point $X = (x_1, \cdots, x_k, 0, \cdots, 0)$, having zero for the last $n - k$ co-ordinates, is an extreme point of the convex set $S$ of solutions to (43) and (44).

PROOF. Suppose $X$ is not an extreme point. Then since $X$ is in $S$, it is a convex combination of two other points $Y$ and $Z$ in $S$,

$$X = kY + (1 - k)Z \qquad (0 \leqq k \leqq 1).$$

Every co-ordinate of $X$ is nonnegative, and the last $n - k$ co-ordinates are zero, so $Y$ and $Z$ must have the form

$$Y = (y_1, \cdots, y_k, 0, \cdots, 0)$$

$$Z = (z_1, \cdots, z_k, 0, \cdots, 0).$$

Also, since $Y$ and $Z$ are feasible solutions, we have

$$AY = B$$

and

$$AZ = B.$$

Rewriting these as vector equations,

$$y_1 P_1 + \cdots + y_k P_k = P_0$$

$$z_1 P_1 + \cdots + z_k P_k = P_0.$$

But the $P_1, \cdots, P_k$ are linearly independent vectors, so the vector $P_0$ can be expressed in at most one way as a linear combination of the $P_1, \cdots, P_k$. This means that $y_i = z_i = x_i$, and that $X$ cannot be expressed as a convex combination of two other points in $S$. The point $X$ is therefore an extreme point of $S$.

THEOREM 4. If $X = (x_1, \cdots, x_k, 0, \cdots, 0)$ is an extreme point of $S$, then there are linearly independent vectors $P_1, \cdots, P_k$ such that

$$x_1 P_1 + \cdots + x_k P_k = P_0$$

$$x_i > 0 \qquad (i = 1, \cdots, k).$$

PROOF. Assume that $P_1, \cdots, P_k$ are linearly dependent. Then

$$y_1 P_1 + y_2 P_2 + \cdots + y_k P_k = 0$$

where not all $y_i = 0$. Multiply the equation above by a constant $t > 0$, then add and subtract the resulting equation from the equation giving $P_0$ as a nonnegative combination of $P_1, \cdots, P_k$. The following equations result,

$$(x_1 + ty_1)P_1 + \cdots + (x_k + ty_k)P_k = P_0$$
$$(x_1 - ty_1)P_1 + \cdots + (x_k - ty_k)P_k = P_0.$$

Since each $x_i > 0$, we can get two feasible solutions from these equations by choosing $t$ sufficiently small so that $(x_i \pm ty_i) > 0$. Suppose $t'$ is the value so chosen. Then two feasible solutions are

$$X_1 = (x_1 + t'y_1, \cdots, x_k + t'y_k, 0, \cdots, 0)$$
$$X_2 = (x_1 - t'y_1, \cdots, x_k - t'y_k, 0, \cdots, 0).$$

But $X = \frac{1}{2}X_1 + \frac{1}{2}X_2$; this means that $X$ is not an extreme point which contradicts the hypothesis. Since the assumption that $P_1, \cdots, P_k$ are linearly dependent leads to a contradiction, it must be false and we conclude that the vectors are linearly independent.

In both Theorems 3 and 4 we assumed for convenience that the first $k$ vectors were linearly independent. There is no loss of generality in doing this, for if the first $k$ vectors are not linearly independent, we can by a suitable relabeling give the subscripts $1, \cdots, k$ to any subset of $k$ linear independent vectors among the $n$ vectors in (43). As a consequence of this, Theorem 3 actually states that an extreme point of the convex set of solutions in $n$-space has $k$ positive coefficients and $n - k$ zero coefficients, and it should be observed that the $k$ positive coefficients need not be the first $k$ co-ordinates of the point.

### Dual Linear Programs

Associated with every linear programming problem is a closely related problem—also one of linear programming—called the *dual*. The original problem, which in our case is a maximization problem, is called the primal, and its dual is a minimization problem. Since the dual of the dual problem is the primal, either problem can be considered the primal and the remaining one the dual. Furthermore, an optimal solution to the primal reveals information concerning the optimal solution of the dual, and if the primal problem has an interpretation, then its dual also has an interpretation—although the dual interpretation may not be of interest.[4]

For convenience, we restate the primal problem in inequality form. It is to maximize

$$f = c_1 x_1 + c_2 x_2 + \cdots + c_n x_n$$

subject to

$$a_{11}x_1 + a_{12}x_2 + \cdots + a_{1n}x_n \leq b_1$$
$$a_{21}x_1 + a_{22}x_2 + \cdots + a_{2n}x_n \leq b_2$$

(45)

$$\cdots \cdots \cdots \cdots \cdots \cdots \cdots \cdots$$

$$a_{m1}x_1 + a_{m2}x_2 + \cdots + a_{mn}x_n \leq b_m$$

[4] The interpretation of the dual problem is almost always of interest in applications of linear programming to economic theory. See Dorfman, Samuelson, and Solow [54], pp. 39–63, 166–84; Koopmans [97], pp. 96–101.

(46) $$x_i \geqq 0 \qquad (i = 1, \cdots, n).$$

The dual problem is to minimize

(47) $$f^* = b_1 u_1 + b_2 u_2 + \cdots + b_m u_m$$

subject to

(48)
$$a_{11} u_1 + a_{21} u_2 + \cdots + a_{m1} u_m \geqq c_1$$
$$a_{12} u_1 + a_{22} u_2 + \cdots + a_{m2} u_m \geqq c_2$$
$$\cdots\cdots\cdots\cdots\cdots\cdots\cdots\cdots\cdots$$
$$a_{1n} u_1 + a_{2n} u_2 + \cdots + a_{mn} u_m \geqq c_n$$

(49) $$u_i \geqq 0 \qquad (i = 1, \cdots, m).$$

If we write vectors as column vectors and indicate row vectors as transposes of column vectors, then the primal and dual problems can be written as follows:

maximize $f = C^T X$  
subject to  
$AX \leqq B$  
$X \geqq 0$

and

minimize $f^* = B^T U$  
subject to  
$A^T U \geqq C$  
$U \geqq 0.$

The similarities in the two problems are more easily seen in matrix form. The components of the transpose, $B^T$, of the column vector of constants in the primal become the coefficients in the linear function in the dual, and the transpose, $C$, of the row vector forming the coefficients in the linear function in the primal becomes the column vector of constants in the dual. The number of constraints in the dual equals the number of variables in the primal and there are as many constant terms in the primal as there are variables in the dual. Also, the matrix of coefficients of the inequalities in the dual is the transpose of the matrix $A$ in the primal. The word "dual" is used to indicate that the variables $u_i$ play the same roles in the second problem that the $x_i$ played in the first problem.

For some interesting interrelationships between the primal and dual, consider the following. The matrices of coefficients $A$ and $A^T$ are

$$A = \begin{pmatrix} \overset{A_1}{a_{11}} & \overset{A_2}{a_{12}} & \cdots & \overset{A_n}{a_{1n}} \\ a_{21} & a_{22} & \cdots & a_{2n} \\ \cdots & \cdots & \cdots & \cdots \\ a_{m1} & a_{m2} & \cdots & a_{mn} \end{pmatrix}, \qquad A^T = \begin{pmatrix} \overset{A_1^T}{a_{11}} & \overset{A_2^T}{a_{21}} & \cdots & \overset{A_m^T}{a_{m1}} \\ a_{12} & a_{22} & \cdots & a_{m2} \\ \cdots & \cdots & \cdots & \cdots \\ a_{1n} & a_{2n} & \cdots & a_{mn} \end{pmatrix}.$$

As the symbols above the columns in the matrices suggest, we denote the $i^{\text{th}}$ column of $A$ by $A_i$ and the $i^{\text{th}}$ column of $A^T$ by $A_i^T$ (note that $A_i^T$ is *not* to be interpreted as the transpose of the column vector $A_i$). We can now write the primal and dual problems in a manner which emphasizes the role of inner products of vectors in linear programming. We have respectively, maximize $f = C^T X$

  subject to

$$
\begin{array}{lll}
a_{11}x_1 + a_{12}x_2 + \cdots + a_{1n}x_n \leqq b_1 & A_1^T \cdot X \leqq b_1 & A_1^T \cdot X - b_1 \leqq 0 \\
a_{21}x_1 + a_{22}x_2 + \cdots + a_{2n}x_n \leqq b_2 & A_2^T \cdot X \leqq b_2 & A_2^T \cdot X - b_2 \leqq 0 \\
\cdots\cdots\cdots\cdots\cdots\cdots\cdots\cdots\cdots \quad \text{or} & \cdots\cdots\cdots \quad \text{or} & \cdots\cdots\cdots\cdots \\
a_{m1}x_1 + a_{m2}x_2 + \cdots + a_{mn}x_n \leqq b_m & A_m^T \cdot X \leqq b_m & A_m^T \cdot X - b_m \leqq 0
\end{array}
$$

(50)

(51) $\qquad\qquad x_i \geqq 0 \qquad\qquad X \geqq 0 \qquad\qquad X \geqq 0,$

and minimize $f^* = B^T U$

  subject to

$$
\begin{array}{lll}
a_{11}u_1 + a_{21}u_2 + \cdots + a_{m1}u_m \geqq c_1 & A_1 \cdot U \geqq c_1 & A_1 \cdot U - c_1 \geqq 0 \\
a_{12}u_1 + a_{22}u_2 + \cdots + a_{m2}u_m \geqq c_2 & A_2 \cdot U \geqq c_2 & A_2 \cdot U - c_2 \geqq 0 \\
\cdots\cdots\cdots\cdots\cdots\cdots\cdots\cdots \quad \text{or} & \cdots\cdots \quad \text{or} & \cdots\cdots\cdots \\
a_{1n}u_1 + a_{2n}u_2 + \cdots + a_{mn}u_m \geqq c_n & A_n \cdot U \geqq c_n & A_n \cdot U - c_n \geqq 0
\end{array}
$$

(52)

(53) $\qquad\qquad u_i \geqq 0 \qquad\qquad U \geqq 0 \qquad\qquad U \geqq 0.$

Now $C^T = (c_1, c_2, \cdots, c_n) \leqq (A_1 \cdot U, A_2 \cdot U, \cdots, A_n \cdot U)$ by (52).

Therefore $C^T X \leqq (A_1 \cdot U, A_2 \cdot U, \cdots, A_n \cdot U) \begin{pmatrix} x_1 \\ \cdot \\ \cdot \\ \cdot \\ x_n \end{pmatrix},$

(54) $\qquad C^T X \leqq (A_1 \cdot U)x_1 + (A_2 \cdot U)x_2 + \cdots + (A_n \cdot U)x_n.$

If we have a maximum for $f = C^T X$, it must occur for that vector $X$ for which (54) is an equality, so for an optimal solution we have

$$(A_1 \cdot U)x_1 + \cdots + (A_n \cdot U)x_n = C^T X,$$

or

$$(A_1 \cdot U)x_1 + \cdots + (A_n \cdot U)x_n - c_1 x_1 - \cdots - c_n x_n = 0.$$

Collecting terms, we have for an optimal solution,

$$(A_1 \cdot U - c_1)x_1 + (A_2 \cdot U - c_2)x_2 + \cdots + (A_n \cdot U - c_n)x_n = 0.$$

Since $x_i \geqq 0$ for $i = 1, \cdots, n$ in any feasible solution and since $(A_i \cdot U - c_i) \geqq 0$ by the inequalities (52), the only way that the sum of these terms can be equal to zero is for at least one of the following to hold:

  a. if $x_i > 0$ in the primal, then $(A_i \cdot U - c_i) = 0$;

  b. if $(A_i \cdot U - c_i) > 0$ in the dual, then $x_i = 0$ in the primal.

In other words, if the $i^{th}$ variable in the primal is positive, then the $i^{th}$ inequality in the dual must be an equality, since $(A_i \cdot U - c_i) = 0$ means that $A_i \cdot U = c_i$, and if the $i^{th}$ inequality in the dual is a strict inequality, then the $i^{th}$ variable in the primal must have a zero value.

These and other concepts can be illustrated by means of a simple example. The primal problem is to maximize

$$(55) \qquad f = 2x_1 + 5x_2 \qquad\qquad f = (2 \;\; 5) \begin{pmatrix} x_1 \\ x_2 \end{pmatrix}$$

subject to                                             or

$$(56) \qquad \begin{aligned} x_1 + 4x_2 &\leq 24 \\ 3x_1 + x_2 &\leq 21 \\ x_1 + x_2 &\leq 9 \\ x_1, x_2 &\geq 0 \end{aligned} \qquad\qquad \begin{pmatrix} 1 & 4 \\ 3 & 1 \\ 1 & 1 \end{pmatrix} \begin{pmatrix} x_1 \\ x_2 \end{pmatrix} \leq \begin{pmatrix} 24 \\ 21 \\ 9 \end{pmatrix}$$

$$\begin{pmatrix} x_1 \\ x_2 \end{pmatrix} \geq 0.$$

The dual is to minimize

$$(57) \qquad f^* = 24u_1 + 21u_2 + 9u_3 \qquad\qquad f^* = (24 \;\; 21 \;\; 9) \begin{pmatrix} u_1 \\ u_2 \\ u_3 \end{pmatrix}$$

subject to                                             or

$$(58) \qquad \begin{aligned} u_1 + 3u_2 + u_3 &\geq 2 \\ 4u_1 + u_2 + u_3 &\geq 5 \end{aligned}$$

$$(59) \qquad\qquad u_i \geq 0 \qquad (i = 1, 2, 3) \qquad \begin{pmatrix} 1 & 3 & 1 \\ 4 & 1 & 1 \end{pmatrix} \begin{pmatrix} u_1 \\ u_2 \\ u_3 \end{pmatrix} \geq \begin{pmatrix} 2 \\ 5 \end{pmatrix}$$

$$U \geq 0.$$

In view of the inequalities (58), we have upon substitution of the left-hand sides of (58) for the coefficients 2 and 5,

$$f = 2x_1 + 5x_2 \leq (u_1 + 3u_2 + u_3)x_1 + (4u_1 + u_2 + u_3)x_2,$$

which can be written

$$(60) \qquad f \leq (x_1 + 4x_2)u_1 + (3x_1 + x_2)u_2 + (x_1 + x_2)u_3.$$

Similarly, from $f^* = 24u_1 + 21u_2 + 9u_3$, in view of the inequalities (56) we get the inequality

$$(61) \qquad f^* \geq (x_1 + 4x_2)u_1 + (3x_1 + x_2)u_2 + (x_1 + x_2)u_3.$$

From (60) we have

$$f \leq (x_1 + 4x_2)u_1 + (3x_1 + x_2)u_2 + (x_1 + x_2)u_3 \leq f^*.$$

Since we want to maximize $f$ we would want the equality to hold on the left above, and $f^*$ is also minimized if the equality holds on the right. We have then $f \leq f^*$ for feasible solutions to the problems, and for an optimal solution (if one exists) we have $f = f^*$. Also, if $f = f^*$, then $f^* - f = 0$, where from (61) and (55),

$$f^* - f = (x_1 + 4x_2)u_1 + (3x_1 + x_2)u_2 + (x_1 + x_2)u_3 - 2x_1 - 5x_2 = 0,$$

which can be written,

$$f^* - f = (u_1 + 3u_2 + u_3 - 2)x_1 + (4u_1 + u_2 + u_3 - 5)x_2 = 0.$$

Note the coefficients of $x_1$ and $x_2$. Since $x_1$ and $x_2$ are nonnegative, if $x_1$, the first variable in the primal, is positive in the optimal solution, then its coefficient must be zero in order to preserve the equality above. This means that $u_1 + 3u_2 + u_3 = 2$, and the first inequality in the dual must become an equality. Similar comments can be made if $x_2 > 0$.

There are four theorems of fundamental importance in the theory of linear programming, the first two of which are suggested by the preceding example, and we state them now without proof. These and other important theorems are proved in Good [69], pp. 18–21 and Kuhn and Tucker [98], pp. 3–18 and 53–97. The symbols below refer to the primal and dual problems as stated above in (50), (51) and (52), (53) respectively.

THEOREM 5.  If $X^*$ and $U^*$ are feasible vectors for their respective programs, then $C^T X^* \leqq B^T U^*$.

THEOREM 6.  If $X^*$ and $U^*$ are feasible vectors and if $C^T X^* = B^T U^*$, then $X^*$ and $U^*$ are optimal vectors.

THEOREM 7.  (Duality Theorem). A feasible vector $X^*$ is an optimal vector for the primal problem if and only if there is a feasible vector for the dual such that $B^T U^* = C^T X^*$.

THEOREM 8.  (Existence Theorem.) A necessary and sufficient condition that one (and therefore both) of the linear programming problems have optimal solutions is that both problems have feasible solutions.

### Degeneracy in Linear Programming

Throughout the preceding discussion of linear programming it was assumed that no restraint equation in the converted linear equation form was a linear combination of the others. This assumption ruled out degeneracy, which we now wish to consider. Suppose the linear programming problem is that of (41) and (42). If $P_0$, the column vector of constants, can be expressed as a nonnegative linear combination of fewer than $m$ linearly independent vectors, then the linear programming problem is said to be degenerate. In this case, more than two hyperplanes of dimension $n - 1$ intersect in a common space of dimension $n - 2$, and at least one of the equations among those in (41) is a linear combination of the others. The equations which are linear combinations of the others are redundant, for they express restraints which are already embodied in the other equations.

For a geometrical picture of degeneracy consider a linear programming problem in which we wish to maximize $f(x_1, x_2) = c_1x_1 + c_2x_2$ subject to the inequalities

(1)                                        $a_{11}x_1 + a_{12}x_2 \leqq b_1$

(2)                                        $a_{21}x_1 + a_{22}x_2 \leqq b_2$

(3)                                        $a_{31}x_1 + a_{32}x_2 \leqq b_3$

(4)                                        $a_{41}x_1 + a_{42}x_2 \leqq b_4$

$$x_i \geqq 0 \qquad (i = 1, \cdots, 4).$$

Suppose we further assume that each $a_{ij} > 0$, and that the graphs of the straight lines forming the boundaries of the half spaces defined by (1)–(4) are those shown below with the corresponding numbers (the dashed line is the graph of $f(x_1, x_2) = c_1x_1 + c_2x_2 = k$). The point $B$ is a degenerate extreme point and (3) is a linear combination of (2) and (4). If we were to adjoin a slack variable to each of the inequalities in order to convert them to equalities and then look at the requirements space, we might be under the mistaken

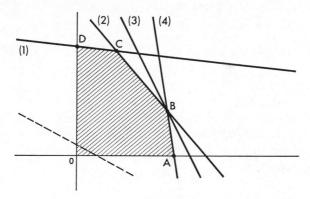

**Figure 13**

impression that the requirements space was four-dimensional and that four linearly independent vectors would provide a basis for requirements space. If we began with a feasible solution and proceeded to find an optimal solution along the path from 0 to $A$ to $B$ by use of the Simplex method, we would discover at the point corresponding to $B$ in solution space that $P_0$ was a linear combination of only three vectors because at this point when the coefficient of some vector became zero in the process of giving the coefficient of another vector the largest possible positive value, the coefficient of a second vector would become zero as well. Since the Simplex method adds vectors one at a time, it could not then move us to the extreme point corresponding to $C$. On the other hand, if the path had been from 0 to $D$ to $C$, the method would arrive at the optimal solution even though there was a degeneracy and even though the correct requirements space is three-dimensional rather than four-dimensional![5]

The Simplex method includes computational procedures for dealing with degeneracy. If at a stage in the solution process two or more vectors assume zero coefficients, then by increasing the coefficients of all vectors having zero coefficients except one by an arbitrarily small positive number $\epsilon$, we can get a feasible solution with an appropriate number of vectors having positive coefficients and then proceed from there.[6]

We have discussed the possibility that there are fewer than $m$ linearly independent vectors in (41), but one might raise the question, can there be more than $m$ linearly independent vectors? The answer is in the negative, and by introducing the concept of the rank of a matrix the reason for this can be made clear. The *rank* of a matrix is defined to be the maximal number of linearly independent column vectors in the matrix. It is a theorem that the maximal number of linearly independent row vectors in a matrix is equal to the maximal number of linearly independent column vectors in the matrix, or as it is more briefly stated, that the row rank and column rank of a matrix are equal. Since there are at most $m$ row vectors in the coefficient matrix of (41), there can be at most $m$ linearly independent row or column vectors.

These considerations suggest the following definitions which are standard in linear programming: *A basic feasible solution* to the linear programming problem in (41) and (42) is a feasible solution with no more than $m$ positive $x_i$, and a *nondegenerate basic feasible solution* is a basic feasible solution with exactly $m$ positive $x_i$.

### APPENDIX

### *The Simplex Method*

The Simplex method consists primarily of a set of operations which will move the linear function from one extreme point of the convex set of feasible solutions to an adjacent extreme point which makes the value of $f$ at least as large. If optimal solutions exist and a degenerate extreme point is not encountered, the technique will move the linear function to an extreme point

---

[5] Since inequality (3) is a linear combination of (2) and (4), the optimal solution to the problem when (3) has been deleted is the same as that for the system with (3) included. However, if (3) is deleted, the requirements space becomes three-dimensional. The Simplex method can give the optimal solution if the path avoids a degenerate extreme point even if we have an incorrect requirements space because all slack vectors have zero coefficients in the linear function.

[6] There is an extensive literature on computational techniques for dealing with degeneracy. For a particularly clear discussion see Dorfman, Samuelson, and Solow [54], pp. 80–93.

most distant from the origin (or to an extreme point closest to the origin in a minimization problem), and this extreme point will yield a maximum (or a minimum) value for $f$.

Although the method will be illustrated by means of a simple problem whose optimal solution is obvious from the appropriate geometry in two-space, most of the techniques that would be used in solving more lengthy problems can be presented in this simple format and only two iterations of the method are required to reach an optimal solution to the problem.

Suppose the problem is to maximize $f = 2x_1 + 5x_2$
subject to

(1)
$$x_1 \leq 4$$

(2)
$$x_2 \leq 6$$

(3)
$$x_1 + x_2 \leq 8.$$

Introducing slack variables we get the equation system

$$x_1 + x_3 = 4$$

$$x_2 + x_4 = 6$$

$$x_1 + x_2 + x_5 = 8,$$

which can be written in the vector equation form,

$$\begin{pmatrix} 1 \\ 0 \\ 1 \end{pmatrix} x_1 + \begin{pmatrix} 0 \\ 1 \\ 1 \end{pmatrix} x_2 + \begin{pmatrix} 1 \\ 0 \\ 0 \end{pmatrix} x_3 + \begin{pmatrix} 0 \\ 1 \\ 0 \end{pmatrix} x_4 + \begin{pmatrix} 0 \\ 0 \\ 1 \end{pmatrix} x_5 = \begin{pmatrix} 4 \\ 6 \\ 8 \end{pmatrix}.$$
$$\quad P_1 \qquad\quad P_2 \qquad\quad P_3 \qquad\quad P_4 \qquad\quad P_5 \qquad\quad P_0$$

The linear programming problem is then to maximize

(4)
$$f = 2x_1 + 5x_2 + 0x_3 + 0x_4 + 0x_5$$

subject to

(5)
$$P_1 x_1 + P_2 x_2 + P_3 x_3 + P_4 x_4 + P_5 x_5 = P_0$$

(6)
$$x_i \geq 0 \qquad (i = 1, \cdots, 5).$$

Consider the Simplex tableau on the following page. The vectors $P_1, \cdots, P_5$, and $P_0$ appear in the first stage but their order of appearance has been changed. $P_0$ appears first, followed by the *basis* vectors $P_3, P_4, P_5$. Then the *structural* vectors $P_1$ and $P_2$ are entered. The $c_j$ values in the first row of the tableau are the coefficients of the vectors in the linear function (4) which we seek to maximize. In the first stage of the tableau the $z_j$ row is filled out with zeros. Also, the elements in the first stage of the tableau which are in the intersection of the $P_i$ row and the $P_j$ column will be denoted $a_{ij}$. For example, $a_{30}$ denotes the number 4 which is in the intersection of the row labeled $P_3$

and the column labeled $P_0$ and $a_{51}$ denotes the number 1 lying in the inter-section of the $P_5$ row and $P_2$ column.

Merely writing down the vectors in this way provides a feasible solution, for all the vectors appearing at the top of the table have been stated in terms of the vectors appearing at the side. If $x_3 = 4$, $x_4 = 6$, $x_5 = 8$, then in order for (4) to be satisfied, $x_1$ and $x_2$ must both be zero. Hence, $(0, 0)$ is a feasible solution and we have for this point $f = 2(0) + 5(0) + 0 + 0 + 0 = 0$.

The following test is used to determine whether the solution is an optimal feasible solution, whether it is necessary to go on, or whether there is no finite solution.

1. If all $z_j - c_j \geq 0$, an optimal solution has been obtained.

2. If $z_j - c_j < 0$ for some column, then one of two things has occurred:

**SIMPLEX TABLEAU**

| $c_j$ | | 0 | 0 | 0 | 0 | 2 | 5 |
|---|---|---|---|---|---|---|---|
| | Vector | $P_0$ | $P_3$ | $P_4$ | $P_5$ | $P_1$ | $P_2$ |
| 0 | $P_3$ | 4 | 1 | 0 | 0 | 1 | 0 |
| 0 ← | $P_4$ | 6 | 0 | 1 | 0 | 0 | 1 |
| 0 | $P_5$ | 8 | 0 | 0 | 1 | 1 | 1 |
| $z_j$ | | 0 | 0 | 0 | 0 | 0 | 0 |
| $z_j - c_j$ | | 0 | 0 | 0 | 0 | $-2$ | $-5$ |
| 0 | $P_3$ | 4 | 1 | 0 | 0 | 1 | 0 |
| 5 → | $P_2$ | 6 | 0 | 1 | 0 | 0 | 1 |
| 0 ← | $P_5$ | 2 | 0 | $-1$ | 1 | 1 | 0 |
| $z_j$ | | 30 | 0 | 5 | 0 | 0 | 5 |
| $z_j - c_j$ | | 30 | 0 | 5 | 0 | $-2$ | 0 |
| 0 | $P_3$ | 2 | 1 | 1 | $-1$ | 0 | 0 |
| 5 | $P_2$ | 6 | 0 | 1 | 0 | 0 | 1 |
| 2 → | $P_1$ | 2 | 0 | $-1$ | 1 | 1 | 0 |
| $z_j$ | | 34 | 0 | 3 | 2 | 2 | 5 |
| $z_j - c_j$ | | 34 | 0 | 3 | 2 | 0 | 0 |

a. if all the $a_{ij}$ in that column are nonpositive, the solution is infinite;

b. if some $a_{ij}$ in that column is nonnegative, further iterations are necessary.

If a new iteration is required we proceed as follows. Some structural vector will be used to replace a basis vector, so we have a "replacing" vector (denoted by subscript $k$) and a "replaced" vector (denoted by subscript $r$). The replacing vector will be that structural vector with the most negative $z_j - c_j$ value. In the first stage of the tableau, for example, we would select $P_2$ to be the replacing vector since for $P_2$ we have $z_j - c_j = -5$.

The replaced vector $P_r$ is determined by means of the rule

$$\theta = \operatorname*{minimum}_{i} \frac{a_{i0}}{a_{ik}}, \ a_{ik} > 0, \ (i = 1, 2, 3),$$

which tells us to divide each of the components of the replacing vector $P_5$ into the corresponding components of the vector $P_0$ (denoted by $a_{i0}$). The vector associated with the smallest such ratio is the vector to be replaced. In the first stage we have for the three ratios

(7) $$\frac{a_{30}}{a_{32}} = \frac{\text{not defined}}{(a_{32} = 0)}; \ \frac{a_{40}}{a_{42}} = \frac{6}{1} = 6; \ \frac{a_{50}}{a_{52}} = \frac{8}{1} = 8.$$

Therefore $P_4$ is selected as the vector to be replaced (this is indicated by an arrow pointing away from the tableau).

The second stage of the tableau is now made to reflect these changes. We first write in the labels of the new basis vectors $P_3$, $P_2$, and $P_5$ in the second column. Then we determine the elements which go into the row opposite the new basis vector $P_2$. The elements in this row are obtained by means of the expression

$$a'_{kj} = \frac{a_{rj}}{a_{rk}}.$$

In the present instance, $r = 4$ and $k = 2$, since the replaced and replacing vectors were $P_4$ and $P_2$ respectively. Thus $a_{rk} = a_{42} = 1$. The rule then tells us to enter as elements in the new row those elements in the same row of the preceding stage divided by 1 (in this case the rule merely indicates that we enter the elements in the former row in the row corresponding to $P_2$ in the second stage). The elements in the remaining rows are determined by the rule

$$a'_{ij} = a_{ij} - \frac{a_{rj}}{a_{rk}} a_{ik} = a_{ij} - (a'_{kj})(a_{ik}).$$

As an example we determine the element to go in the intersection of the $P_3$ row and the $P_0$ column in the second stage. In this case, $i = 3, j = 0$, and we have from above, $r = 4$ and $k = 2$. Hence for this element the rule states

$$a'_{30} = a_{30} - (a'_{20})(a_{32}) = 4 - 6(0) = 4.$$

To determine the next element in the same row, $a'_{33}$, the rule states, since $i = 3$ and $j = 3$,

$$a'_{33} = a_{33} - (a'_{23})(a_{32}) = 1 - (0)(0) = 1.$$

Finally, to determine the elements in the $z_j$ row, multiply each element in each column by the corresponding element in the $c_j$ column in that stage and then add these products. For example, the elements in the $P_0$ column in the second stage are 4, 6, and 2. Multiplying each of these by the corresponding elements in the $c_j$ column and then adding, we get $0 \cdot 4 + 5 \cdot 6 + 0 \cdot 2 = 30$, the first element in the $z_j$ row.

In the last stage of the tableau all $z_j - c_j = 0$, so we have arrived at the optimal solution, $x_1 = 2$, $x_2 = 6$, $x_3 = 2$, and

$$f = 2(2) + 5(6) + 0(2) + 0 + 0 = 34.$$

Note that $x_3$, the coefficient of the slack vector $P_3$, has a zero coefficient in the linear function and so does not contribute to the value of $f$.

If at a given stage in carrying out the Simplex procedure it is discovered that as a replacing vector is added to the basis not one but two or more vectors are replaced, then the linear programming problem is degenerate. Degeneracy is indicated when several of the ratios of the type (7) are tied for being the smallest. In this instance, if all the vectors having the smallest ratios were taken out of the basis there would not be a sufficient number of vectors remaining to continue the procedure. Since only one vector should be replaced in each stage of the solution, a convention is needed to resolve a tie when it occurs. One rule is to select that vector associated with one of the smallest ratios which has the smallest subscript; another rule is to drop the vector associated with one of the smallest ratios whose subscript occurs first in a table of random numbers. Although there are more complicated rules for resolving ties, experience has shown that either of these two rules will permit further iterations to be made and an optimal solution to be reached if one exists.

# AN ANALYTICAL AND GRAPHICAL COMPARISON OF MARGINAL ANALYSIS AND MATHEMATICAL PROGRAMMING IN THE THEORY OF THE FIRM*

*by* YUAN-LI WU
*and* CHING-WEN KWANG

## INTRODUCTION

Mathematical programming has been widely recognized as an important development in applied mathematics in the postwar period. Motivated initially by the need for more effective methods of solving military and business problems, its methods of analysis have found an increasing field of application in recent years. Yet in spite of this success, comparatively little effort has been directed toward the systematic introduction of the basic concepts and techniques of mathematical programming to economic theory at a level of mathematical sophistication that can be readily understood by economists with little background in mathematics.[1]

The purpose of this paper is to clarify some aspects of the relationship between mathematical programming and conventional marginal analysis in the theory of the firm. It is intended to provide an exposition of mathematical

---

* The authors are grateful to Professor K. E. Boulding and Dr. W. A. Spivey for helpful comments and suggestions; they are especially indebted to Dr. Spivey for his careful reading of, and comments on, the first draft of this paper. They also wish to acknowledge their indebtedness to Dean J. W. Culliton of the College of Commerce, University of Notre Dame, and the Reverend T. F. Divine, S.J., former Dean of the College of Business Administration, Marquette University, for their encouragement and support.

[1] Some notable contributions in this area are: Dorfman [53], [52]; Baumol [15]; Dorfman, Samuelson, and Solow [54]. Some basic papers on linear programming are collected in Koopmans [96]. Also important are Koopmans [97], and the group of articles by Cooper and others [41].

programming analysis of the firm without the use of advanced mathematical techniques. Although parts of the material presented may appear somewhat complicated and technical, to follow the mathematical treatment requires only a familiarity with some basic concepts of modern mathematics and a knowledge of elementary algebra and analytic geometry.[2] Some knowledge of intermediate economic analysis is the only other prerequisite.

The theory and techniques of mathematical programming as a practical tool for business decision-making are of special significance to the theory of the firm.[3] First, mathematical programming provides a new tool of analysis which brings to light certain economic problems that tend to be neglected in the conventional analysis. Second, the experience and knowledge gained from the application of mathematical programming to managerial problems may serve as an empirical test of traditional assumptions concerning business behavior. It may indeed be argued that developments in the whole field of management science offer the economist new empirical data on, and fresh insights into, business behavior which, one may hope, will enrich the contents of economic theory and eventually increase its "usefulness." In this paper, however, we shall be concerned only with mathematical programming as a new tool of economic analysis.

The economic theory of the firm is essentially a formulation of the basic principles governing the rational behavior of business enterprises. Traditionally the central problem of the economics of the firm is the analysis of pricing and output decisions under assumptions of profit maximization and rationality. The principal analytical tool in this part of economic theory is that of marginal analysis. In the following sections we shall consider in detail how the basic concepts of mathematical programming can be incorporated in the analysis of the firm and the way in which the standard economic problems of the firm can be restated in mathematical programming form. For this purpose, a number of mathematical programming models of the firm have been constructed. These are similar to the models frequently found in textbooks on intermediate economic analysis. Attention is focused upon the cost functions of the firm as the latter seem to constitute the initial point of discussion in most conventional texts.

[2] The basic mathematical knowledge required to follow these recent developments is presented in Dr. W. A. Spivey's chapter, "Basic Mathematical Concepts," in this volume.

[3] Recent management literature abounds with the application of mathematical programming to business problems. For a nonmathematical survey see Henderson and Schlaifer [77]. A more comprehensive survey of such applications can be found in Vazsonyi [165]. Discussions of such applications may also be found in books on operations research. See, for instance, Sasieni, Yaspan, and Friedman [143]; Churchman, Ackoff, and Arnoff [35]; McCloskey, Trefethen [104].

For current developments in this field, one should consult the journals *Management Science* and *Operations Research*. A summary of some operations research problems is presented in the paper "Operations Research: Its Nature and Scope, with Some Comments concerning its Impact on the Smoothing of Cyclical Fluctuations," by Dr. H. H. Jenny in this volume.

The results yielded by these mathematical programming models are then compared with the conclusions derived from conventional marginal analysis. It is intended that such a comparison will demonstrate both the similarities and differences between mathematical programming and the usual marginal analysis. This procedure will also indicate the limitations and advantages of both approaches. It should be clear that the formal and abstract models presented here cannot be perfect representations of economic reality: they are only designed to facilitate the analysis of complex, multivariate systems. While one must always guard against the many pitfalls in the use of mathematical models, such abstract constructions are nevertheless necessary in order to reveal in full the underlying correspondence, or the lack of it, between the two methods of analysis.

In this paper we shall be concerned entirely with short-run output decisions of the firm. The short-run period is a time interval during which the range of choice open to the firm is limited by the presence of one or more fixed factors (constraints). Examples of these are machine-tool capacity, available plant and equipment, warehouse space, working capital, supervisory staff, etc. In the short run, output can be varied only by variations in the level of utilization of the fixed factors.

The first section of this paper will be devoted to an examination of short-run output decisions of a firm with given input and output prices. The assumption of constant input and output prices necessarily confines this part of our analysis to a firm in a purely competitive market.[4] It will be seen that the methods of linear programming can be most effectively applied under these conditions.[5]

The assumption of pure competition will be relaxed in the second section. We shall present a few models of the determination of price and output by a firm under variable input and output prices. There it will be found necessary to employ nonlinear programming techniques. Because of limitations of space, this topic is not given extensive treatment.

Most applications of mathematical programming to the theory of the firm have been concerned with short-run problems. It is possible, and indeed necessary, to consider the applicability of mathematical programming methods to the long-run analysis of the firm. Similarly, dynamic programming can be used in the analysis of the equilibrium of the firm through time. These extensions and further analyses, however, are not considered in this paper.[6]

---

[4] This does not, however, imply that practical applications of mathematical programming can be made only by firms in markets approximating the pure competition model. In fact, most of the pioneering work in the application of the technique to business problems is done in large firms which quite obviously do not operate in a purely competitive market.

[5] For a general mathematical exposition of linear programming, see Spivey, *op. cit.*, pp. 61–79.

[6] These topics will be given fuller treatment in a forthcoming study by the authors.

## SHORT-RUN ANALYSIS OF THE FIRM WITH
## GIVEN INPUT AND OUTPUT PRICES

The analysis of the firm usually begins with an inquiry into the short-run pricing and output decisions of a single-product firm in a purely competitive market. The basic characteristics of such a market are: first, that the firms in the market produce a homogeneous product; second, that the number of firms and their individual size relative to the market are such that none of them can exert any perceptible influence on market price by its own action. Consequently, the demand curve for the product of the firm will appear as a horizontal straight line at the level of the prevailing market price. The firm, under such circumstances, will have no "price policy" or "price decision" to make. In seeking to maximize profit, it will only have to select that rate of output which offers the largest aggregate profits for the period under consideration.

In the short-run period the firm employs by definition a given amount of fixed factors—or a fixed plant—with certain variable factors. Output is varied by changing the amount of variable inputs used.[7] Correspondingly, the firm has certain fixed costs which would be incurred even at zero output. If it does not produce at all, its net loss would be equal to its total fixed costs. The goal of profit maximization in the short run therefore requires that the firm should select that level of output which will either maximize positive profit or minimize loss (negative profit).

It is evident that as long as the market price is above average variable costs, the firm would be able to recover through production some part of the fixed costs. The general rule which the firm follows to maximize profit or minimize loss is to produce at an output at which marginal cost is equal to marginal revenue provided that price exceeds the average variable costs of output.

This analysis of the short-run behavior of the firm is generally illustrated in graphical form as in Figure 1. Here the price line is the demand curve for the firm's output showing the going market price at which it can sell any output. The cost curves show the variation of its average total costs, average variable costs, average fixed costs, and marginal cost of production with variation in output at given factor prices. As the size of the firm is small relative to the market, its purchases of factor services are also assumed to have no perceptible effect on factor prices.

Under this set of demand and cost conditions, the output which will maximize the aggregate profit of the firm for the period under consideration is $OX_1$. This level of output also implies a given proportion between the fixed and variable factors. Thus both output and factor combinations are uniquely determined.

---

[7] One might add that output may also be varied by changing the level of utilization of the fixed factors. While this may happen independently of variations in the amount of variable input used, the difference between the two types of changes is not always clearly brought out in conventional analysis even though it is sometimes implied.

The transition from the marginal analysis to mathematical programming requires essentially a new way of looking at the economic problem of the firm. In conventional theory the firm is conceived of as varying the level of inputs so as to produce that output which will maximize its profit in the time period under consideration. The firm's choice is from among different rates of consumption of factor inputs and of production of outputs.

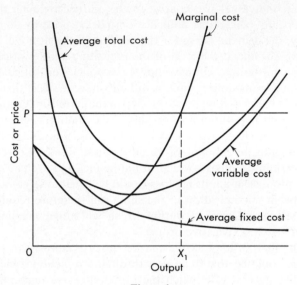

**Figure 1**

The basic concept in mathematical programming is that of a "process" or "activity."[8] The firm is viewed as producing an output by one or more processes. Instead of making decisions directly as to the quantities of productive factors to be employed, the typical economic choice confronting the firm, in this analysis, consists of decisions as to the levels at which various processes of production are utilized.

A process of production is simply a specific way of producing a given output. It is defined as soon as the relationship among the rates of inputs and the rates of output is specified. Each process implies a given set of relationships among factor inputs and between factor inputs and output. Thus, for example, if in any time period the production of one unit of product A requires the use of two units of capital and one unit of labor, the ratio of 1 to 2 to 1 would represent a specific process of producing A at unit level. The amounts of inputs required to produce a specific quantity of output is determined by the technological conditions of production: the output being the maximum obtainable from the given set of input rates. In this view, a firm can

---

[8] On the basic concept of a process or activity, see Dorfman [52], pp. 797–8, 803–5; Dorfman, Samuelson, Solow [54], pp. 132–3; Koopmans [97], pp. 71–9.

vary its output only by changing the level of utilization of a process or by substitution among the processes available to it. In either case there will be changes in the quantities of inputs employed. But these changes would have been brought about indirectly by the firm's decisions concerning changes in the levels of operation of the various processes.

In fact, the usual short-run average variable cost curve may be viewed as representing an infinite number of processes. Each point on the average variable cost curve implies a given proportion between fixed and variable factors. In mathematical programming terminology every point corresponds to a separate process. In order to apply the methods of mathematical programming to the analysis of the firm, it is necessary to restate the economic problem of the firm in terms of processes. The following five cases are formulated to illustrate this approach. These cases will also be analyzed by means of the familiar cost and demand curves to bring out both the similarities and differences of these two approaches.

In considering the conditions under which a firm makes its decision regarding the choice of its production processes and the size of its output, distinctions may be made: (1) between single- and multiple-product firms, (2) between the presence of a single constraint (fixed factor) and that of multiple constraints, and (3) between fixed factors that are specialized with respect to production processes and those that are used by more than one production process. Furthermore, in the case of multiple-product firms, there may be joint products, or there may be joint demand for some of the products, or some of the products may constitute at the same time inputs for other products. Leaving out the complications that arise out of the last statement, we may classify all firms into at least the following categories:

*Type I.* A single-product firm subject to a single constraint, but the fixed factor is nonspecialized with respect to available processes. This is examined in Case I, and again in Case III.

*Type II.* A single-product firm subject to multiple constraints, but each of the fixed factors is specialized with respect to a different process. This is examined in Case II.

*Type III.* A single-product firm subject to multiple constraints, and some or all of the fixed factors are nonspecialized with respect to processes.

*Types IV, V,* and *VI* parallel types I–III and deal with multiple-product firms.

Since a firm belonging to Type V above (i.e., multiple-product, multiple-constraint, fixed factor being specialized) may be looked upon as a number of separate firms in effect, each producing a separate product, the analysis in Case II may be extended to it (again ignoring the complication of joint demand). Similarly, Type IV may be regarded as an extension of Type I if all the processes are regarded as means of producing the same product, i.e., revenue, irrespective of the physical nature of the products in question. Accordingly, only Types III and VI have also to be discussed. Case IV discusses them under the assumption that the fixed factors are perfectly divisible while Case V adopts the assumption that the fixed factors are divisible only in discrete units.

### Case I: A Single Product Firm with one Nonspecialized Fixed Factor

We consider first a simple case in which a firm produces a single product, $A$, with two processes utilizing one nonspecialized fixed factor and one variable factor. The fixed factor is assumed to be continuously divisible. The productive activities of the firm can be represented by the following table:

|  | PROCESS | | AVAILABLE |
| *Factor requirement per unit of output:* | I | II | RESOURCES |
| Fixed factor | $a_1$ | $a_2$ | $F$ |
| Variable factor | $b_1$ | $b_2$ | Unlimited |
| Variable cost per unit output | $vc_1$ | $vc_2$ | |

In this table, $a_1$, $a_2$, $b_1$, $b_2$, $vc_1$, $vc_2$, and $F$ are all constants. Let $a_1$ be less than $a_2$ and $vc_1$ greater than $vc_2$. Denote the market price of the product by $p$. It is to be noted that each process is defined in terms of a set of constant rates of consumption of inputs per unit of output of $A$. Since the firm is assumed to be operating in a purely competitive market, both the market price for its product and the prices it has to pay for productive factors can be regarded as given constants. Consequently, the dollar values of the variable factor requirements per unit of output, $vc_1$ and $vc_2$, are also constant. Following Dorfman, we shall refer to the difference between gross revenue (sales price × quantity of output sold) and total variable, or direct, cost (variable cost per unit × quantity of output produced) as the net revenue.[9]

Under the above assumptions, the net revenue per unit for each of the two processes is therefore also constant. In order to maximize profit (or minimize loss) in the short-run period, the firm will seek to maximize total net revenue. The economic choice of the firm is the selection of the levels at which either of the two processes, or a combination of both, should be employed so as to maximize net revenue subject to the restriction that no more than 100 per cent of the fixed factor can be used. The existence of the fixed factor sets a limit to the total output that can be produced in the short-run period.

GRAPHIC SOLUTION. This situation is portrayed graphically in Figure 2. In this diagram, output by process I is measured along the horizontal axis and

[9] There is no standard term for this magnitude in economic literature. In management accounting terminology it is called the marginal income or marginal balance. "Net revenue" is usually used in economic analysis for the difference between gross revenue and *total* cost. But its use as the difference between gross revenue and variable cost seems to be established in linear programming literature. It will be noted that changes in inventory are not explicitly considered in this formulation, since this is usually ignored in conventional analysis.

output by process II along the vertical axis. $OX_1$ is the output by process I when the full amount of the fixed factor, i.e., $F$, is employed; $OX_2$ represents total output when process II alone is fully utilized. The line segment $X_1X_2$ then represents the levels of output that can be produced by all possible combinations of the two processes which absorb 100 per cent of the fixed factor.[10] At point $A$, for instance, output is $AV + AW (= OV + OW)$, $OV$ being produced by process II, $OW$

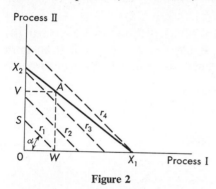

**Figure 2**

being produced by process I. At any point on $X_1X_2$ the full fixed capacity of the firm would be absorbed. $X_1X_2$, therefore, is a "production possibility curve" of the firm: it defines the boundary between the attainable and the unattainable positions in the short-run period. The set of feasible outputs and the corresponding combinations of processes are represented by the triangle $OX_1X_2$, including its three sides. The absolute value[11] of the slope of the line segment $X_1X_2$ measures the rate of output substitution of process I for process II.[12] This rate is the decrease in the number of units produced by process II required to permit an increase of one unit in output by process I.

Let $x_1$ be the output by process I; $x_2$, the output by process II. $x_1$ and $x_2$ are referred to as "process levels" or "levels of activity." Also, let $r$ denote total net revenue from any level of output. Total net revenue, then, is given by

$$r = (p - vc_1)x_1 + (p - vc_2)x_2.$$

This is the "objective function" that the firm seeks to maximize in the short-run period. In Figure 2, the dashed lines $r_1, r_2, r_3, r_4, \cdots$, are iso-revenue lines. Each one of the iso-revenue lines represents a given level of net revenue;

[10] Mathematically, all points on $X_1X_2$ are convex linear combinations of $X_1$ and $X_2$ and are given by $(\lambda X_1 + (1 - \lambda)X_2)$ where $0 \leqq \lambda \leqq 1$.

[11] The absolute value of a real number $x$ is $x$ itself if $x$ is nonnegative, or the positive number $-x$ if $x$ is negative. It is denoted by $|x|$. See Richardson [138], p. 227. In subsequent discussions in this paper, we shall refer to the absolute value of the slope of a curve simply as its slope.

[12] PROOF: By definition, the absolute value of the slope of

$$X_1X_2 = \frac{OX_2}{OX_1}.$$

By assumption, $\quad OX_2 = F/a_2, OX_1 = F/a_1.$

Therefore, $\quad \dfrac{OX_2}{OX_1} = \dfrac{a_1}{a_2}.$

$a_1/a_2$ gives us the number of units produced by process II which employs the same amount of the fixed factor as one unit output by process I. For instance, if $a_1 = 1$, $a_2 = 2$, then to increase output by process I by one unit, one-half unit by process II must be given up.

every point on a given iso-revenue line corresponds to a combination of the two processes that yields the same net revenue. The system of iso-revenue lines is defined by the equation

$$r = (p - vc_1)x_1 + (p - vc_2)x_2$$

where $r$ is a parameter. In Figures 2, 3, and 4 the iso-revenue lines are drawn in the first quadrant. This implies that both $(p - vc_1)$ and $(p - vc_2)$ are greater than zero. If $(p - vc_1) < 0$, and $(p - vc_2) > 0$, then the iso-revenue lines will lie in the second quadrant. If $(p - vc_1) > 0$, and $(p - vc_2) < 0$, the $r$ lines will be in the fourth quadrant. If net revenues per unit from both processes are negative, the iso-revenue lines will be in the third quadrant.[13]

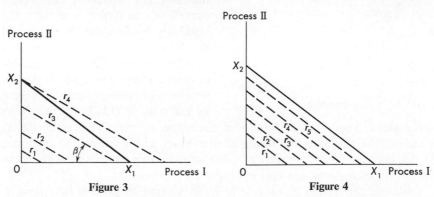

**Figure 3**                          **Figure 4**

Given $p$, $vc_1$, and $vc_2$, all the iso-revenue lines will be parallel since their slope is equal to $(p - vc_1)/(p - vc_2)$.[14] In the diagram, the greater the net revenue, the higher will be the iso-revenue line.

The graphical solution of the maximizing problem is to find the point in the triangle $OX_1X_2$ that lies on the highest possible iso-revenue line. This is the familiar procedure of indifference-curve analysis. We impose on the field of choice open to the firm a system of indifference curves, i.e., the iso-revenue lines, and seek to determine the optimum position among those which are possible.

Since net revenue increases as the iso-revenue lines move away from the origin in Figure 2, the combinations of processes that need to be considered are those represented by points lying on $X_1X_2$. The choice of the optimal

[13] Although no process can be operated at a negative level and hence the second, third, and fourth quadrants have no "real" meaning, it will be seen from what follows that our analytical tool will yield a meaningful solution in every possible case.

[14] Consider, for example, $r_1$ in Figure 2. We have by definition

$$OW(p - vc_1) = OS(p - vc_2);$$

hence,

$$\frac{OS}{OW} = \frac{p - vc_1}{p - vc_2}.$$

But $\tan \alpha = OS/OW$ which is the measure of the slope of $r_1$. Given $p$, $vc_1$, and $vc_2$, $OS/OW$ is a constant. The same can be shown for all the "$r$" lines.

level of process combination is made by selecting that point on $X_1X_2$ which lies on the highest iso-revenue line. If the slope of $X_1X_2$ differs from that of the iso-revenue lines, the optimal process level will correspond to either $X_1$ or $X_2$.[15]

In Figure 2, the absolute value of the slope of the iso-revenue lines is greater than that of $X_1X_2$ $\left[\dfrac{p - vc_1}{p - vc_2} > \dfrac{OX_2}{OX_1}\right]$. $X_1$ is the point that lies on the highest attainable iso-revenue line. Output is $OX_1$; only process I will be used. In Figure 3, the slope of the iso-revenue lines is less than that of $X_1X_2$ $\left[\dfrac{p - vc_1}{p - vc_2} < \dfrac{OX_2}{OX_1}\right]$. The highest possible iso-revenue line will intersect $X_1X_2$ at $X_2$. There output will be $OX_2$ and process II only will be used. In both cases, the output and factor combinations, which follow as a result of the process combination selected, are uniquely determined.

If the iso-revenue lines are parallel to $X_1X_2$ $\left[\dfrac{p - vc_1}{p - vc_2} = \dfrac{OX_2}{OX_1}\right]$, there will be no unique solution. Geometrically, the highest possible iso-revenue line will coincide with $X_1X_2$. Consequently, all combinations of the two processes represented by points on $X_1X_2$ will yield the same net revenue which in this case is the highest attainable. This is illustrated in Figure 4. In this situation, however, $X_1$ and $X_2$ are also optimal points since both lie on the line segment $X_1X_2$.

The criterion by which the firm will determine the optimal process combinations is whether the slope of the iso-revenue lines is greater than, equal to, or less than the slope of the production possibility line $X_1X_2$. Algebraically, the criterion is whether

$$\frac{p - vc_1}{p - vc_2} \gtreqless \frac{OX_2}{OX_1}\left[= \frac{a_1}{a_2}\right].$$

In the situation depicted in Figure 4, we have seen that

$$\frac{p - vc_1}{p - vc_2} = \frac{OX_2}{OX_1};$$

simplifying and collecting terms, we get

$$(OX_1 - OX_2)p = OX_1 \cdot vc_1 - OX_2 \cdot vc_2.\text{[16]}$$

---

[15] The formal similarity between this analysis and the linear programming illustration of the classical theory of international trade presented by Dorfman, Samuelson, and Solow should be noted. See Dorfman, Samuelson, and Solow [54], pp. 31–2. Also, the similarity between this presentation and Leontief's discussion in [101] is to be noted.

[16] Since

$$\frac{(p - vc_1)}{(p - vc_2)} = \frac{OX_2}{OX_1},$$

$$(p - vc_1)OX_1 = (p - vc_2)OX_2, \text{ and}$$

$$OX_1 \cdot p - OX_1 \cdot vc_1 = OX_2 \cdot p - OX_2 \cdot vc_2;$$

therefore,

$$(OX_1 - OX_2)p = OX_1 \cdot vc_1 - OX_2 \cdot vc_2.$$

This expression shows that if process I is substituted for process II, the increase in gross revenue due to a larger output would be exactly offset by an equal increase in variable cost. Conversely, any decrease in gross revenue would be offset by an equal saving in variable cost. The firm is therefore indifferent to the substitution of one process for the other.

LINEAR PROGRAMMING FORMULATION. We can express the economic problem of the firm in linear programming terms. The short-run problem of the firm is to maximize:

(1)                              $r = (p - vc_1)x_1 + (p - vc_2)x_2$

subject to

(2)                              $a_1x_1 + a_2x_2 \leqq F,$

(3)                              $x_1 \geqq 0$ and $x_2 \geqq 0.$

It should be noted that although the condition is not stated explicitly, $r$ is required to be either greater than or equal to zero. The economic nature of the problem requires that $p$, $vc_1$, and $vc_2$ be positive numbers; and $x_1$ and $x_2$ are positive or zero. If $p$ should be less than $vc_1$ and/or $vc_2$, then the corresponding process or processes will not be used. Consequently, $r \geqq 0$ is implied in the problem.

In this formulation, $r$ is a linear function defined over a closed, convex set (triangle $OX_1X_2$ together with the boundary lines). The linear function in such a case will take on its maximum or minimum value at an extreme point of the convex polygon; if colinearity should arise, then the maximum or minimum may also be at a nonextreme point.[17] The extreme points of the convex set are the origin, $O$, and $X_1$ and $X_2$. The origin obviously gives a minimum value of $r$. The solution will therefore be either $X_1$ or $X_2$, or an infinite number of points if colinearity occurs.

If we substitute the co-ordinates of $X_1(OX_1, O)$ into the linear function, the value of $r$ is $(p - vc_1)OX_1$. Similarly, substituting the co-ordinates of $X_2(O, OX_2)$ into the equation for $r$, we obtain $(p - vc_2)OX_2$. Whether $X_1$ or $X_2$ will give the maximum value of $r$ depends on the slope of the $r$ lines. The requisite conditions may be specified as follows:

1. If $X_1$ gives the maximum value of $r$, then $(p - vc_1)OX_1 > (p - vc_2)OX_2$. Transposing, we get

$$\frac{p - vc_1}{p - vc_2} > \frac{OX_2}{OX_1}.$$

This is the situation depicted in Figure 2. The firm will use process I only and produce output $OX_1$.

[17] On this theorem of the maximization of a linear function defined over a convex polygon, see, for instance, Kemeny, Snell, and Thompson [91], p. 256; Spivey, *op. cit.*, p. 61–65. Colinearity is defined as follows: the graphs of two linear functions are colinear if the coefficients of one are constant multiples of the coefficients of the other. See Spivey, *op. cit.*, p. 29–32.

2. Similarly we can show that if $X_2$ gives the maximum value of $r$, then

$$\frac{p - vc_1}{p - vc_2} < \frac{OX_2}{OX_1}.$$

This situation is portrayed in Figure 3. Only process II will be used and output is $OX_2$.

3. In the case of colinearity,

$$\frac{p - vc_1}{p - vc_2} = \frac{OX_2}{OX_1}.$$

Net revenue is maximized at either $X_1$ or $X_2$, or any other point on the line segment $X_1X_2$. This is illustrated in Figure 4.

The above conclusions are exactly the same as those obtained from the graphical analysis. We find that the optimal program of the firm requires under all circumstances no more than one process. In this case there is one effective constraint in addition to the requirements that $x_1$ and $x_2$ must be nonnegative. Our result is an illustration of an important theorem in linear programming, namely, that the number of processes involved in an optimal solution will be no more than the number of constraints in the problem.[18] Also, if the firm produces at all, the optimal program requires the full utilization of the single fixed factor in question.

This analysis can be extended immediately to a firm with more than two processes. If there are $n$ processes available, we can denote the unit fixed factor requirement of a process by $a_i(i = 1, 2, \cdots, n)$; unit variable cost of a process by $vc_i(i = 1, 2, \cdots, n)$; output by a process, $x_i(i = 1, 2, \cdots, n)$. The linear programming problem is then to maximize:

(1) $$r = (p - vc_1)x_1 + (p - vc_2)x_2 + \cdots + (p - vc_n)x_n$$

subject to

(2) $$a_1x_1 + a_2x_2 + \cdots + a_nx_n \leqq F, \text{ and}$$

(3) $$x_1 \geqq 0, x_2 \geqq 0, \cdots, x_n \geqq 0.$$

AN ALTERNATIVE GRAPHIC SOLUTION. The solution of this case can also be represented by a process ray diagram as in Figure 5. In this diagram process I is represented by the ray $OA$; process II by $OB$. The axes are scaled in units of the factors. $OF$ measures the quantity of the fixed factor. The horizontal line $FF'$ is the fixed factor limitation line which divides the diagram into the attainable (or feasible) region and the unattainable (or nonfeasible) region.[19]

The process rays $OA$ and $OB$ are scaled respectively in units of output. Each point on a process ray corresponds to a given output, the co-ordinates

[18] Dorfman, Samuelson, and Solow [54], pp. 78, 160–5.
[19] The closed half space defined by $FF'$ and the area below it is the feasible region. The open half space above $FF'$ represents the nonfeasible region.

of which being the factor inputs required. We shall denote unit output on $OA$ by $\lambda_1$ and that on $OB$ by $\lambda_2$. In Figure 5, $OA_1 = \lambda_1$ and $OB_1 = \lambda_2$. The scale unit on each process ray is determined uniquely by the unit factor

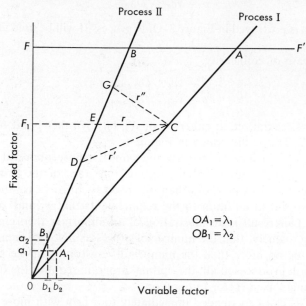

**Figure 5**

requirements of the process. The line segment corresponding to one unit of output on one ray need not, therefore, be equal in length to that on the other ray.[20] Since $OX_1$ and $OX_2$ are the outputs produced by process I and process II respectively when the fixed factor is fully utilized, $OA$ corresponds to $OX_1$ and $OB$ corresponds to $OX_2$. We may write:

$$OA = \lambda_1 \cdot OX_1$$

$$OB = \lambda_2 \cdot OX_2.$$

Furthermore, since price and unit variable costs are constant, each point on a process ray will also represent a given amount of net revenue. To maximize net revenue the firm will choose that point in the feasible section of the diagram which lies on the highest iso-revenue line. Three iso-revenue lines with different slopes are shown and labeled $r$, $r'$, and $r''$. The relevant range of choice for the firm consists of points on the line segment $AB$; the point on $AB$ which will correspond to the maximum net revenue clearly depends on the slope of the iso-revenue lines.

[20] From the Pythagorean theorem, we have in Figure 5:

$$OA_1 = \lambda_1 = \sqrt{a_1^2 + b_1^2}.$$

$$OB_1 = \lambda_2 = \sqrt{a_2^2 + b_2^2}.$$

Consider first an iso-revenue line such as $r(CE)$ which is parallel to $FF'$. It is clear that the line segment $AB$ will then coincide with the highest attainable iso-revenue line. Hence any point on $AB$ is an optimum program. In other words, the firm will maximize net revenue as long as it utilizes fully the fixed factor. This is the situation portrayed in Figure 4. We shall show that the same criterion established there holds also in Figure 5.

In Figure 5, $OC$ corresponds to the output produced by process I with $F_1$ of the fixed factor, i.e., $OC/\lambda_1$; $OE$ represents the output produced by process II with the same quantity of fixed factor, i.e., $OE/\lambda_2$. We can write immediately

$$\frac{OE}{OC} = \frac{OB}{OA} = \frac{\lambda_2}{\lambda_1} \frac{OX_2}{OX_1}.$$

Since we assume now that $CE$ is an iso-revenue line,

$$\frac{OC}{\lambda_1} (p - vc_1) = \frac{OE}{\lambda_2} (p - vc_2),$$

i.e.,

$$\frac{OE}{OC} = \frac{\lambda_2}{\lambda_1} \frac{(p - vc_1)}{(p - vc_2)};$$

therefore,

$$\frac{p - vc_1}{p - vc_2} = \frac{OX_2}{OX_1}.$$

We have thus proved that in Figure 5, if the iso-revenue lines $(r)$ are parallel to the horizontal axis, the condition $\dfrac{p - vc_1}{p - vc_2} = \dfrac{OX_2}{OX_1}$ holds and the line segment $AB$ corresponds to all programs that will maximize net revenue.

If the iso-revenue lines have a positive slope such as $r'(CD)$, then $B$ will correspond to the optimum program. Output will be $OX_2 = \left(\dfrac{OB}{\lambda_2}\right)$ and process II will be employed. By construction

$$OD = k \cdot OE \, (0 < k < 1).$$

We can write:

$$\frac{OD}{OC} = k \cdot \frac{OE}{OC} < \frac{OE}{OC}.$$

But

$$\frac{OE}{OC} = \frac{OB}{OA} = \frac{\lambda_2}{\lambda_1} \frac{OX_2}{OX_1}.$$

Therefore,

$$\frac{OD}{OC} < \frac{\lambda_2}{\lambda_1} \frac{OX_2}{OX_1}.$$

Since $CD$ is an iso-revenue line,

$$\frac{OD}{\lambda_2}(p - vc_2) = \frac{OC}{\lambda_1}(p - vc_1).$$

Thus,

$$\frac{OD}{OC} = \frac{\lambda_2}{\lambda_1}\frac{p - vc_1}{p - vc_2}$$

and

$$\frac{p - vc_1}{p - vc_2} < \frac{OX_2}{OX_1}.$$

This is the case illustrated above in Figure 3. Process I is here seen to be altogether inefficient and therefore should be left out completely.

If the iso-revenue lines slope downward such as $r''$, point $A$ will correspond to the output that maximizes net revenue. Process I will be used and output will be at $OX_1 \left( = \dfrac{OA}{\lambda} \right)^{21}$. Figure 2 illustrates this situation. This completes our demonstration that the diagram used in this section will yield identical results as the diagrams in the preceding section.

The advantage of the process ray diagram lies in the fact that it can be used in a two-dimensional figure to portray a single-product firm with more than two processes. Each different process can be represented by a different ray. In the diagram employed in Figures 2, 3, and 4, only a firm with two processes can be represented since we measure output by the processes on the two axes. The disadvantage of the process ray diagram is that it can portray only two inputs.

ANALYSIS IN TERMS OF COST AND DEMAND CURVES. The determination of the optimal program of production can also proceed by specifying for each process the relationship between the variable unit costs (which are also the marginal costs) and the going market price of the product. Three different cases can be distinguished.

---

[21] In this case,

$$OG = h \cdot OE, \qquad h > 1$$

$$\frac{OG}{OC} = \frac{h \cdot OE}{OC} = h \cdot \frac{\lambda_2}{\lambda_1}\frac{OX_2}{OX_1} > \frac{\lambda_2}{\lambda_1}\frac{OX_2}{OX_1}.$$

Again,

$$\frac{OG}{\lambda_2}(p - vc_2) = \frac{OC}{\lambda_1}(p - vc_1).$$

Therefore,

$$\frac{OG}{OC} = \frac{\lambda_2}{\lambda_1}\frac{p - vc_1}{p - vc_2}$$

and

$$\frac{p - vc_1}{p - vc_2} > \frac{OX_2}{OX_1}.$$

1. First we consider the situation where the market price of the product is less than the variable costs per unit of both processes. Clearly in this case the firm will minimize loss by not producing at all.[22]

2. If market price is less than the variable cost per unit in process I but greater than the variable cost per unit in process II, the firm will use only process II and output will be $OX_2$. This is represented in Figure 6.

It should be noted that we assume that $a_1 < a_2$ and $vc_1 > vc_2$. This is a necessary assumption because the firm is assumed to have two efficient

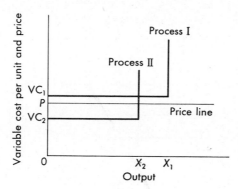

**Figure 6**

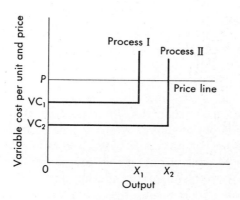

**Figure 7**

[22] If

$$p < vc_1, \text{ i.e., } p - vc_1 < 0,$$

and

$$p < vc_2, \text{ i.e., } p - vc_2 < 0,$$

then

$$r = (p - vc_1)x_1 + (p - vc_2)x_2 \leqq 0$$

and attains its maximum value when both $x_1$ and $x_2$ are equal to zero. In Figures 2, 3, 4, the iso-revenue lines will lie in the third quadrant.

processes available. Otherwise if $a_1$ were greater than $a_2$, and $vc_1$ greater than $vc_2$, then process I would be inferior to process II and there would be no effective problem of choice at all. This situation is depicted in Figure 7.

3. The market price is greater than the variable cost per unit both in process I ($vc_1$) and in process II ($vc_2$). The firm's problem is whether to use one of the processes or a combination of the two. This is illustrated in Figure 8.

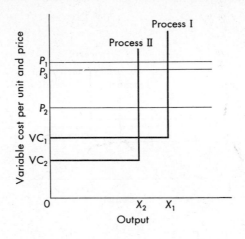

**Figure 8**

Suppose first that the firm is producing an output $OX_1$, utilizing process I fully. At this level of output the firm is earning a net revenue of $(p - vc_1)OX_1$. The question is whether it is possible to increase its net revenue by substituting process II for process I.

For each unit of output, the two processes require different amounts of the fixed factor which, in the short run, constitutes the effective limitation to the amount of total output produced. We have denoted this requirement for process I by $a_1$ and that for process II by $a_2$. The ratio $a_1/a_2$ ($= OX_2/OX_1$) gives us the number of units of output that can be produced by process II with the fixed capacity released from producing one unit less by process I. It is, therefore, the rate of output substitution of process II for process I.

Whether it will be profitable for the firm to substitute process II for process I depends on the relative magnitude of the net revenue lost by giving up one unit by process I—$(p - vc_1)$—and the net revenue gained by producing $a_1/a_2$ unit by process II—$(p - vc_2)OX_2/OX_1$—instead. The conditions that determine the firm's choice of process can be classified as follows:

a. If the net revenue gained is less than the net revenue lost, it will not be profitable for the firm to substitute process II for process I. This is depicted in Figure 2 where the slope of the iso-revenue lines is greater than that of $X_1 X_2$.[23] The firm will maximize net revenue by utilizing process I fully. Output will be $OX_1$. In Figure 8 this condition holds at market price $p_1$.

b. If the net revenue gained is greater than the net revenue lost by substituting process II for process I, the firm will continue to substitute process II for process I until process II alone is used and output will be $OX_2$. This is illustrated above in Figure 3. In Figure 8 this is illustrated when market price is $p_2$.

c. If the net revenue gained is equal to the net revenue lost, the firm will be indifferent as to which process to use. As long as the fixed factor is fully utilized, any one process or a combination of the two processes will yield the same net revenue. This is the colinearity case represented in Figure 4. In Figure 8 this situation corresponds to a market price of $p_3$.

DERIVATION OF THE SUPPLY CURVE. The preceding section has presented an analysis of the economic choice of the firm in terms of the concepts of marginal analysis. This analysis, however, has not been formulated in terms of the familiar marginal cost curve and supply curve of the firm which occupy such a prominent place in the conventional approach. We shall now illustrate the construction of the conventional marginal cost curve from the production processes assumed.

Since we assume that the unit fixed factor requirement of process II is greater than that of process I ($a_2 > a_1$) but that the unit variable cost of process II is lower than that in process I ($vc_2 < vc_1$), for any output up to $OX_2 (= F/a_2)$, process II will be used. For output exceeding $OX_2$, process I will have to be used. If the firm is producing an output $OX_2$, then in order to produce one more unit, output by process II must be reduced by $a_1/(a_2 - a_1)$ so that sufficient fixed capacity may be released for production by process I. The corresponding increase in output by process I will be $a_2/(a_2 - a_1)$ units.[24]

---

[23] If

$$(p - vc_2) \frac{OX_2}{OX_1} < (p - vc_1),$$

then,

$$(p - vc_2)OX_2 < (p - vc_1)OX_1,$$

i.e.,

$$\frac{(p - vc_1)}{(p - vc_2)} > \frac{OX_2}{OX_1}.$$

A similar procedure can be used to demonstrate the results stated in the following two cases.

[24] PROOF: When the total output is $OX_2$, for each unit increase in output by process I, the firm must give up $a_1/a_2$ units by process II. If output by process I is increased by $x$ units, then output by process II must be reduced by $[a_1/a_2] x$ units. If the change should increase total output by 1, i.e., resulting in a total output of $(OX_2 + 1)$, we must require

$$x - [a_1/a_2] x = 1,$$

i.e.,

$$x [(a_2 - a_1)/a_2] = 1.$$

From this we get

$$x = a_2/(a_2 - a_1).$$

Consequently, the corresponding decrease in the number of units of output by process II will be

$$\frac{a_1}{a_2} \cdot x = \frac{a_1}{a_2} \cdot \frac{a_2}{a_2 - a_1} = \frac{a_1}{a_2 - a_1}.$$

We may therefore tabulate marginal cost as follows:

| Total Output $x$ | Lowest attainable total variable cost TVC | Marginal cost MC |
|---|---|---|
| 0 to $OX_2 (= F/a_2)$ | $vc_2 \cdot x$ | $vc_2$ |

$OX_2 + 1\left(= \dfrac{F}{a_2} + 1\right)$ 

$vc_2 \cdot \left[OX_2 - \left(\dfrac{a_1}{a_2 - a_1}\right)\right]$ 

$vc_1 \cdot \dfrac{a_2}{a_2 - a_1}$ [25]

$+ vc_1 \cdot \left[\dfrac{a_2}{a_2 - a_1}\right]$ 

$- vc_2 \cdot \dfrac{a_1}{a_2 - a_1}$

$= vc_2 \cdot OX_2 + \left[vc_1 \cdot \dfrac{a_2}{a_2 - a_1} - vc_2 \cdot \dfrac{a_1}{a_2 - a_1}\right]$

$(OX_2 + 1) + 1$
$= OX_2 + 2$ 

$vc_2 \cdot \left[OX_2 - 2 \cdot \dfrac{a_1}{a_2 - a_1}\right]$ 

$vc_1 \cdot \dfrac{a_2}{a_2 - a_1}$

$+ vc_1 \left[2 \cdot \dfrac{a_2}{a_2 - a_1}\right]$ 

$- vc_2 \cdot \dfrac{a_1}{a_2 - a_1}$

$= vc_2 \cdot OX_2 + 2\left[vc_1 \cdot \dfrac{a_2}{a_2 - a_1} - vc_2 \cdot \dfrac{a_1}{a_2 - a_1}\right]$

. . . . . . . . . . . . . . . . . . . . . . . . . . . . . . . . . . . . . . . . . . . . . . . .

$OX_2 + [OX_1$
$- (OX_2 + 1)]$
$= OX_1 - 1$ 

$vc_2 \left\{OX_2 - \left[OX_1 - (OX_2 + 1)\right]\dfrac{a_1}{a_2 - a_1}\right\}$ 

$vc_1 \cdot \dfrac{a_2}{a_2 - a_1}$

$+ vc_1 \left\{\left[OX_1 - (OX_2 + 1)\right]\dfrac{a_2}{a_2 - a_1}\right\}$ 

$- vc_2 \cdot \dfrac{a_1}{a_2 - a_1}$

$= vc_2 \cdot OX_2 + \left[OX_1 - (OX_2 + 1)\right]$

$\left[vc_1 \cdot \dfrac{a_2}{a_2 - a_1} - vc_2 \cdot \dfrac{a_1}{a_2 - a_1}\right]$

$OX_2 + [OX_1 - OX_2]$
$= OX_1$ 

$vc_2 \cdot OX_2$

$+ \left[OX_1 - OX_2\right]\left[vc_1 \cdot \dfrac{a_2}{a_2 - a_1} - vc_2 \cdot \dfrac{a_1}{a_2 - a_1}\right]$ 

$vc_1 \cdot \dfrac{a_2}{a_2 - a_1}$

$= vc_1 \cdot OX_1$ 

$- vc_2 \cdot \dfrac{a_1}{a_2 - a_1}$

This is a step function which rises after the maximum output by process II has been reached. The graph of the *MC* curve is shown in Figure 9. The broken

[25] This is the marginal cost of producing the $(OX_2 + 1)^{\text{th}}$ unit.

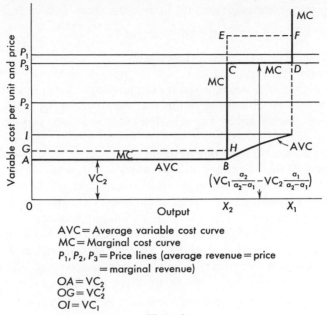

AVC = Average variable cost curve
MC = Marginal cost curve
$P_1, P_2, P_3$ = Price lines (average revenue = price
= marginal revenue)
$OA = VC_2$
$OG = VC_2'$
$OI = VC_1$

**Figure 9**

marginal cost curve means that marginal cost assumes different values at the point of discontinuity depending on whether the change in output is an increase or a decrease.

The average cost schedule can also be derived as in the following table:

| Total output $(x)$ | Total variable cost $(TVC)$ | Average variable cost $(AVC)$ |
|---|---|---|
| $0 < x \leqq OX_2$ | $vc_2 \cdot x$ | $vc_2$ |
| $OX_2 + 1$ | $vc_2 . OX_2 + \left[ vc_1 \cdot \dfrac{a_2}{a_2 - a_1} - vc_2 \cdot \dfrac{a_1}{a_2 - a_1} \right]$ | |
| | $= vc_2 . OX_2 + MC$ (marginal cost) | $\dfrac{vc_2 . OX_2 + MC}{OX_2 + 1}$ |
| $OX_2 + 2$ | $vc_2 . OX_2 + 2MC$ | $\dfrac{vc_2 . OX_2 + 2MC}{OX_2 + 2}$ |
| $\cdots\cdots\cdots$ | $\cdots\cdots\cdots\cdots\cdots\cdots\cdots$ | $\cdots\cdots\cdots$ |
| $\begin{aligned} &OX_2 + [OX_1 \\ &- (OX_2 + 1)] \\ &= OX_1 - 1 \end{aligned}$ | $vc_2 \cdot OX_2 + [OX_1 - (OX_2 + 1)]MC$ | |
| | | $\dfrac{vc_2 \cdot OX_2 + [OX_1 - (OX_2 + 1)] MC}{OX_1 - 1}$ |
| $\begin{aligned} &OX_2 + [OX_1 - OX_2] \\ &= OX_1 \end{aligned}$ | $vc_2 \cdot OX_2 + [OX_1 - OX_2] MC$ | $\dfrac{vc_2 \cdot OX_2 + [OX_1 - OX_2] MC}{OX_1}$ |
| | $= vc_1 \cdot OX_1$ | $= vc_1.$ |

We may express the average cost for all outputs above $OX_2$ in general form:

For $OX_2 < x \leqq OX_1$ the average variable cost $= \dfrac{vc_2 \cdot OX_2 + (x - OX_2)MC}{x}$

which represents a rectangular hyperbola.[26]

The average cost curve is also shown in Figure 9. Both curves turn up to infinity at output $OX_1$ which is the maximum output the firm can produce. Three price lines are also drawn in this diagram to depict the firm's decisions under various market prices. The price lines are, of course, also the marginal revenue curves.

At a price $p_2$, the firm will obviously maximize net revenue at output $OX_2$, using process II only. Contrary to conventional analysis, however, marginal cost is not equal to marginal revenue at this point because the marginal cost curve is not a continuously rising, smooth curve. Although this formal marginal condition does not hold, it is still a valid principle that if market price is greater than average variable cost, the firm should continue to increase its output as long as marginal revenue is more than marginal cost. We may formulate the marginal condition for profit maximization in the following way: if net revenue is maximized at an output of $n$ units, then at this output

$$\text{marginal cost of} \atop \text{the } n^{\text{th}} \text{ unit} \quad \underset{=}{\leqq} \quad {\text{marginal revenue} \atop (= \text{market price})} \quad < \quad {\text{marginal cost of the} \atop (n + 1)^{\text{th}} \text{ unit}}$$

It is to be noted that this condition embraces the second-order equilibrium condition in conventional analysis. In other words, the second-order condition that marginal cost be above marginal revenue to the right of the equilibrium point and below marginal revenue to the left of that point is always satisfied if such an output exists.

If market price is at $p_3$, the firm will maximize net revenue by producing either $OX_2$ or $OX_1$. It can be seen in Figure 9 that total net revenue is measured by the area $ABCp_3$ at either output. At $p_1$, net revenue will be maximized at an output of $OX_1$. The supply schedule of the firm can be constructed from Figure 9 as follows:

| Price ($p$) | Output ($x$) | Process employed |
|---|---|---|
| $0 < p < vc_2$ | 0 | None |
| $vc_2 \leqq p < \left[ vc_1 \dfrac{a_2}{a_2 - a_1} - vc_2 \dfrac{a_1}{a_2 - a_1} \right]$ | $OX_2$ | II |
| $p = \left[ vc_1 \dfrac{a_2}{a_2 - a_1} - vc_2 \dfrac{a_1}{a_2 - a_1} \right]$ | $OX_2 - OX_1$ | II, or I, or a combination of both |
| $p > \left[ vc_1 \dfrac{a_2}{a_2 - a_1} - vc_2 \dfrac{a_1}{a_2 - a_1} \right]$ | $OX_1$ | I |

[26] Since $vc_2$, $OX_2$, and $MC$ are all constants, the average cost function is of the type:

$$y = \frac{a_1 x + b_1}{a_2 x + b_2}$$

which represents a rectangular hyperbola; and, for the range of output specificed, the corresponding average cost curve is a section of the hyperbola.

The supply curve in Figure 9 is the broken line OABCD. It will be observed that (1) the firm will not produce in the short-run until market price is equal to the minimum average variable cost ($= vc_2$); (2) for a wide range of price variation, output is completely inelastic; (3) the firm will either produce at full capacity or not at all.

This analysis can be readily reconciled with the criteria developed in the linear programming graphic solution. For $vc_2 \leq p < p_3$ in Figure 9 output is $OX_2$. It can be shown that if $p < p_3$ $\left( = vc_1 \dfrac{a_2}{a_2 - a_1} - vc_2 \dfrac{a_1}{a_2 - a_1} \right)$ then $\dfrac{p - vc_1}{p - vc_2} < \dfrac{OX_2}{OX_1}$, which is the case illustrated in Figure 3.[27] The case of colinearity illustrated in Figure 4 corresponds to $p = p_3$ in Figure 9. Finally, if $p > p_3$ in Figure 9, we can show that $\dfrac{p - vc_1}{p - vc_2} > \dfrac{OX_2}{OX_1}$, which is shown in Figure 2.

Changes in input prices will be reflected in Figure 9 in the form of downward or upward shifts of the $MC$ and $AVC$ curves without changes in their shape. If factor price rises, the marginal cost curve may shift upward from $ABCD$ to the dashed line $GHCEF$. If the product price was $p_1$ before the rise in factor price, then the equilibrium output would now fall from $OX_1$ to $OX_2$. We observe again that output does not vary continuously with changes in factor price. In this illustration, at a product price of $p_1$, output will fall from $OX_1$ to $OX_2$ only after factor price has risen to such an extent so that $\left( vc_1 \dfrac{a_2}{a_2 - a_1} - vc_2 \dfrac{a_1}{a_2 - a_1} \right) > p_1$. This analysis can be readily extended to cover decreases in factor price and for different product prices.

THE TRANSPORTATION PROBLEM: AN ILLUSTRATION. The transportation problem is one of the earliest problems to have been solved successfully by linear programming techniques. The solution also has important applications to other business and economic problems. It may therefore be instructive to compare briefly the marginal analysis approach with linear programming in

[27] PROOF: If $p < \left( vc_1 \dfrac{a_2}{a_2 - a_1} - vc_2 \dfrac{a_1}{a_2 - a_1} \right)$,

then $\qquad (a_2 - a_1)p < (vc_1 \cdot a_2 - vc_2 \cdot a_1)$,

i.e., $\qquad (p - vc_1)a_2 < (p - vc_2)a_1$, and

$$\frac{p - vc_1}{p - vc_2} < \frac{a_1}{a_2}.$$

But $\qquad \dfrac{a_1}{a_2} = \dfrac{F}{a_2} \Big/ \dfrac{F}{a_1} = OX_2 / OX_1 \text{: therefore}$

we have $\qquad \dfrac{p - vc_1}{p - vc_2} < \dfrac{OX_2}{OX_1}.$

This proof can be easily extended to the other two conditions.

the transportation problem.[28] Consider, for example, a transportation problem in which there are two warehouses and three retail stores. In this type of problem we assume the capacity of each warehouse, the requirement of each retail store, and unit cost of shipping the product from each warehouse to each store to be given. Hence the total quantity of the product to be shipped from the available warehouses and the total quantity required at all the retail stores are also constant. The problem is to determine the pattern of shipments with the least total shipping cost.

Each routeing, or pattern of shipment, can be regarded as a "process," or "activity." The total output of every process, i.e., the total quantity of product shipped, is equal to the total requirements of the retail stores. For each route we can compute a total cost. This total cost will generally be different for different patterns of shipment.

Since each pattern of shipment is either used to ship the total quantity required or is not used at all,[29] the average cost of a route pattern may be regarded as the ratio of its total cost to total requirements. This magnitude can also be taken as the marginal cost per unit of that process. For each route pattern, or process, we can plot a graph of its average cost (and/or marginal cost). In Figure 10, a few average variable cost curves are drawn. All average cost curves turn up to infinity at the capacity quantity shipped because increases in variable cost will not increase the quantity shipped after the full capacity of the warehouses has been utilized.

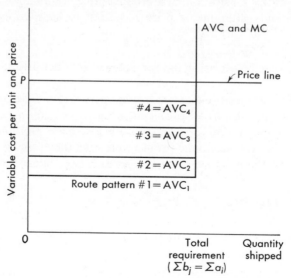

**Figure 10**

[28] For discussion of the linear programming solution of the transportation problem, see, for instance, Vazsonyi [165], Chap. 2; Gass [68], Chap. 10.

[29] The problem can be readily modified by setting up "dummy" stores if the warehouses do not have to be emptied entirely.

If we assume the product shipped to the retail stores can all be sold at a given market price, then in order to maximize net revenue the firm will select a pattern of shipment that will result in the lowest average cost.[30] In terms of Figure 10, if market price is $p$, the firm will select the route pattern represented by the lowest $AVC$ curve. If the $AVC$ curves are known to the firm, then the optimum process can be determined. This is what conventional marginal analysis would tell us.

The above discussion can be clarified by defining the following terms:

$x_{ij}$ = the amount shipped from the $i^{\text{th}}$ warehouse to the $j^{\text{th}}$ store;

$c_{ij}$ = the unit shipping cost from the $i^{\text{th}}$ warehouse to the $j^{\text{th}}$ store;

$a_i$ = the total capacity of the $i^{\text{th}}$ warehouse;

$b_j$ = total requirement of the $j^{\text{th}}$ store.

Then the average direct cost of any route pattern is given by $\sum_{i=1}^{m} \sum_{j=1}^{n} c_{ij} \cdot x_{ij} \Big/ \sum_{j=1}^{n} b_j$. This is what the firm would seek to minimize subject to the conditions:

(1) $\sum_{j=1}^{n} x_{ij} = a_i$ for $i = 1, 2, \cdots, m$; (2) $\sum_{i=1}^{n} x_{ij} = b_j$ for $j = 1, 2, \cdots, n$; and

(3) $x_{ij} \geqq 0$.

In actual fact, of course, the problem of the firm is to discover the route pattern which yields the lowest total cost. A trial-and-error method will generally be tedious and often impractical because of the sheer number of alternatives available. Moreover, a rule is required to determine when the best possible program is achieved. In other words, the information on which the "marginal solution" is based requires linear programming techniques to obtain. The marginal analysis in this case can indicate the property of the optimum solution but it does not provide a rule that leads to the best possible program.

### Case II: A Single-product Firm with several Specialized Fixed Factors and Multiple Processes

In this case we assume that the firm has available a number of processes which can be used simultaneously in the production of a single product $A$. Each process requires the use of a specialized fixed factor in combination with the variable factor. The production processes can be summarized in the following table.

---

[30] Usually, there will be more than one pattern of shipment that will give the lowest possible total cost.

|  |  | PROCESS |  |  |
| --- | --- | --- | --- | --- |
| *Factor requirement per unit output* | I | II | III | IV $\cdots$ N |
| Fixed factor | $a_1$ | $a_2$ | $a_3$ | $a_4 \cdots a_n$ |
| Variable factor | $b_1$ | $b_2$ | $b_3$ | $b_4 \cdots b_n$ |
| Variable cost per unit | $vc_1$ | $vc_2$ | $vc_3$ | $vc_4 \cdots vc_n$ |
| *Total resources available* |  |  |  |  |
| Fixed factor | $F_1$ | $F_2$ | $F_3$ | $F_4 \cdots F_n$ |
| Variable factor |  |  | unlimited |  |
| Process levels (output per process) | $x_1$ | $x_2$ | $x_3$ | $x_4 \cdots x_n$ |
| Capacity output $F_i/a_i$ | $OX_1$ | $OX_2$ | $OX_3$ | $OX_4 \cdots OX_n$ |
| Market price of output | $p$ | $p$ | $p$ | $p \cdots p$ |

where $a_i$, $b_i$, $vc_i$, $F_i$, and $p$ are all constants.

The available processes can be arranged in an array with respect to unit variable cost such that

$$vc_1 < vc_2 < vc_3 < \cdots < vc_n.$$

The economic problem of the firm is to find the combination of processes, and hence the corresponding output, that maximizes net revenue,

$$r = (p - vc_1)x_1 + (p - vc_2)x_2 + \cdots + (p - vc_n)x_n.$$

GRAPHIC SOLUTION. In the graphical representation of this case shown in Figure 11, we utilize a number of pairs of rectangular axes. Thus $OL_1$ and $OL_2$ are co-ordinate axes with origin at $O$; $O'L_3$ and $O'L_4$ are co-ordinate axes with origin at $O'$, etc. We measure output by process I on $OL_1$ and output by process II on $OL_2$. Similarly, outputs by process III and process IV are measured by reference to the co-ordinate axes $O'L_3$ and $O'L_4$; and so on. The capacity output by each process is marked off on the appropriate axis.

Here the $r_i$ ($i = 1, 2, 3, \cdots$) lines again represent a family of iso-revenue curves. The slope of the $r_i$ lines is equal to $\tan \alpha = (p - vc_1)/(p - vc_2)$. The $r_i'$ ($i = 1, 2, \cdots$) lines are another set of iso-revenue curves drawn with reference to the co-ordinate axes $O'L_3$ and $O'L_4$. Each line represents combinations of process III and process IV that yield a given net revenue. The slope of this family of iso-revenue lines is $\tan \beta = (p - vc_3)/(p - vc_4)$. It may be noted that the net revenue represented by $r_1'$ is the same as the net revenue represented by $r_5$ as both pass through $O'$. But $r_1'$ should be read with reference to $O'$ as the origin and $O'L_3$ and $O'L_4$ as the co-ordinate axes. It is clear that we can draw iso-revenue lines for processes V and VI with reference to co-ordinate axes $O''L_5$ and $O''L_6$, and so forth. These, however, are not shown in Figure 11.

The rectangle $OX_1O'X_2$ represents all feasible combinations of process I and process II and their corresponding outputs. At $O'$, for instance, process I and process II are simultaneously fully employed and output is $(OX_1 + OX_2)$. Similarly, the rectangle $O'X_3O''X_4$ represents all feasible combinations of process III and process IV and the corresponding outputs. We can represent the available processes of the firm and all feasible combinations by a series of rectangles such as $OX_1O'X_2$ and $O'X_3O''X_4, \cdots$ .

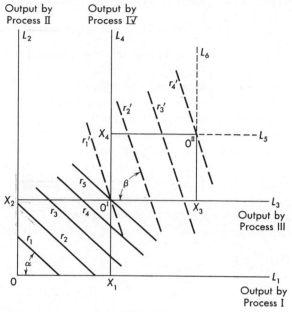

**Figure 11**

Consider first the rectangle $OX_1O'X_2$. If both $(p - vc_1)$ and $(p - vc_2)$ are positive, clearly the combination of process I and process II that lies on the highest iso-revenue line is represented by $O'$. At $O'$, output is $(OX_1 + OX_2)$; the net revenue from process I and process II is maximized and is equal to $(p - vc_1)OX_1 + (p - vc_2)OX_2$. The same reasoning can be applied to process III and process IV. Here the set of all feasible combinations of the two processes is represented by the rectangle $O'X_3O''X_4$. The point in this rectangle that touches the highest relevant iso-revenue line $(r'_4)$ is $O''$. Output is $(OX_3 + OX_4)$ and net revenue is $(p - vc_3)OX_3 + (p - vc_4)OX_4$. If we limit our investigation to the case where the firm has four processes, obviously total net revenue will be maximized when the net revenue from process I and process II and the net revenue from process III and process IV are both maximized. The optimal production plan of the firm is represented by $O'$ and $O''$: all four processes will be fully utilized; output will be $(OX_1 + OX_2 + OX_3 + OX_4)$.

This analysis can be extended immediately to a firm with any finite number of processes. In Figure 11 the set of rectangles $OX_1O'X_2$, $O'X_3O''X_4$, etc., represents all feasible combinations of the available processes and their corresponding outputs. Profit maximization requires moving from $O$ to $O'$ to $O''$, etc., that is, from an extreme point of one rectangle to an extreme point of another rectangle in a northeasterly direction as long as the net revenues yielded from the processes are positive. In the diagram this condition is shown by the slope and position of the iso-revenue lines: when the net revenue from a combination of the two processes $(i)$ and $(i + 1)$ is nonnegative, i.e.,

$$(p - vc_i)x_i + (p - vc_{i + 1})x_{i + 1} \gtreqless 0, \ (i = 1, 3, 5, 7, \cdots)$$

the family of iso-revenue lines will be in the first quadrant with reference to the appropriate axes.

The above argument indicates that, for a firm with $n$ processes, profit will be maximized (or loss minimized) in the short run by employing fully all processes from process I to process $i$, where $i = 1, 2, \cdots, n$, if the market price of the product, $p$, is greater than the variable cost per unit in process $i(vc_i)$ but less than the unit variable cost in process $i + 1(vc_{i + 1})$. Since we assumed $vc_1 < vc_2 < vc_i < vc_{i + 1} \cdots < vc_n$, if $(p - vc_i) > 0$, then $(p - vc_1)$, $(p - vc_2)$, $\cdots$, $(p - vc_{i - 1})$ must all be positive. Furthermore, $(p - vc_1) > (p - vc_2) > \cdots > (p - vc_i)$. Consequently, net revenue will be maximized by utilizing all processes up to the $i^{\text{th}}$ process fully.

If $i = n$, then all processes will be employed to their full extent.

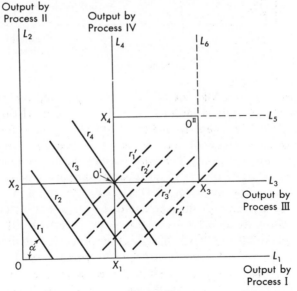

**Figure 12**

If $(p - vc_3) > 0$ but $(p - vc_4) < 0$, the $r'$ lines will be in the fourth quadrant of the $O'L_3L_4$ plane and sloping upward. This is shown in Figure 12. Net revenue will be maximized at $X_3$ as this will be the point in the rectangle $O'X_3O''X_4$ that lies on the highest iso-revenue line $r'_4$ in the diagram. This means that the firm will utilize processes I, II, and III fully and produce an output $(OX_1 + OX_2 + OX_3)$. Note that if $(p - vc_4) < 0$, then by assumption $(p - vc_5)$, $(p - vc_6)$, $\cdots$, are all negative.

If both $(p - vc_3)$ and $(p - vc_4)$ are negative, then the net revenue from any level of output by process III and process IV will be negative. This is portrayed in Figure 13. The higher the iso-revenue line, then, the greater is the negative

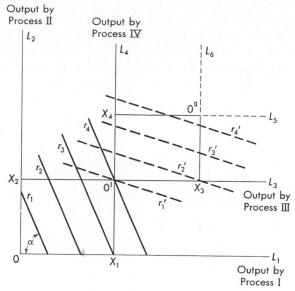

**Figure 13**

net revenue or loss. The firm will clearly minimize loss from these two processes by selecting a combination of the processes represented by $O'$ which lies on the zero net revenue line $r_1'$. At $O'$, process III and process IV are not employed (or employed at zero level). Total output by the firm then will be $(OX_1 + OX_2)$ with process I and process II fully utilized.

In case the net revenue from any process is equal to zero, the process may or may not be employed. The criterion of net revenue maximization will not suffice to indicate the firm's decision.

LINEAR PROGRAMMING FORMULATION. The mathematical formulation of the firm's short-run problem is to maximize:

(1) $$r = (p - vc_1)x_1 + (p - vc_2)x_2 + \cdots + (p - vc_n)x_n$$

subject to

$$a_1x_1 \leqq F_1,$$

$$a_2x_2 \leqq F_2,$$

(2) $$\cdot \ \cdot \ \cdot \ \cdot \ \cdot \ \cdot$$

$$\cdot \ \cdot \ \cdot \ \cdot \ \cdot \ \cdot \ \cdot$$

$$a_nx_n \leqq F_n; \text{ and}$$

(3) $$x_1 \geqq 0, \ x_2 \geqq 0, \cdots, \ x_n \geqq 0.$$

As we have seen above, the decision as to whether a process, $i$, ($i = 1, 2,$ $3, \cdots$) is to be used depends on whether ($p - vc_i$) is greater or less than zero. Total net revenue would be maximized by utilizing in full all processes up to and including the $i^{\text{th}}$ process if

$$vc_i < p < vc_{i+1} \qquad (i = 1, 2, 3, \cdots).$$

CONVENTIONAL MARGINAL ANALYSIS. The traditional marginal analysis pictures the preceding problem graphically as in Figure 14. We have assumed that variable cost per unit is constant for all processes. Consequently, marginal cost per unit of each process is constant. Since the processes are of varying degrees of efficiency, the more efficient processes will be used first.

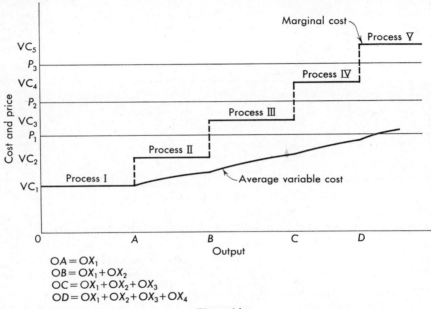

$$OA = OX_1$$
$$OB = OX_1 + OX_2$$
$$OC = OX_1 + OX_2 + OX_3$$
$$OD = OX_1 + OX_2 + OX_3 + OX_4$$

**Figure 14**

Thus, process I (with the lowest unit variable cost) will be employed first. After the fixed factor for process I ($F_1$) has been fully utilized, further increases in output will require the use of process II. Process III again will be used only after the fixed factor for process II has been fully utilized, and so on. We can therefore construct a marginal cost schedule for the firm as follows:

| Output $(x)$ | Marginal cost per unit $(MC)$ |
|---|---|
| $0 < x \leq OX_1$ | $vc_1$ |
| $OX_1 < x \leq (OX_1 + OX_2)$ | $vc_2$ |
| $(OX_1 + OX_2) < x \leq (OX_1 + OX_2 + OX_3)$ | $vc_3$ |
| $\cdots\cdots\cdots\cdots\cdots\cdots\cdots\cdots\cdots\cdots$ | $\cdots$ |
| $(OX_1 + OX_2 + \cdots + OX_{i-1}) < x$ $\leq (OX_1 + OX_2 + \cdots + OX_i)$ | $vc_i$ |

Figure 14 is the graph of this step function. It will be recognized immediately that this is also the short-run supply curve of the firm.

The supply schedule can be tabulated as follows:

| Market price (p) | Output (x) |
|---|---|
| $o < p < vc_1$ | $0$ |
| $p = vc_1$ | $0$ to $OX_1$ |
| $vc_1 < p < vc_2$ | $OX_1$ |
| $p = vc_2$ | $OX_1$ to $(OX_1 + OX_2)$ |
| $vc_2 < p < vc_3$ | $OX_1 + OX_2$ |
| $p = vc_3$ | $(OX_1 + OX_2)$ to $(OX_1 + OX_2 + OX_3)$ |
| $vc_3 < p < vc_4$ | $OX_1 + OX_2 + OX_3$ |
| . . . . . . . . . . . . . | . . . . . . . . . . . . . . . . . . . |
| $vc_i < p < vc_{i+1}$ | $OX_1 + OX_2 + \cdots + OX_i$ |
| . . . . . . . . . . . . . | . . . . . . . . . . . . . . . . . |

It will be observed that, as in case I, output does not change continuously with variations in price. Again, if output attains $OX_i$ at the optimum process level, the following condition must hold:

marginal cost at $OX_i \leq$ marginal revenue $<$ marginal cost at $(OX_i + 1)$
(market price)

Changes in input price will be reflected by downward or upward shifts of the marginal cost curve in Figure 14. Given the product price, output will also not vary continuously with input price changes. If the marginal equilibrium condition was originally satisfied at an output $OX_i$, then output will change only after input price has changed to such an extent that the above inequality no longer holds for $OX_i$.

We may also derive the average variable cost schedule as in the following table:

| Output (x) | Total variable cost (TVC) | Average variable cost (AVC) |
|---|---|---|
| $0 < x \leq OX_1$ | $vc_1 \cdot x$ | $vc_1$ |
| $OX_1 < x \leq (OX_1 + OX_2)$ | $vc_1 \cdot OX_1 + vc_2 \cdot (x - OX_1)$ $= (vc_1 - vc_2)OX_1 + vc_2 \cdot x$ | $vc_2 + \dfrac{(vc_1 - vc_2)OX_1}{x}$ |
| $(OX_1 + OX_2) < x \leq (OX_1 + OX_2 + OX_2)$ | $vc_1 OX_1 + vc_2 \cdot OX_2 + vc_3 \cdot$ $(x - OX_1 - OX_2) = (vc_1 - vc_2) \cdot$ $OX_1 + (vc_2 - vc_3)OX_2 + vc_3 \cdot x$ | $vc_3 + \dfrac{(vc_1 - vc_3)OX_1 + (vc_2 - vc_3)OX_2}{x}$ |
| . . . . . . . . . . . . . . . . . . . . . . . . . . . | . . . . . . . . . . . . . . . | . . . . . . . . . . . . . . . . . |
| $(OX_1 + OX_2 + \cdots + OX_{i-1}) < x \leq (OX_1 + OX_2 + \cdots + OX_i)$ | $vc_1 \cdot OX_1 + vc_2 \cdot OX_2 + \cdots +$ $vc_i (x - OX_1 - \cdots - OX_{i-1})$ $= (vc_1 - vc_i) OX_1 +$ $(vc_2 - vc_i)OX_2 + \cdots + vc_i \cdot x$ | $vc_i + \dfrac{(vc_1 - vc_i) OX_1 + \cdots + (vc_{i-1} - vc_i)OX_{i-1}}{x}$ |

We see from this table that the rising $MC$ curve gives rise to a rising $AVC$ curve. The $AVC$ curve is also shown in Figure 14; it is, however, not a smooth curve. For all outputs above $OX_1$, the average variable cost curve consists of a series of hyperbolas each of which corresponds to the output range listed in the table at foot of page 123.

### Case III: A Single-product Firm with One Nonspecialized Fixed Factor and Multiple Processes (a Variant of Case I)

In this case, the firm is confronted with a finite number, $n$, of processes the direct unit costs (unit variable costs) of which may be visualized as:

$$vc_1 > vc_2 > \cdots > vc_{n-(t+1)} > vc_{n-t}$$

and

$$vc_{n-t} < vc_{n-(t-1)} < vc_{n-(t-2)} < \cdots < vc_n$$

where $vc_{n-t}$ is the direct unit cost of the cheapest process available. This case differs from the preceding one in that the fixed factor, $F$, is not composed of groups of subsidiary fixed factors such as machines of varying degrees of efficiency. On the contrary, it is assumed that the different processes represent different ratios of the variable input to the same fixed factor as in Case I.

However, two additional assumptions are made here. First, the given amount of the fixed factor limits the maximum level of each process. But, by virtue of some other quality it possesses, the full utilization of one process does not prevent the use of the same fixed factor again in other processes. Thus, instead of one fixed factor, we may speak of pseudo-multiple fixed factors which cannot be physically separated. Second, the various processes must be used in such an order that, for instance, if process IV is employed, processes I, II, and III must be employed also. In general terms, the only feasible combinations are process I + process II + $\cdots$ + process $h$, where $h \leq n$ and $h$ represents the last of the processes used. This added restriction actually distinguishes the present case from Case II by making it impossible for the available processes to be arranged neatly in an order of uninterruptedly increasing unit direct costs. These assumptions result in a discontinuous U-shaped marginal cost curve. It is therefore the case that corresponds most closely to the textbook model of conventional marginal analysis while assuming the perfect divisibility of the fixed factors. A hypothetical example that comes to mind is production at a mine by using methods of strip-mining (i.e., removal of the surface cover) where up to a point the mineral content of the ore becomes progressively more concentrated as the depth of excavation increases and then becomes progressively poorer beyond that point.

GRAPHIC SOLUTION. Let us assume that process IV is the cheapest so that $vc_1 > vc_2 > vc_3 > vc_4$ and $vc_4 < vc_5 < \cdots < vc_n$. It follows then

$$p - vc_1 < p - vc_2$$
$$p - vc_2 < p - vc_3$$

$$p - vc_3 < p - vc_4$$
$$p - vc_4 > p - vc_5$$
$$p - vc_5 > p - vc_6$$

. . . . . . . . . . . . . .

Given $p$, the signs of all the unit net revenues are known. Let $p - vc_1$ and $p - vc_2$ be negative, but let $p - vc_3$ be positive.

Again, suppose that the unit fixed factor requirements by processes are $a_1$ for process I; $a_2$ for process II; etc. Let $x_j$ ($j = 1, 2, \cdots, n$) be the process level of the $j^{th}$ process, and $OX_j$ ($j = 1, 2, \cdots, n$) be the maximum output by the $j^{th}$ process. The fixed factor requirement in each process at full capacity is equal to $F$, the total fixed factor available. In other words, $a_j \cdot OX_j = F$, or $a_j \cdot x_j \leqq F$ for $j = 1, 2, \cdots, n$.

The above assumptions enable us to compute the sum $(p - vc_1)OX_1 + (p - vc_2)OX_2$ which is a constant and may be designated by $L$.

Then, in Figure 15, using $O'$ as the origin, we can construct a series of rectangles as in Case II to represent the feasible process combinations and their respective outputs in the same manner as before. If $p - vc_8$ becomes less than 0, process VII would be the last one used and the optimum process combination would be processes I, II, $\cdots$, VII. The $r''$ lines lie in the 4th

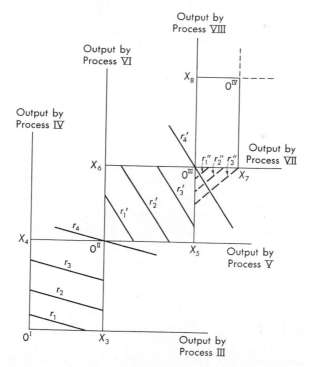

**Figure 15**

quadrant and are dotted, because a process cannot be operated at a negative level. The optimum solution is found at the extreme point $X_7$ in the series of convex sets denoted by the rectangles. Note that the slope of the $r$ lines with respect to the horizontal axis is less than that of the $r'$ lines because $p - vc_3 < p - vc_4$ while $p - vc_5 > p - vc_6$ as given above.

LINEAR PROGRAMMING FORMULATION. Under the given assumptions, we may write $r$ as the total net revenue which is equal to

$$(p - vc_1)\, x_1 + (p - vc_2)x_2 + \cdots + (p - vc_t)x_t$$
$$+ (p - vc_{t+1})x_{t+1} + \cdots + (p - vc_n)x_n$$

where

$$(p - vc_i) < 0, \text{ for } i = 1, 2, \cdots, t;\ (p - vc_{t+1}) > 0.$$

This may be abbreviated as

$$r = \sum_{k=t+1}^{n}(p - vc_k)x_k - \sum_{i=1}^{t}(vc_i - p)x_i$$
$$= \sum_{k=t+1}^{n}(p - vc_k)x_k - L, \text{ where } L = \sum_{i=1}^{t}(vc_i - p)x_i > 0.$$

Let $r + L = Z$. Then the linear programming problem is to maximize

(1) $$Z = \sum_{k=t+1}^{n}(p - vc_k)x_k \text{ subject to}$$

(2) $$a_k x_k \leqq F(k = t+1, t+2, \cdots, n), \text{ or alternatively,}$$

$$\sum_{k=t+1}^{n} a_k x_k \leqq (n - t)F$$

i.e., $$\left(\sum_{k=t+1}^{n} \frac{x_k}{OX_k} \leqq (n - t), \text{ since } \frac{F}{OX_k} = a_k\right);$$

(3) $$x_k \geqq 0 \text{ or, in the alternative formulation,}$$

$$0 \leqq x_k \leqq OX_k$$

(this condition means that a process cannot be extended indefinitely at the expense of other processes in the feasible combination); and

(4) $$Z - L > 0.$$

Since $p - vc_k$ must be positive with maximization, the optimum solution will make $x_k$ equal to $OX_k$ for all processes used, and there will be no slack. The total output at optimum would be $OX_1 + OX_2 + OX_3 + \cdots + OX_k$, the $k^{\text{th}}$ process being the last one used.

CONVENTIONAL MARGINAL ANALYSIS. The same problem may be graphed by using the marginal cost curve which will be a step function. The marginal cost schedule is defined by the condition that the available processes must be employed in a fixed order. This tabulation is presented below:

| Output (x) | Marginal cost (MC) |
|---|---|
| $0 < x \leqq OX_1$ | $vc_1$ |
| $OX_1 < x \leqq (OX_1 + OX_2)$ | $vc_2$ |
| $(OX_1 + OX_2) < x \leqq (OX_1 + OX_2 + OX_3)$ | $vc_3$ |
| ........................................... | .... |
| ........................................... | .... |
| $(OX_1 + OX_2 + \cdots + OX_{i-1}) < x \leqq (OX_1 + OX_2 + \cdots + OX_i)$ | $vc_i$ |

In the above example, we assume $vc_4$ to be the lowest variable cost among the available processes. The graph of the marginal cost schedule is shown in

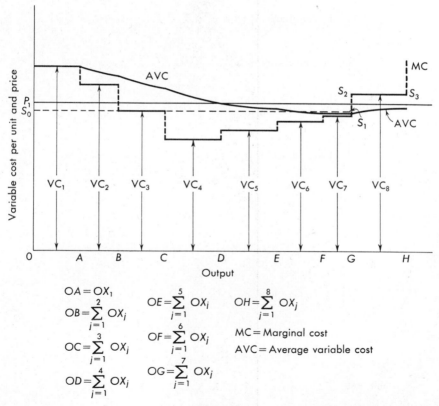

$OA = OX_1$

$OB = \sum\limits_{j=1}^{2} OX_j$

$OC = \sum\limits_{j=1}^{3} OX_j$

$OD = \sum\limits_{j=1}^{4} OX_j$

$OE = \sum\limits_{j=1}^{5} OX_j$

$OF = \sum\limits_{j=1}^{6} OX_j$

$OG = \sum\limits_{j=1}^{7} OX_j$

$OH = \sum\limits_{j=1}^{8} OX_j$

MC = Marginal cost
AVC = Average variable cost

**Figure 16**

Figure 16. In this case, the *MC* curve first falls and then rises as output expands. It thus corresponds to the U-shaped *MC* curve in conventional analysis. The criterion developed above that at the output that maximizes net revenue, $OX_e$,

marginal cost $\leqq$ marginal revenue $<$ marginal cost of
  at $OX_e$         (market price)         producing $(OX_e + 1)$ unit

remains valid. A second-order condition, however, is required in this case to ensure that a true equilibrium exists, namely, that total net revenue must be positive. This is the restraint $Z - L > 0$ in the linear programming formulation.

From Figure 16, the supply schedule can be constructed in the following way:

| *Market price* $(p)$ | *Output* $(x)$ |
|---|---|
| $0 < p \leqq vc_4$ | 0 |
| $vc_4 < p \leqq vc_5$ | 0 |
| | $\left\{ \because \text{ by construction } \left[ (p - vc_4)OX_4 + \sum_{i=1}^{3} (p - vc_i)OX_i \right] < 0 \right\}$ |
| $vc_5 < p \leqq vc_6$ | 0 |
| | $\left\{ \because \text{ by construction } \left[ \sum_{k=4}^{5}(p - vc_k)OX_k + \sum_{i=1}^{3} (p - vc_i)OX_i \right] < 0 \right\}$ |
| $vc_6 < p < vc_7$ | 0 |
| | $\left\{ \because \text{ by construction } \left[ \sum_{k=4}^{6} (p - vc_k)OX_k + \sum_{i=1}^{3} (p - vc_i)OX_i \right] < 0 \right\}$ |
| $p = vc_7$ | 0 |
| | $\left\{ \because \text{ by construction } \left[ \sum_{k=4}^{7} (p-vc_k)OX_k + \sum_{i=1}^{3} (p - vc_i)OX_i \right] < 0 \right\}$ |
| $vc_7 < p < vc_8$ | (i)     0 |
| | if $\left\{ \left[ \sum_{k=4}^{7} (p - vc_k)OX_k + \sum_{i=1}^{3} (p - vc_i)OX_i \right] < 0 \right\}$ |
| | (ii)     $\sum_{j=1}^{7} OX_j$ |
| | if $\left\{ \left[ \sum_{k=4}^{7} (p - vc_k)OX_k + \sum_{i=1}^{3} (p - vc_i)OX_i \right] > 0* \right\}$ |
| $p = vc_8$ | $\sum_{j=1}^{7} OX_j$ or $\sum_{j=1}^{8} OX_j$ |
| . . . . . . . . . . . . . | |
| . . . . . . . . . . . . . | |
| **IN GENERAL** | |
| $vc_h < p < vc_{h+1}$ | $\sum_{j=1}^{h} OX_j$ |
| $p = vc_{h+1}$ | $\sum_{j=1}^{h} OX_j$ or $\sum_{j=1}^{h+1} OX_j$ |

\* This condition is satisfied in Figure 16.

This supply curve is drawn as the dashed broken line $OS_0S_1S_2S_3$ in Figure 16. It coincides with the marginal cost curve beyond the point $S_1$. It will also be noted that, similar to the two preceding cases, output does not vary continuously with changes in product price. After market price has reached $OS_0$, when total net revenue will be positive, the ranges within which price variations will not bring about output changes depend on the differences among the unit direct costs of the various processes.

The effect of changes in factor prices can be readily analyzed by our diagram. Increase in factor prices will result in proportional increases in unit variable cost since constant variable input per unit is assumed. This will be shown as an upward shift of the $MC$ curve as well as the supply curve. This means that the price at which total net revenue becomes positive (i.e., $Z - L > 0$) will be higher than that before the increase in factor prices. In general, then, given the product price, increases in factor price will either reduce output (to zero or a lower level) or does not affect output at all.

The average variable cost schedule, which can be derived by the same procedure illustrated in Case I and Case II, is also shown in Figure 16.

### Case IV: A Multiple-product Firm with more than One Fixed Factor

The preceding cases illustrate mathematical programming formulations of the economic choice confronting a single-product firm under various assumptions as to the number and nature of constraints and processes. We now consider a firm producing more than one product and having more than one fixed factor and process.

Let us assume that there are $n$ different products and $m$ fixed factors. Further, we shall denote the output of each product by $x_1, x_2, \cdots, x_n$; the quantity of fixed factors by $F_1, F_2, \cdots, F_m$; the unit fixed factor requirements of the $j^{th}$ product by $a_{1j}, a_{2j}, \cdots, a_{mj}$, where $j = 1, 2, \cdots, n$. The production of each product is conceived as a process or activity. Thus the firm has $n$ processes utilizing $m$ fixed factors. Suppose also that the unit variable cost for each process, $vc_j$, and the price of the $j^{th}$ product ($j = 1, 2, 3, \cdots, n$), $p_j$, are given and constant.

In the short run, the firm's problem is to select the combination of processes that yields the maximum net revenue

$$r = (p_1 - vc_1)x_1 + (p_2 - vc_2)x_2 + \cdots + (p_n - vc_n)x_n$$

subject to the restriction that no more than 100 per cent of any fixed factor can be used. This is the typical mathematical programming problem: the selection of a pattern of processes and corresponding outputs which maximizes profit and yet does not violate the limitation imposed by the available capacities of the firm.

GRAPHIC SOLUTION. Up to now we have dealt with cases in which for each process there is only one limiting fixed factor. The situation of a firm producing more than two products and having more than two fixed factors, however, cannot be represented by a two-dimensional diagram. In order to illustrate the nature of the problem, we shall depict with our diagram a firm with two products and a number of fixed factors.[31] In Figure 17 the output of

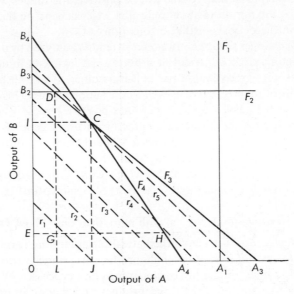

**Figure 17**

product $A$ is scaled horizontally and that of product $B$ is scaled vertically. We shall assume that there are four fixed factors, $F_1$, $F_2$, $F_3$, $F_4$; that $F_1$ is used in the production of $A$ only (i.e., $a_{12} = 0$), and $F_2$ in the production of $B$ only ($a_{21} = 0$). $F_3$ and $F_4$, however, are required by both products, ($a_{31} > 0$, $a_{32} > 0$, $a_{41} > 0$, $a_{42} > 0$). We define the production of $A$ as process I and the production of $B$ as process II in terms of input requirements per unit of output.

Instead of a rectangle of feasible process combinations as in Case II and Case III, the effect of the four fixed factor restrictions is to limit the feasible combinations of processes and the corresponding outputs to the convex polygon $OA_4CDB_2$. The lines $F_1$, $F_2$, $F_3$, and $F_4$ represent all combinations of outputs of $A$ and $B$ that require 100 per cent of the fixed factors respectively. These lines are therefore called fixed factor limitation lines.

Now suppose that we impose on this figure the iso-revenue lines $r_1$, $r_2$, $\cdots$. As in the previous cases, the firm's problem consists in selecting that point in $OA_4CDB_2$ which lies on the highest iso-revenue line. The optimum production program depends on the slope and location of the fixed factor limitation lines and the slope of the $r$ lines. Clearly, in this case, the combination

---

[31] This type of diagram is first employed by Dorfman, see [52], p. 799.

of outputs corresponding to point $C$ is that which yields the maximum net revenue. The similarity between Figure 17 and Figures 2, 3, and 4 in Case I should be noted. Figure 17 may also be interpreted as representing a single-product firm with two processes and two fixed factors which are specialized and two fixed factors which are nonspecialized. Such a situation will represent a variant of Case I above. The convex set $OA_4CDB_2$ represents all feasible combinations of the two processes in the production of the single product. The iso-revenue lines will in this case indicate the combinations of the two processes which yield the same net revenue. The optimum program of the firm will also correspond to the extreme point $C$ in the convex polygon $OA_4CDB_2$, which lies on the highest possible iso-revenue line in Figure 17.

The addition of further constraints in the problem can be easily handled in this diagram. Each constraint will simply be represented by a "production possibility" line. The intersection of the closed half planes defined by these production possibility lines will correspond to the feasible programs of the firm. The only limitation to the use of this type of diagram in a single-product firm is the number of available processes. In a two-dimensional graph, only two axes can be used to measure the output by two processes. Such a diagram consequently cannot be used when the number of processes exceeds two.

AN ALTERNATIVE GRAPHIC SOLUTION. The solution of this problem can also be portrayed by the process ray diagram illustrated above in Case I, Figure 5. This graphical representation is shown in Figure 18.

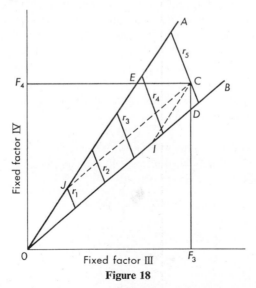

**Figure 18**

In this diagram the fixed factors $F_3$ and $F_4$ are measured on the horizontal and vertical axes respectively. The specialized fixed factors $F_1$ and $F_2$ are not represented explicitly in Figure 18. It will be recalled that, in Figure 17 above, the optimum program of the firm, namely, point C, requires less than 100 per cent of both $F_1$ and $F_2$. In other words, there is excess capacity in both $F_1$ and $F_2$ at the optimum output combination of $A$ and $B$. The effective restraints to the firm consist of $F_3$ and $F_4$ only. We can therefore solve the maximization problem of the firm with reference to the only two constraints that are binding.

It should be noted that a process ray diagram such as Figure 18 can be used to portray a situation where there are more than two products. Every process of producing every product of the firm can be represented by a separate process ray. Since the two axes must represent two constraints, this type of diagram will be applicable as long as there are not more than two effective constraints. In other words it can be readily applied either to a firm having more than two products but only two effective constraints or to a single-product firm having more than two processes but with two effective constraints.

In Figure 18, the fixed factors $F_3$ and $F_4$ are measured along the horizontal and vertical axes respectively. $OF_3$ represents the amount of $F_3$ available; $OF_4$, the quantity of $F_4$ available. The process ray $OA$ represents the output of $A$; and the process ray $OB$, the output of $B$. The process rays are necessarily linear since we have assumed constant unit fixed factor requirements. The fixed factor limitation lines are $F_3C$ and $F_4C$. The feasible production programs of the firm correspond to the rectangle $OF_3CF_4$. The economic choice of the firm, however, will consist only of the factor combinations in the polygon $OIDCEJ$.

. The "$r$" lines in the diagram are the iso-revenue lines. The selection of the optimum program is then the selection of that point in $OIDCEJ$ which lies on the highest iso-revenue line. This, in Figure 18, is clearly point C. The combination of outputs at $C$ is $OJ$ of $A$ and $OI$ of $B$. This follows immediately from the fact that the point $C$ represents the sum of the two vectors $OJ$ and $OI$.

Both Figure 17 and Figure 18 are drawn on the same set of assumptions. $OJ$ and $OI$ in Figure 18 therefore represent the same amounts of output of $A$ and $B$ as $OJ$ and $OI$ in Figure 17.

LINEAR PROGRAMMING FORMULATION. We can state the general case of a firm producing $n$ products with $m$ fixed factors in linear programming form. The firm will seek to maximize:

(1)         $r = (p_1 - vc_1)x_1 + (p_2 - vc_2)x_2 + \cdots + (p_n - vc_n)x_n$

     subject to

$$a_{11}x_1 + a_{12}x_2 + \cdots + a_{1n}x_n \leqq F_1,$$
$$a_{21}x_1 + a_{22}x_2 + \cdots + a_{2n}x_n \leqq F_2,$$

(2)         $\cdots\cdots\cdots\cdots\cdots\cdots\cdots\cdots\cdots\cdots$
          $\cdots\cdots\cdots\cdots\cdots\cdots\cdots\cdots\cdots\cdots$

$$a_{m1}x_1 + a_{m2}x_2 + \cdots + a_{mn}x_n \leqq F_n;$$

    and

(3)         $x_1 \geqq 0,\ x_2 \geqq 0,\ \cdots,\ x_n \geqq 0.$

CONVENTIONAL ANALYSIS. The conventional analysis of a multiple-product firm distinguishes between situations in which demands for the various products are interrelated and situations in which cost interdependence among the products exists.[32] Here we have abstracted from both these complications except to the extent that the production of both $A$ and $B$ is limited by the existence of the fixed factors. Under such circumstances where the demand curves and the marginal cost curves of the various products are unrelated, traditional analysis holds that profits will be maximized when marginal cost and marginal revenue (equals price) are equal for each of the products. The marginal cost of producing one product can be defined for each given level of production of the other product. Proceeding from any given combination of the two outputs, we may inquire as to the profitability of increasing either one or both of the products further. If the marginal cost of one product is less than its price, profits can be increased by increasing its output. This process will be continued until marginal cost, which rises as production expands, is equal to price for both products. The firm will then be in short-run equilibrium.

Under our present assumptions, the marginal costs for both products are constant ($vc_1$ and $vc_2$). The above criterion therefore does not define an equilibrium level of output for the firm and must be modified. Let us consider any point, say $G$, in Figure 17, which represents an output of $OL$ units of $A$ and $OE$ units of $B$. We may ask what is the most profitable output of $A$, given the production of $B$ at $OE$? As long as ($p_1 - vc_1$) > 0, the answer will be as much as possible. But the firm can only expand output of $A$ up to $H$ at which point the fixed factor $F_4$ will have been exhausted. In fact, for any given output of $B$, the most profitable output of $A$ will correspond to a point on the broken line $DCA_4$. Similarly, if we suppose the output of $A$ as given, $B_2DCA_4$ will represent the most profitable outputs of $B$ to be produced at given levels of production of $A$. The point corresponding to the combination of outputs of $A$ and $B$ that will maximize profits, assuming the net revenue from both to be positive, must then lie on $B_2DCA_4$.

The conventional graphic solution of this problem usually employs the construction of constant revenue curves and constant outlay curves and the derivation of an output expansion path.[33] Since we know that the optimum combination of output must lie on the production boundary curve $B_2DCA_4$, there is no need to construct constant outlay curves. We may inquire immediately which point on $B_2DCA_4$ corresponds to the optimum output of the firm. The iso-revenue lines are superimposed in the diagram for this purpose. This is exactly what we have done in our previous graphic analysis. It is nevertheless instructive to examine the line of reasoning in terms of the familiar concepts of marginal analysis.

We note first that movement along $B_2DCA_4$ represents substitution of

---

[32] See, for instance, Weintraub [166], Chaps. 13 and 14.
[33] See, for example, Stigler [155], pp. 314–19; cf. Boulding [21], pp. 769–71.

output between $A$ and $B$ (with the exception of movement along $B_2D$). Suppose that the firm is producing $OA_4$ of product $A$. The effective limitation to the firm's output at this point is set by $F_4(OA_4 \cdot a_{41} = F_4)$. The firm will change the pattern of its output if such a change will increase its profit. Since $OA_4$ is the maximum of $A$ that it can produce, the only change the firm can make is to substitute product $B$ for $A$. The rate of output substitution of $B$ for $A$, which is the number of units of $B$ that can be produced by giving up one unit of $A$, depends on $F_4$ alone as there are excesses in all other factors. This rate is given by the slope of line $F_4$ (or $A_4B_4$) which is equal to

$$\frac{OB_4}{OA_4} = \left(\frac{a_{41}}{a_{42}}\right).$$

To determine whether it is profitable to substitute $B$ for $A$ the firm must also know the rate of "net revenue" substitution of $B$ for $A$. This rate is defined as the number of units of $B$ which must be substituted for one unit of $A$ in order to leave total net revenue from total output unchanged. It is the slope of the $r$ lines $(p_1 - vc_1)/(p_2 - vc_2)$. By construction the slope of $F_4$ is greater than the slope of the $r$ lines in Figure 17. Hence,

$$\frac{a_{41}}{a_{42}} > \frac{p_1 - vc_1}{p_2 - vc_2}, \qquad \text{i.e.,} \quad \left[\frac{a_{41}}{a_{42}} \cdot (p_2 - vc_2)\right] > (p_1 - vc_1),$$

which means: if one unit of $A$ is given up, the number of units of $B$ that can be produced in its stead will yield an amount of net revenue greater than the revenue lost from the decrease in the production of $A$. Under these circumstances the firm will continue to substitute $B$ for $A$ until point $C$.

The limiting factor after point $C$ is reached becomes $F_3$. The rate of output substitution of $B$ for $A$ is measured by $a_{31}/a_{32}$. The rate of revenue substitution remains at $\dfrac{p_1 - vc_1}{p_2 - vc_2}$.

Again by construction,

$$\frac{a_{31}}{a_{32}} < \frac{p_1 - vc_1}{p_2 - vc_2}, \qquad \text{i.e.,} \quad \left[\frac{a_{31}}{a_{32}} \cdot (p_2 - vc_2)\right] < (p_1 - vc_1).$$

This condition means that the revenue yielded from the increased number of $B$ produced at point $C$ will be less than the revenue lost from the decrease in the output of $A$. Point $C$ then corresponds to the optimum production program.

In conventional analysis, the equilibrium of the firm with respect to the substitution of output $B$ for $A$ requires that the marginal rate of output substitution of $B$ for $A$ be equal to the ratio of the unit net revenue from $A$ to the unit net revenue from $B$. In this case, the equilibrium conditions are expressed by two inequalities in the neighborhood of the optimum combination. This is the result of the kinked production boundary curve. The rate of output substitution is not defined at point $C$. On the other hand, the concepts of marginal analysis remain applicable. Furthermore, the second-order condition of equilibrium, that the rate of output substitution of $B$ for $A$ must decrease as the quantity of $B$ increases, holds true in the mathematical programming model.[34]

This analysis has indicated the underlying correspondence between mathematical programming and marginal analysis. While the conventional marginal analysis can indicate the logical nature of the optimum position, it does not provide any direct means of finding the optimum except by way of trial and error. Mathematical programming, on the other hand, sets forth a technique whereby a numerical solution can be found once the necessary information is available.

DERIVATION OF THE SUPPLY SCHEDULE OF THE FIRM. The above analysis provides us with the tools for the derivation of the supply schedule of the firm. It is noted in the discussion of the linear programming graphical solution in Figure 17 that the optimum solution depends on the slope and position of the fixed factor limitation lines and the slope of the iso-revenue lines. In the short run, the firm is confronted with a fixed plant. The fixed factor limitation lines are therefore given in a short-run analysis. Given the available fixed factors, the optimum solution will depend on the slope of the iso-revenue lines. The slope of the iso-revenue lines depends, for a two-product firm, on $p_1$, $p_2$, $vc_1$, and $vc_2$. The optimum program of production then will change as a result of changes in these variables. Since $vc_1$ and $vc_2$ are assumed to be constant, we can deduce from Figure 17 the supply schedule of the firm by relating $p_1$, $p_2$, and the outputs of $A$ and $B$.

In Figure 17, however, the relationship between $p_1$, $p_2$, and the output of the firm is not immediately apparent. We may first construct the supply schedule by relating the slope of the iso-revenue lines to output. It is then a simple mathematical operation to deduce the relationship between $p_1$, $p_2$, and the production of $A$ and $B$. The relationship between the slope of the iso-revenue lines and output levels is presented in the table at top of page 136.

Consider for example the situation in which the slope of the iso-revenue lines is equal to zero. In Figure 17 the family of iso-revenue lines will be parallel to the horizontal axis. The highest possible iso-revenue line that can touch the area $OA_4CDB_2$ will be coincident with the line segment $B_2D$. All combinations of output corresponding to points on $B_2D$ will yield the same net revenue. Consequently, the output of $B$ will be $OB_2$ while that of $A$ may

---

[34] This condition means that the slope of the production boundary $B_2DCA_4$ (or transformation curve) must increase as output of $A$ is increased at the expense of $B$; or, equivalently, it must decrease as output of $B$ is increased at the expense of $A$. An excellent exposition of the conditions of equilibrium of the firm is given in Baumol [16], pp. 66–80.

| Slope of r lines | Output A | Output B | Optimum program in Figure 17 |
|---|---|---|---|
| *r* lines in 2nd quadrant | | | |
| $p_1 - vc_1 < 0$ | 0 | $OB_2$ | |
| *r* lines in 4th quadrant | | | |
| $p_2 - vc_2 < 0$ | $OA_4$ | 0 | |
| *r* lines in 3rd quadrant | | | |
| $p_1 - vc_1 < 0$ | 0 | 0 | |
| $p_2 - vc_2 < 0$ | | | |
| *r* lines in 1st quadrant | | | |
| $\dfrac{p_1 - vc_1}{p_2 - vc_2} = 0$ | | | |
| i.e., $p_1 - vc_1 = 0$ | $0{-}OL$ | $OB_2$ | $B_2D$ |
| $0 < \dfrac{p_1 - vc_1}{p_2 - vc_2} < \dfrac{a_{31}}{a_{32}}$ | $OL$ | $OB_2$ | $D$ |
| $\dfrac{p_1 - vc_1}{p_2 - vc_2} = \dfrac{a_{31}}{a_{32}}$ | $OL{-}OJ$ | $OI{-}OB_2$ | $DC$ |
| $\dfrac{a_{31}}{a_{32}} < \dfrac{p_1 - vc_1}{p_2 - vc_2} < \dfrac{a_{41}}{a_{42}}$ | $OJ$ | $OI$ | $C$ |
| $\dfrac{p_1 - vc_1}{p_2 - vc_2} = \dfrac{a_{41}}{a_{42}}$ | $OJ{-}OA_4$ | $0{-}OI$ | $CA_4$ |
| $\dfrac{p_1 - vc_1}{p_2 - vc_2} > \dfrac{a_{41}}{a_{42}}$ | $OA_4$ | 0 | $A_4$ |

vary from zero up to *OL*. The derivation of the other entries in the above table proceeds on the same line of reasoning.

For any given $p_2$ (assume $p_2 > vc_2$) we can derive the supply schedule of *A* and *B* as follows:

| $p_1$($p_2$ given and $> vc_2$) | Output A | B |
|---|---|---|
| $0 < p_1 < vc_1,\ (p_1 - vc_1 < 0)$ | 0 | $OB_2$ |
| $p_1 = vc_1,\ (p_1 - vc_1 = 0)$ | $0{-}OL$ | $OB_2$ |
| $vc_1 < p_1 < \left[ vc_1 + \dfrac{a_{31}(p_2 - vc_2)}{a_{32}} \right]$ | $OL$ | $OB_2$ |
| $p_1 = vc_1 + \dfrac{a_{31}(p_2 - vc_2)}{a_{32}}$ | $OL{-}OJ$ | $OI{-}OB_2$ |
| $\left[ vc_1 + \dfrac{a_{31}(p_2 - vc_2)}{a_{32}} \right] < p_1 < \left[ vc_1 + \dfrac{a_{41}(p_2 - vc_2)}{a_{42}} \right]$ | $OJ$ | $OI$ |
| $p_1 = vc_1 + \dfrac{a_{41}(p_2 - vc_2)}{a_{42}}$ | $OJ{-}OA_4$ | $0{-}OI$ |
| $p_1 > \left[ vc_1 + \dfrac{a_{41}(p_2 - vc_2)}{a_{42}} \right]$ | $OA_4$ | 0 |

It is readily seen that for any given value of $vc_1$, $vc_2$, and $p_2$, a rise in $p_1$ will tend to increase the output of $A$ at the expense of $B$. Graphically, an increase in $p_1$ relative to $p_2$ means an increase in the numerical slope of the iso-revenue lines. The limit of the increase in the output of $A$ is reached when $F_4$ is fully absorbed with an output of $OA_4$ of $A$ and zero of $B$. Contrary to the continuous curves employed in conventional analysis, the proportion between the outputs of $A$ and $B$ does not vary continuously with variations in $p_1$. A short-run supply curve of $A$ drawn on the assumption of a specific level of $p_2$ is shown in Figure 19. For certain intervals of $p_1$, output may remain constant,

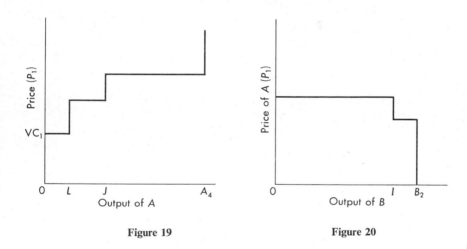

Figure 19                          Figure 20

changing only after $p_1$ has reached a new level. For any short-run supply curve of $A$, there will be a related short-run supply curve of $B$ as defined in the supply schedule above. The supply curve of $B$ corresponding to the supply curve of $A$ in Figure 19 is shown in Figure 20. For a given set of $vc_1$ and $vc_2$, there is a family of such short-run supply curves of $A$ and $B$, each corresponding to a given level of $p_2$. These short-run supply curves are similar in shape, the only difference being the range of price variations over which the output of $A$ remains constant at $OL$ and $OJ$.

Similarly, we can derive the supply schedule of $A$ and $B$ for any given level of $p_1$ as in the table on page 138; the graphs of the supply schedules are shown in Figures 21 and 22 (assume $p_1 > vc_1$).

The analytical tools we have developed can also be used to deal with changes in the unit variable costs of $A$ and $B$. Given $p_1$ and $p_2$, a change in $vc_1$ and/or $vc_2$ will result in a change in the slope of the iso-revenue lines. It is therefore possible to derive a schedule relating changes in $vc_1$ and/or $vc_2$ to output. The graph of such a schedule will be similar to Figures 19, 20, 21, and 22.

| $p_2$ ($p_1$ given and $> vc_1$) | Output | |
| --- | --- | --- |
| | A | B |
| $0 < p_2 < vc_2, (p_2 - vc_2 < 0)$ | $OA_4$ | 0 |
| $p_2 = vc_2, (p_2 - vc_2 = 0)$ | $OA_4$ | 0 |
| $vc_2 < p_2 < \dfrac{a_{42}(p_1 - vc_1)}{a_{41}} + vc_2$ | $OA_4$ | 0 |
| $\left[\text{i.e., } \dfrac{p_1 - vc_1}{p_2 - vc_2} > \dfrac{a_{41}}{a_{42}}\right]$ | | |
| $p_2 = \dfrac{a_{42}(p_1 - vc_1)}{a_{41}} + vc_2$ | $OJ-OA_4$ | $0-OI$ |
| $\dfrac{a_{42}(p_1 - vc_1)}{a_{41}} + vc_2 < p_2 < \dfrac{a_{32}(p_1 - vc_1)}{a_{31}} + vc_2$ | $OJ$ | $OI$ |
| $p_2 = \dfrac{a_{32}(p_1 - vc_1)}{a_{31}} + vc_2$ | $OL-OJ$ | $OI-OB_2$ |
| $p_2 > \dfrac{a_{32}(p_1 - vc_1)}{a_{31}} + vc_2$ | $OL$ | $OB_2$ |
| as $p_2$ tends to $\infty$ | $0-OL$ | $OB_2$ |

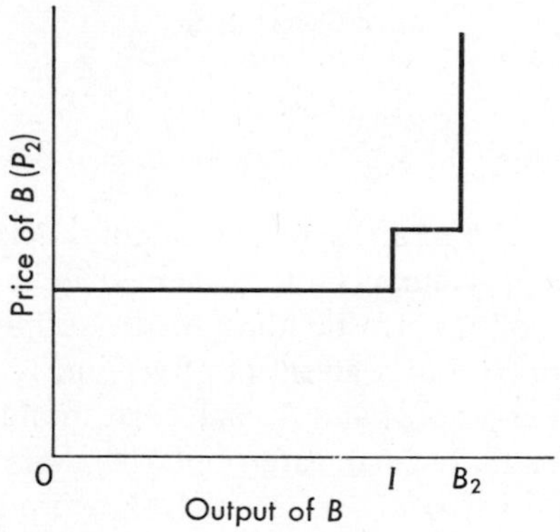

Figure 21

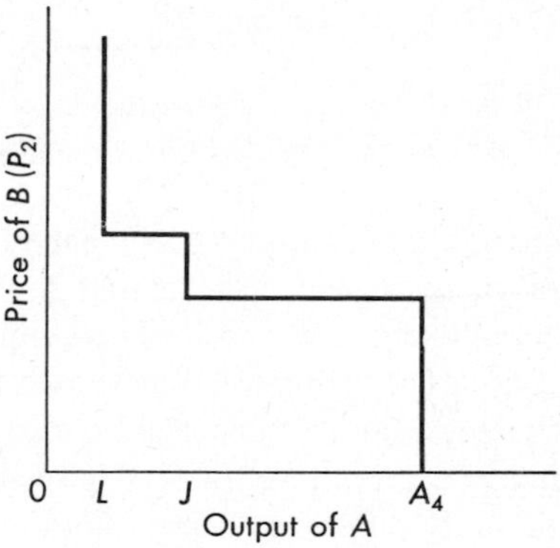

Figure 22

FURTHER ANALYSIS: CHANGES IN FACTOR PROPORTIONS AND CHOICE OF PROCESSES. It is noted above that the process ray diagram employed in the alternative graphic solution can be used to portray a firm with more than two processes (or products) but with no more than two effective constraints. Figure 23 presents graphically the case of a firm with three processes, each of which corresponds to the production of a different product, and two non-specialized fixed factors. In this diagram we can also think of net revenue instead of physical output as being measured along the process rays. This interpretation presents no special difficulty, as we assume product prices and variable factor prices as constant in the short run.

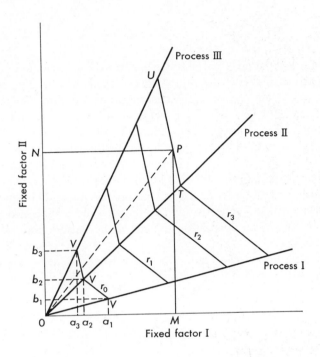

**Figure 23**

The production processes of the firm may be defined as follows:

| Input of fixed factor per unit output | PROCESS I | II | III | Resources available |
|---|---|---|---|---|
| Fixed factor I ($F_1$) | $Oa_1$ | $Oa_2$ | $Oa_3$ | $OM$ |
| Fixed factor II ($F_2$) | $Ob_1$ | $Ob_2$ | $Ob_3$ | $ON$ |
| Variable cost per unit output | $vc_1$ | $vc_2$ | $vc_3$ | |
| Unit net revenue (net revenue per unit output) | $\lambda_1$ | $\lambda_2$ | $\lambda_3$ | |
| Process levels (output) | $x_1$ | $x_2$ | $x_3$ | |

In Figure 23, $OMPN$ is the rectangle of feasible programs. The process combination that yields the maximum net revenue is the one which corresponds to the highest iso-revenue line that touches the rectangle $OMPN$. $P$, therefore, represents the program that yields the maximum net revenue.

At $P$ the process levels are:

$$x_1 = 0$$

$$x_2 = \frac{UP}{UT} \cdot OT$$

$$x_3 = \frac{PT}{UT} \cdot OU.$$

In this solution, the position of $P$ depends on the relative amounts of the fixed factors available. It is the ratio between their supplies that determine the position of $P$, and, consequently, the optimum program.

In Figure 23, if $P$ lies between process I and process II, the optimum program would then require the use of these two processes. If the intersection of the fixed factor limitation lines should fall to the left of process III or to the right of process I, then only one process (III or I) would be required in the optimum program. Similarly, if $P$ should fall on a process ray, then the optimum program would require the use of that process alone. Our analysis then has shown that with two effective constraints, no more than two processes need be used. This is an illustration of one of the basic theorems of linear programming.[35]

This generalization applies readily in a case where there is only one fixed factor. Such a situation is illustrated in Figure 24. In this diagram, the point

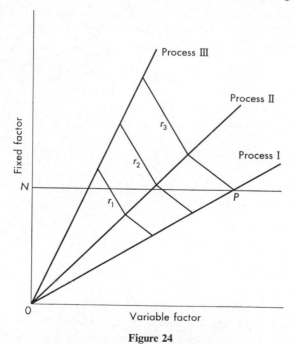

**Figure 24**

---

[35] See Dorfman, Samuelson, and Solow [54], p. 78.

at which the highest iso-revenue line touches the fixed factor limitation line, $P$, will lie on one process ray only. Hence, the output that will yield the maximum net revenue is obtained by using one process. The position of $P$ depends on the slope of the iso-revenue lines and the position of the fixed factor limitation line.

The relationship between the intersection point, $P$, of the two fixed factor limitation lines and the selection of the optimum program provides us with the tool to analyze the effect of changes in the proportion between available fixed resources on the choice of processes. With respect to Figure 23, we may summarize this analysis as follows:

The ratios of $F_2$ and $F_1$ required per unit of output are:

$$\begin{array}{ll} \text{Process I} & Ob_1/Oa_1 \\ \text{Process II} & Ob_2/Oa_2 \\ \text{Process III} & Ob_3/Oa_3. \end{array}$$

Since by assumption $Ob_3 > Ob_2 > Ob_1$ and $Oa_3 < Oa_2 < Oa_1$ we have

$$\frac{Ob_1}{Oa_1} < \frac{Ob_2}{Oa_2} < \frac{Ob_3}{Oa_3}.$$

Let $\alpha$ be the ratio of the total amount of the second fixed factor to that of the first fixed factor. In Figure 23, $\alpha$ will be equal to $ON/OM\ (= MP/NP)$. If we draw a straight line from $O$ to $P$, $\alpha$ will be the numerical value of the slope of the vector $OP$. It is therefore possible to represent the various ratios between the amounts of the two fixed factors by vectors of different slopes. This has been done in Figure 25.

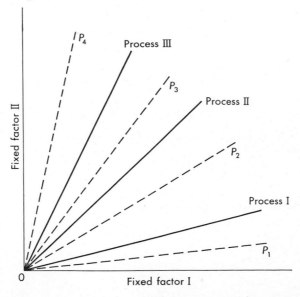

**Figure 25**

In Figure 25, the three process rays are reproduced together with the four dotted vectors $OP_1$, $OP_2$, $OP_3$, $OP_4$, each of which represents a different proportion between $F_1$ and $F_2$. The relationships between $\alpha$ and the choice of processes in the optimum program is summarized in the following table.

| $\alpha$ | *Processes used in the optimum program* |
|---|---|
| $\alpha \geqq \dfrac{Ob_3}{Oa_3}$ | Process III |
| $\dfrac{Ob_2}{Oa_2} < \alpha < \dfrac{Ob_3}{Oa_3}$ | Process III and Process II |
| $\alpha = \dfrac{Ob_2}{Oa_2}$ | Process II |
| $\dfrac{Ob_1}{Oa_1} < \alpha < \dfrac{Ob_2}{Oa_2}$ | Process II and Process I |
| $\alpha \leqq \dfrac{Ob_1}{Oa_1}$ | Process I |

In other words, the choice of processes is determined by the relative scarcity of the two fixed factors. In the process or combination of processes used, the ratio of the factors in use must equal the ratio of the factors available unless the latter ratio such as represented by $OP_1$ and $OP_4$, falls outside the range of the factor requirement ratios in the efficient processes. In the latter case one of the fixed factors is not scarce. Thus the number of processes in use is the same as the number of scarce factors. Given two fixed factors, not more than two processes will be in use and two will actually be used only if both fixed factors are scarce.

LINEAR PROGRAMMING FORMULATION. For the firm portrayed in Figure 23, the linear programming problem is to maximize

(1)              $r$ (total net revenue) $= \lambda_1 x_1 + \lambda_2 x_2 + \lambda_3 x_3$

subject to

$$Oa_1 x_1 + Oa_2 x_2 + Oa_3 x_3 \leqq OM,$$

(2)              $Ob_1 x_1 + Ob_2 x_2 + Ob_3 x_3 \leqq ON$; and

(3)              $x_1 \geqq 0, \ x_2 \geqq 0, \ x_3 \geqq 0.$

For a firm with $n$ processes and $m$ fixed factors, the problem may be generalized. It will then be the maximization of

(1)              $$r = \sum_{j=1}^{n} \lambda_j x_j$$

subject to

(2)              $\sum_{j=1}^{n} a_{ij} \cdot x_j \leqq F_i$              for $i = 1, 2, 3, \cdots, m$; and

(3) $\qquad x_j \geqq 0 \qquad j = 1, 2, 3, \cdots, n;$

where $a_{ij}$ represents the unit requirement of the $j^{\text{th}}$ process for the $i^{\text{th}}$ fixed factor; $F_i$ represents the available amount of the $i^{\text{th}}$ fixed factor.

### Case V: A Multiple Product Firm with Imperfectly Divisible Fixed Factors and or Products

SIMPLE CASES OF IMPERFECT DIVISIBILITY. So far we have assumed that the firm can adjust the levels of its production processes continuously. This is predicated on the implicit assumption that both the fixed factors and the products are continuously divisible. The question must now be raised as to what would happen once this assumption is abandoned. Let us consider some simple illustrations.

First, given the continuous divisibility of the product, if there is a single nonspecialized fixed factor as in Case I, and if this factor is altogether in-divisible so that the firm has only one unit of it, the optimum solution of the problem—i.e., the choice of the process to be used from among the feasible ones—is unaffected. This can be clearly perceived as we refer to Figure 5. If we look upon $OF$ as an indivisible unit of the fixed factor, then, given two processes only, the points $A$ and $B$ would be the only two possible choices. If more processes were available, all the feasible solutions would still remain on the line $FF'$ and the optimum solution as determined by the criterion $\dfrac{p - vc_i}{p - vc_j} \gtreqless \dfrac{OX_j}{OX_i}$ $(i \neq j)$ would be unaffected. If the number of available processes becomes very large, as one moves along the line $FF'$, one passes successively from one process to another. If all obviously "inefficient" processes have been eliminated, one can imagine successive processes using the same indivisible fixed factor that would yield total outputs increasing by one unit at a time. Suppose that the available processes number $1, 2, \cdots, k,$ $\cdots, n$. Process $k$ would be discarded in favor of process $k + 1$ if

$$\frac{p - vc_{k+1}}{p - vc_k} > \frac{OX_k}{OX_{k+1}}$$

i.e.,

$$(p - vc_{k+1}) \cdot OX_{k+1} > (p - vc_k)OX_k.$$

Since by assumption $OX_{k+1} = OX_k + 1$, we have

$$(p - vc_{k+1})(OX_k + 1) = (p \cdot OX_k + p - vc_{k+1} \cdot OX_k - vc_{k+1})$$
$$> (p \cdot OX_k - vc_k \cdot OX_k).$$

From this we get

$$p > (vc_{k+1} - vc_k)OX_k + vc_{k+1}.$$

The right-hand side of the inequality represents the increase in direct cost due to the substitution of process $k + 1$ for process $k$ which results in an increase of total output by one unit. This is, of course, the traditional concept of marginal cost. Thus we have reconstructed the case of conventional marginal analysis. Since points below the line $FF'$ are not feasible due to the indivisibility of the fixed factor, there is not a series of constant marginal cost curves as in Case I, but a single marginal cost curve to be derived from a continuous average cost curve. The latter itself can be easily derived from Figure 5, the only modification being an increase in the number of processes.

The above analysis will, however, have to be modified if the product is not continuously divisible, because in this case not all the points on the line $FF'$ would belong to the feasible set. It would then be possible for a process to be ruled out as nonfeasible even if it would have been optimal under the condition of continuous divisibility of the product.

Second, as long as the fixed factors are specialized with respect to production processes, the level of any process that is used by a firm is in no way restricted by the levels at which other processes are being simultaneously employed. In other words, the opportunity cost of each process in terms of other processes is zero. The only effective limit to the level of any process is the amount available of the fixed factor or factors peculiar to that process. Hence, if any process is employed at all and if there is continuous divisibility of the product(s), it would be employed at the maximum level with the specialized fixed factors fully employed. One important deduction from this is then that the general assumption in linear programming of the continuous divisibility of the fixed factors is again unnecessary for the straightforward solution of an optimization problem under these conditions. The optimum solution of the problem would remain the same as if the fixed factors were perfectly divisible.

The outcome of this discussion is that given continuous product divisibility and the continuous divisibility of the variable input, the indivisibility of fixed factors has no effect on the optimum solution of the production problem faced by the firm as long as the fixed factors are completely specialized with respect to processes or as long as there is only one nonspecialized fixed factor. If any of these conditions is not satisfied, the firm's optimum production plans may be quite different from what it would have been had perfect divisibility existed.

GRAPHIC ILLUSTRATIONS OF DISCRETE PROGRAMMING. The problem of indivisibility exists not only with respect to factors of production, but also with respect to products. For instance, it may not be possible to use a certain machine at less than one machine-hour at a time just as one cannot build, say, $35\frac{1}{2}$ ships of certain standard specifications. Given imperfect divisibility of factors and products, unit level of any process may be defined as that level at which both the inputs and outputs are in the smallest number of units of integral value that are technically feasible. This condition may be relaxed either with respect to the products or with respect to the factors if continuous divisibility prevails in either case. Once the unit level has been thus defined, the optimal solution must consist of processes operated at levels of integral value. Such a solution will in general be different from what it would be if continuous divisibility prevailed throughout.

As a first example, we may turn to a modified version of Figure 17. Let us disregard the specialized fixed factors and omit the lines $F_1$ and $F_2$. In Figure 26, the simplified model shows a feasible set represented by the polygon $OB_3CA_4$ and point $C$ represents the best choice the firm can make.

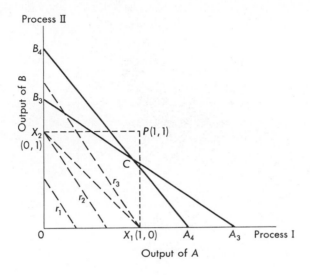

**Figure 26**

If we now alter the model by assuming that the firm's products are divisible in discrete units only, and furthermore, that $OA_4$ is greater than one unit of product $A$, but smaller than two units and that the same applies to $OB_3$ with respect to product $B$, we may add the two lines $X_1P$ and $X_2P$. Visual inspection will show (1) that the point $P$ with co-ordinates (1, 1) is ruled out by the fixed factor constraints represented by $A_3B_3$ and $A_4B_4$; (2) that the former optimum point $C$ is ruled out because of the imperfect divisibility of the products; and (3) that the choice of the new optimum is confined to the three points—$O$, $X_2$, and $X_1$—with their co-ordinates equal to (0, 0), (0, 1), and (1, 0). In this particular case, $X_1$ represents the optimal choice because the slope of $r_3$, which is equal to $\dfrac{p_1 - vc_1}{p_2 - vc_2}$, is found to be greater than the slope of $X_1X_2$, which is equal to

$$\frac{OX_2}{OX_1}\left[\frac{p_1 - vc_1}{p_2 - vc_2} > \frac{OX_2}{OX_1}\right].$$

Since $\dfrac{OX_2}{OX_1} = \dfrac{1}{1} = 1$ by construction, we have $p_1 - vc_1 > p_2 - vc_2$. This is

reminiscent of Case I discussed earlier. The firm will now produce $OX_1$ of product $A$ by process I instead of producing both $A$ and $B$ by a combination of two processes as in Case IV.

A second simple graphic illustration is presented in Figure 27. In this

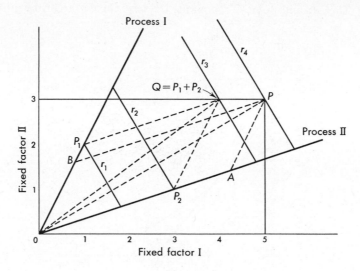

**Figure 27**

diagram we depict a firm producing a single product by two processes subject to the constraint of the two fixed factors. The productive processes of the firm may be described as follows:

| Unit Factor Requirement | PROCESS | | |
|---|---|---|---|
| | I | II | *Resource available* |
| Fixed factor I | 1 | 3 | 5 |
| Fixed factor II | 2 | 1 | 3 |
| Variable factor | $vc_1$ | $vc_2$ | Unlimited |

It has been demonstrated in Case IV that given continuous product and factor divisibility, the optimal solution would be represented by point $P$ which shows a combination of processes I and II at the levels of $OB$ and $OA$ respectively. Now if the factors are divisible only in discrete units as above, the entire feasible set consists of four points only—$0$, $P_1$, $Q$, and $P_2$—and the optimal solution becomes $Q$ which represents processes I and II both at unit levels. Obviously, if more processes were available and the resources available were larger, the set of feasible points would be expanded and the optimal position would no longer be so readily discernible graphically. Of course, it would still be possible to enumerate the feasible points on the single process rays as well as points representing combinations of these processes even though this may become a tedious task.

LINEAR PROGRAMMING FORMULATION. The condition that some processes a firm might adopt could be operated at levels of integral value only imposes an additional constraint on its decision. The optimal solution is no longer necessarily at an extreme point of the convex set bounded by the inequalities as only a subset of a finite number of points within the convex set is now relevant as the field of choice. However, it is still possible to formulate an equivalent linear programming problem.

Let the levels of the available processes for producing $k$ products be represented by $x_1, x_2, \cdots, x_n$ for each product. The problem is to maximize net revenue.

$$(1) \qquad\qquad r = \sum_{t=1}^{k} \sum_{j=1}^{n} (p_t - vc_{tj}) x_{tj}$$

($t = 1, 2, \cdots, k; j = 1, 2, \cdots, n; vc_{tj}$ being the unit direct cost of the $j^{\text{th}}$ process of producing the $t^{\text{th}}$ product)

subject to

$$(2) \qquad\qquad \sum_{t=1}^{k} \sum_{j=1}^{n} (a_{itj} x_{tj}) \leqq F_i \text{ for } i = 1, 2, \cdots, m$$

($F_i$ being the fixed resources available; $a_{itj}$ being the unit requirement of the $(tj)^{\text{th}}$ process for the $i^{\text{th}}$ fixed factor);

$$(3) \qquad\qquad x_{tj} = \text{a nonnegative integer.}$$

The solution of the problem may be carried out as in Markowitz and Manne[36] by writing out for each product the $x_j$ into $x_{1j} + x_{2j} + x_{3j} + \cdots + \cdots + \cdots + x_{qj}$ with $q$ representing the highest integral value a single process may assume given the availability of the fixed factors. Thus modified, the last condition ($x_{tj} = $ a nonnegative integer) may be replaced by the condition that the level of each process must be either 0 or 1. If, for instance, for the $j^{\text{th}}$ process of a product, $x_{1j}, x_{2j}$, and $x_{3j} = 1$ while $x_{4j}, x_{5j}, \cdots, x_{qj} = 0$, the process would be carried on at a level of 3. The modified problem may then be solved by iteration through solving actually a series of linear programming problems.

COMPARISON WITH MARGINAL ANALYSIS. Mention has already been made earlier in this section of marginal analysis in the case of a firm with a fixed factor that is completely indivisible. Apart from this, it would seem that the problem of discreteness can arise in the traditional marginal analysis of the firm only with respect to the imperfect divisibility either of the product or of

---

[36] Markowitz and Manne [116].

the variable input. Whenever one of these conditions prevails, the marginal cost schedule becomes a series of line segments instead of a continuous curve. Accordingly, a small change in either the price of the commodity or in that of the variable input may not have any noticeable effect on the firm's production. This, however, is a situation which we have already found in Case IV where no assumption was made of imperfect divisibility. On the other hand, the problem of discrete programming as described above, which arises out of the imperfect divisibility of two nonspecialized fixed factors, does not occur in the conventional marginal approach for the simple reason that the fixed factor is usually implicitly treated as if it were homogeneous.

## THE FIRM UNDER CONDITIONS OF IMPERFECT MARKETS

In all the preceding cases we have examined, the assumption of constant prices has been made both for the firm's product(s) and for its variable inputs. Under this assumption the total net revenue to be derived from any process will change proportionately as the level of the process changes. In other words, the unit net revenue which is the coefficient of the process level in the objective function is a constant, and the objective function is accordingly linear.

As we abandon the assumption of constant product and input prices, these coefficients of the objective function—$(p_1 - vc_{11})$, $(p_1 - vc_{12})$, $\cdots$, $(p_1 - vc_{1m})$; $(p_2 - vc_{21})$, $\cdots$, $(p_2 - vc_{2m})$; $\cdots$, $(p_n - vc_{n1})$, $\cdots$, $(p_n - vc_{nm})$ for a firm producing $n$ products each with $m$ processes—become themselves variables so that the objective function can no longer be linear. We can, therefore, no longer speak of *linear* programming. Our preceding graphic analysis with convex sets must also be modified through changes in the properties of the iso-revenue curves. As a result of such modifications we shall find that the optimum solution will no longer necessarily be at an extreme point of the convex set, but may be elsewhere on the boundary of the set or even inside the set, and that other rules applicable to linear programming also may no longer hold. A survey of several cases corresponding to those studied under pure competition will throw further light on this generalization.

### A Single-product Firm with Two Processes

Let us assume that the product price, $p_p$ is a continuous function of the firm's output, $x$, and that the price of its variable input, $p_f$, is a continuous function of the amount of variable input purchased or $v$. For simplicity we shall assume these functions to be

$$p_p = f(x) = a - bx$$

and

$$p_f = \phi(v) = d + ev,$$

$a$, $b$, and $e$ being positive numbers, $d$ being either positive or negative.

Since the amount of the variable input purchased depends upon the level at which individual processes are used, if there are two processes, we may indicate the amounts produced under the two processes by $x_1$ and $x_2$ ($x_1 + x_2 = x$). If $\mu_1$ and $\mu_2$ are used to denote the amounts of the variable input in physical units required per unit of $x_1$ and $x_2$ respectively ($\mu_1 \neq \mu_2$), then we may write the amounts of the variable input used in the two processes as $v_1$ and $v_2$ so that

$$v_1 = \mu_1 x_1$$

and

$$v_2 = \mu_2 x_2.$$

The corresponding "direct costs" will then be $p_f \mu_1$ for each unit of $x_1$ and $p_f \mu_2$ for each unit of $x_2$.

The total net revenue, $r$, i.e., the objective function to be maximized, now becomes

$$r = (p_p - p_f \mu_1)x_1 + (p_p - p_f \mu_2)x_2.$$

Since

$$p_p = a - b(x_1 + x_2)$$

and

$$p_f = d + e(v_1 + v_2) = d + e(\mu_1 x_1 + \mu_2 x_2),$$

we may write

$$r = [a - b(x_1 + x_2) - d\mu_1 - e\mu_1(\mu_1 x_1 + \mu_2 x_2)]x_1$$
$$+ [a - b(x_1 + x_2) - d\mu_2 - e\mu_2(\mu_1 x_1 + \mu_2 x_2)]x_2$$
$$= (a - d\mu_1)x_1 + (a - d\mu_2)x_2 - 2(b + e\mu_1\mu_2)x_1 x_2$$
$$- (b + e\mu_1^2)x_1^2 - (b + e\mu_2^2)x_2^2.$$

Comparing this objective function with the quadratic function in its general form, viz., $Ax^2 + Bxy + Cy^2 + Dx + Ey + F = 0$, we find that the value of ($B^2 - 4AC$) is less than zero. This means that the graph of the function is an ellipse. By substituting different values for $r$, a series of ellipses may be drawn to represent the iso-revenue curves. These are plotted in Figure 28 with the following assumed arbitrary constants:

$$a = 3, b = 0.1, d = 2, e = 0.5, \mu_1 = 0.5, \text{ and } \mu_2 = 0.3.$$

The objective function may then be reduced to

$$r = 2x_1 + 2.4x_2 - 0.35x_1 x_2 - 0.225x_1^2 - 0.145x_2^2.$$

By setting $r$ equal to zero, we may draw the iso-revenue curve $r_0$. Now the entire set of nonnegative net revenues with $x_1$ and $x_2$ nonnegative is represented by the space bounded by $OX_1$, $OX_2$ and the section of $r_0$ that is in the first quadrant (including the boundaries). The maximization of net revenue

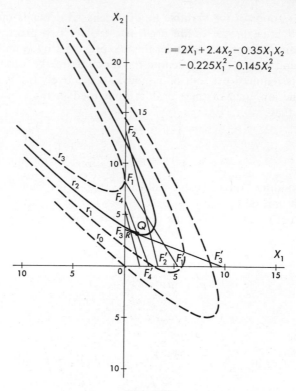

**Figure 28**

must, however, take place within the convex set defined by the fixed constraints. Several points may now be noted.

1. If there is a single constraint such as $F_1F_1'$, the optimum program would be represented by the co-ordinates of point $F_1$. The same would be true if $F_2F_2'$ were the only constraint. On the other hand, if $F_3F_3'$ is the single constraint, the optimum net revenue would be obtained at $Q$ which is on the boundary of the convex set but away from the extreme points.

2. If there are two constraints such as $F_1F_1'$ and $F_2F_2'$, $F_1$ would represent the point of optimum net revenue. The same would be true even if $F_1F_1'$ should intersect the vertical axis at a point above $F_1$. Alternatively, if the fixed constraints were represented by $F_3F_3'$ and $F_4F_4'$, which intersect at $Q$, $Q$ would become the optimum solution. On the other hand if $F_4F_4'$ should cut $F_3F_3'$ to the left of $Q$, a new optimum would be found at the corner of the convex set, $R$.

3. The preceding points demonstrate quite clearly: (a) that both processes I and II could be employed in the optimum solution even in the case of a single fixed constraint; and (b) that in the case of more than one fixed constraint, it is nevertheless possible to have an optimum solution containing only one process, and that neither fixed factor need be fully utilized. The first possibility arises because, unlike linear programming, the profitability of substituting one process by another now

varies also with the degree to which substitution has already taken place. For instance, if $F_3F_3'$ is the single fixed constraint, starting from $F_3$ it will be profitable to substitute process I for process II up to the point $Q$, but not beyond $Q$. The rate of net revenue substitution of process I for process II, which is measured by the slope of the iso-revenue curves,[37] will not remain constant as output by process I is substituted for output by process II along the production boundary line $F_3F_3'$. This, of course, is merely another way of saying that the iso-revenue curves are nonlinear. The second possibility arises because if the net revenue function does not have a maximum *inside* the set defined by the physical constraints, together with the two axes and the curve $r_0$, the maximum feasible net revenue must then lie on the boundary of the set. If it further lies on $OX_1$ or $OX_2$, then the optimum solution would contain one process only. This is the case if $F_1F_1'$ and $F_2F_2'$ are the two relevant fixed constraints.

4. Finally, it should be noted that the scale of the plant in this case exercises an influence on the choice of the processes used. If, for instance, another fixed constraint line were drawn from $F_1$ parallel to $F_3F_3'$, then the optimum solution would be represented by $F_1$, whereas $Q$ is the optimum if $F_3F_3'$ is the fixed constraint. The larger plant would employ one process only as against two processes by the smaller plant. Again, this is due to the fact that the rate of net revenue substitution is not a constant as the scale of the plant changes; or more precisely, the slope of the successive iso-revenue curves intersecting a scale line emerging from the origin (the $OX_2$-axis being such a line) are not equal.

## An *n*-Product Firm with *n*-Processes

A simple case in this category may be represented by a two-product firm using one process for each product. This differs from the preceding example which may be regarded as a special case of this broader category in that there are now two product prices and two separate demand functions for the products.

Let us assume that $x_1$ and $x_2$ are the outputs of two separate products, each representing one particular production process, so that $p_1$ and $p_2$, representing the product prices, are functions of $x_1$ and $x_2$ respectively. Then $r$ becomes

$$(p_1 - p_f\mu_1)x_1 + (p_2 - p_f\mu_2)x_2.$$

Given the linear functions $p_1 = f(x_1) = a_1 - b_1x_1$ and $p_2 = f(x_2) = a_2 - b_2x_2$,

$$r = a_1x_1 - b_1x_1^2 - d\mu_1x_1 - e\mu_1^2x_1^2 - e\mu_1\mu_2x_1x_2$$
$$+ a_2x_2 - b_2x_2^2 - d\mu_2x_2 - e\mu_2^2x_2^2 - e\mu_1\mu_2x_1x_2$$

$$= -(e\mu_1^2 + b_1)x_1^2 - 2e\mu_1\mu_2x_1x_2 - (e\mu_2^2 + b_2)x_2^2$$
$$+ (a_1 - d\mu_1)x_1 + (a_2 - d\mu_2)x_2.$$

---

[37] The slope $dx_2/dx_1$ is equal to

$$\frac{(a - d\mu_1) - 2(b + e\mu_1\mu_2)x_2 - 2(b + e\mu_1^2)x_1}{(a - d\mu_2) - 2(b + e\mu_1\mu_2)x_1 - 2(b + e\mu_2^2)x_2}.$$

If we now assign the following arbitrary values to the constants:

$$\mu_1 = 0.5, \qquad \mu_2 = 0.3, \qquad a_1 = 2.5, \qquad a_2 = 1.5,$$
$$b_1 = 1, \qquad b_2 = 2, \qquad d = 5, \qquad e = -4,{}^{38}$$

the resulting objective function would then be

$$r = 1.2x_1x_2 - 1.64x_2^2$$

which is a hyperbola $\{(B^2 - 4AC) = [(1.2)^2 + 4(0)(1.64)] > 0\}$.

### Graphic Solution

The graphic solution of this problem is presented in Figure 29. It can be easily seen from the diagram that if there is only a single fixed constraint $F_1F_1'$, the graphic solution would yield an optimum at $S$ which is on the

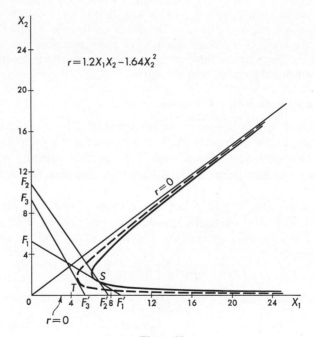

**Figure 29**

boundary, though not an extreme point of the convex set $OF_1F_1'$. If an additional fixed constraint is added, such as $F_2F_2'$, the optimum solution $S$ would then be an extreme point. On the other hand, if the second fixed constraint were $F_3F_3'$, the new optimum solution would be represented by

---

[38] For the sake of variety, the input market is assumed to be "pluperfect" so that its price actually declines as the quantity employed increases.

point $T$ which, however, is not an extreme point. In this case the scale of the fixed plant as such will not affect the choice of the processes.[39]

These two examples suffice to show some of the differences between pure competition and imperfect markets. Under pure competition, if a process is profitable at all, net revenue will continue to rise as the level of the process increases. Thus in the figures used in the cases under competition, zero net revenue always corresponds to the origin alone in the graphs. Hence the entire convex set bounded by the axes and the fixed constraints represents the field of choice. Since the net revenue function is linear, the optimum solution must correspond to an extreme point and, with colinearity as an exception, to only one extreme point.

With imperfect markets, zero value of the net revenue function is no longer limited to the origin. The iso-revenue curve corresponding to zero net revenue may divide the first quadrant of our two-dimensional diagram into two sets, only one of which consists of points of nonnegative net revenue. It is the intersection of this set and the convex set defined by the fixed capacities that now constitutes the field of choice. It should be noted that the intersection of the two sets is *always* a *subset* of the convex set defined by the fixed capacities; the field of choice may therefore also be narrower.

Furthermore, if the net revenue function has a maximum value that is inside the original convex set, the optimum solution would not lie on the boundary of the convex set. On the other hand, if there is a maximum value outside the convex set or if there is no finite maximum at all, the optimum solution would then lie on the boundary of the convex set. But there does not appear to be any general rule requiring the optimum solution to be an extreme point.

The same analysis may also be carried out in terms of the process rays. As long as only two fixed constraints are present, this can be presented on a two-dimensional diagram as before. The principal difference from the graphic analysis under pure competition is that if two points are taken from two process rays representing equal net revenue and a straight line is drawn between them, points on this line are no longer an iso-revenue curve as before. The latter, however, can be easily derived from the net revenue function expressed in terms of process levels by substituting the quantities of the fixed factors used as the independent variables.

For instance, let $\alpha_1$ and $\beta_1$ represent the quantities of fixed factors I and II required by process I at unit level and $\alpha_2$ and $\beta_2$ the corresponding unit requirements in process II. If $f_1$ and $f_2$ are the amounts of the fixed factors employed at process levels $x_1$ and $x_2$, then we have

$$f_1 = \alpha_1 x_1 + \alpha_2 x_2$$

and

$$f_2 = \beta_1 x_1 + \beta_2 x_2.$$

[39] The reader may prove this for himself as an exercise.

From this we may write:

$$x_1 = \frac{\beta_2 f_1 - \alpha_2 f_2}{\alpha_1 \beta_2 - \alpha_2 \beta_1} = \frac{\begin{vmatrix} f_1 & \alpha_2 \\ f_2 & \beta_2 \end{vmatrix}}{\begin{vmatrix} \alpha_1 & \alpha_2 \\ \beta_1 & \beta_2 \end{vmatrix}} \, ,$$

and

$$x_2 = \frac{\begin{vmatrix} \alpha_1 & f_1 \\ \beta_1 & f_2 \end{vmatrix}}{\begin{vmatrix} \alpha_1 & \alpha_2 \\ \beta_1 & \beta_2 \end{vmatrix}} \, .$$

If we take the net revenue function of the previous example with $r = 1.2x_1x_2$ — $1.64x_2^2$ and assume that $\alpha_1 = 2$, $\alpha_2 = 1$, $\beta_1 = 1$, and $\beta_2 = 2$, the net revenue function may then be rewritten as

$$r = 1/9 \, (- \, 4.04f_1{}^2 + 12.56f_1f_2 - 8.96f_2{}^2).$$

The graphic solution of this problem is presented in Figure 30. The diagram shows that the iso-revenue curves, which are hyperbolas, will reach

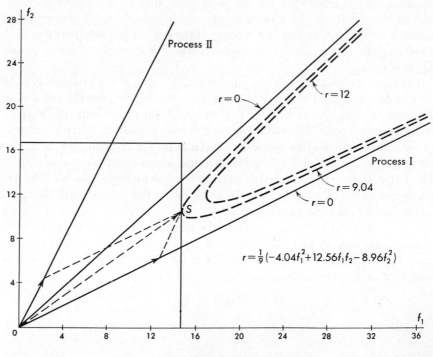

**Figure 30**

the maximum feasible value while using both processes although only one fixed factor will act as the effective constraint, a result that is again contrary to the general theorem in linear programming.

### Mathematical Programming Formulation

The preceding cases can be easily formulated as a problem of maximizing

(1) $$r = \phi(x_1, x_2, \cdots, x_n) = \phi(x_j) \qquad j = 1, 2, \cdots, n$$

subject to

(2) $\sum\limits_{j=1}^{n} a_{ij}x_j \leqq F_i$ for $i = 1, 2, 3, \cdots, m$; $F_1, F_2, \cdots, F_m$ being the fixed con-

straints;

(3) $$x_j \geqq 0; \text{ and}$$

(4) $$r > 0.$$

It is necessary to add the last condition because positive values of the $x$'s may now be associated with negative net revenue even if only processes that are profitable at unit level are included.

It should be noted that the net revenue function is derived from the demand functions for the firm's product(s) and the supply function(s) of the variable input(s) employed by the firm in its various processes. The demand and supply functions assumed in the preceding examples are linear and the result is a quadratic net revenue function. Where the demand and supply functions are not linear, the net revenue function would be of a higher degree. While it is fairly easy to state the problem in a mathematical programming form, there is no standard method of solution for some of these problems other than that of numerical approximation. This is a penalty that one has to pay for leaving the familiar ground of linear programming.

### Conventional Marginal Analysis

It is in this light that one must view again the merits of the conventional marginal analysis in which the general rule is to equate marginal cost to marginal revenue. We can imagine the case of a firm producing a single product with $n$ available processes. We can construct iso-product curves to show the respective levels both of single processes and of process combinations which will yield the same physical output. We can then compute for each of these possibilities of process combinations the total variable costs that would be incurred, allowing for changes in input prices as determined by their supply functions. Then from among the many possible ways of producing the same level of output, we can select one particular arrangement which will incur the least cost in terms of expenditure on the variable input. In this manner, we can determine the lowest total variable cost for successive levels of output and derive from this schedule the data on marginal cost. The latter may then be compared with the demand function for the firm's output and the marginal revenue schedule derived therefrom. If a point of intersection exists between the marginal cost and revenue schedules within the limits set by the fixed capacities, then we have constructed precisely the same result as would be obtained in the marginal analysis in the usual textbook treatment.

Starting from zero output, as long as there is idle capacity in all the fixed factors, the process that has the lowest variable cost will remain to be the cheapest process provided that there is a single product, as well as a single variable input. For such a single-product firm, there is therefore no difficulty in establishing the level of marginal cost. Once idle capacity no longer exists in one of the fixed factors, process substitution must take place, and maximization will be at the boundary. But marginal cost can still be ascertained easily. However, in the case of multiple products and/or multiple variable inputs employed in different processes, while we can continue to think in terms of the least outlay for producing any given level of gross revenue, the same process or process combination will not necessarily remain as the cheapest at all levels of gross revenue even when idle capacity exists all around. While the concept of marginal cost is still quite clear, it may not be readily ascertainable in practice even though mathematical programming may be able to provide a solution for the optimum at which marginal cost and marginal revenue must be conceptually equal. Here again, as we have already observed in the case of pure competition, the formal equality between marginal cost and marginal revenue in the conventional analysis loses much of its significance, while the methods of mathematical programming may still offer a practical approach in the firm's decision-making.[40]

## CONCLUDING REMARKS

In the preceding sections we have examined a number of mathematical programming models of the firm under various assumptions as to market structure, the number and divisibility of the product(s), and the nature of the constraints. These mathematical programming formulations of the economic choice of the firm are also analyzed in terms of the familiar concepts of the marginal analysis. In the case of a single-product firm, it has been shown that the conventional average variable cost curve and the marginal cost curve can be readily constructed from the programming models. Even here, however, as in the transportation problem, the determination of the lowest cost of performing a given task may depend on programming techniques. When we move to multiple-product firms with multiple constraints, the derivation of the cost curves becomes complicated and cumbersome. It is much easier to

[40] For discussions on nonlinear programming and its techniques see, for instance, Dorfman [53], Dorfman, Samuelson and Solow [54]. The basic paper on nonlinear programming is Kuhn and Tucker [99]. Some recent research results are published in Arrow, Hurwicz, and Uzawa [9]; Barankin and Dorfman [12]; Charnes and Cooper [31]; Charnes and Lemke [32]; Frank and Wolfe [67]; and Markowitz [115]. All these papers are mathematically advanced. A general discussion of convex programming may be found in Vazsonyi [165], Chap. 7.

construct the supply schedule of the firm by utilizing the concepts of mathematical programming.

When the analysis is extended to a firm under conditions of imperfect markets, it is indicated that the marginal cost of production is not readily ascertainable in practice when there are multiple products and multiple variable inputs employed in different processes. The practical solution of a firm's production problem may therefore depend on the successful application of mathematical programming methods.

Our analysis has therefore demonstrated that, in all these cases, the familiar concepts of the marginal analysis can be applied to indicate the logical properties of the optimum solution. On the other hand, the traditional tools of marginal analysis may fail to provide a convenient method of arriving at the optimum solution. The availability of techniques for the numerical solution of economic and business problems is indeed the basis of the importance of mathematical programming.

Throughout this discussion, our analysis has proceeded mainly by means of two-dimensional graphical solutions.[41] Mathematical programming formulations have been presented in general form only. The mathematical concepts underlying programming techniques and methods of numerical solution are being presented elsewhere in this volume.[42]

In conclusion, it may be well to point out some other significant omissions of this paper. In the first place, we have already mentioned that limitations of space have confined the scope of this paper mainly to the short-run analysis of the firm with given input and output prices. Consequently, the output decisions of the firm under imperfect markets have not been given extensive treatment; nor have we considered the long-run analysis of the firm. Second, no mention has been made of the dual theorem in linear programming. This omission is caused both by lack of space and by the fact that the dual problem is more relevant in connection with factor pricing.[43] Last, we may mention the problem of uncertainty in decision-making which we have not discussed. As we visualize the general form of a mathematical programming problem, it is clear that the coefficients of the objective function as well as the values of the constraints may be functions of the process levels and that their values may be subject to various degrees of uncertainty. In other words, both the "pay-off" and the "boundaries" are not necessarily given to the firm and are somewhat "fuzzy." Clearly, the substitution of probability functions in these cases would be called for when we deal with dynamic conditions in the long run and/or with an oligopolistic market. The extension of the present analysis along these lines would seem to be a most fruitful area for future research.

[41] The interested reader is referred to Vazsonyi [165] Chap. 6, "The Geometry of Linear Programming," for a delightful tour of three-dimensional diagrams; see also Spivey, *op. cit.*, pp. 61–72.

[42] See Spivey, *op. cit.*, pp. 72–79.

[43] See, however, Spivey, *op. cit.*, pp. 83–87, for a discussion of the dual theorem.

|  | OPERATIONS RESEARCH: |
| --- | --- |
| *Chapter* | *ITS NATURE AND SCOPE,* |
| **5** | *WITH SOME COMMENTS* |
|  | *CONCERNING ITS IMPACT* |
|  | *ON THE SMOOTHING* |
|  | *OF CYCLICAL FLUCTUATIONS** |

*by* HANS H. JENNY

### ECONOMICS AND THE LARGE CORPORATION

Economics, as the writer sees it, is ultimately a *policy science*. In order to formulate workable public policies with respect to large modern corporations, economics must first develop appropriate models. These, though necessarily simplified, must be as accurate as prevailing methodology and knowledge permit. Among other things, they must take into account political and social reality, as well as economic efficiency. The following comments point to a necessary change in the traditional emphasis for economics if such models are to be developed and they underline the importance of Operations Research (O.R.) to the future evolution of an economic theory of the large modern corporation.

I

Large, professionally managed, modern corporations, as they exist in the United States today, represent both a symbol and a threat. They are a symbol of all that is gigantic and successful, and they tell of the dramatic culmination of technological and managerial knowhow which we and the world somehow

* The author wishes to thank all those whose aid has facilitated the completion of this essay. Space limitation does not permit a detailed listing, but a special word of appreciation is due the Trustees of the College of Wooster for providing the financial support and for granting a leave of absence for research. Thanks go also to Dr. N. J. Demerath, Director of the Social Science Institute at Washington University in St. Louis for arranging a meeting of social scientists and businessmen during which some of the ideas contained in this chapter were discussed.

expect of and associate with the American economy. As a threat, they signify monopoly power and a danger not only to the democratic organization of the economy, but also to the socially efficient long-run allocation and use of both human and material resources.

Since the passage of the Sherman Act of 1890, public policy toward large corporations has been concerned chiefly with the threat of monopoly power. This concern is still very much with us. However justified the economist's pre-occupation with the monopoly problem may be, he must remain aware of the social and political realities, as well as of the true nature of the large modern corporation, in his attempts to formulate workable public policies.

Antimonopoly policy has the solid support of an economic theory of the market which makes the (purely) competitive firm not only a thing of beauty and virtue, but also the yardstick for economic efficiency throughout the private economic sector. Economic theory has but recently begun to describe with some accuracy the markets where large corporations operate. Thus, the theory of heterogeneous oligopoly at long last deals with what must be acknowledged as one of the most common market forms in America today.[1] Some exceptions notwithstanding, economists have been reluctant to say anything good about oligopolies. At the same time they have been unable to formulate as clean a policy package as the one resulting from the theory of pure competition. This is largely so because, in spite of the increased realism which oligopoly theory brings to it, the theory of the firm is on the whole ill suited to describe satisfactorily the workings and the multiple motivations characteristic of different types of large corporations.

In order to formulate an economic policy which accords the large corporation its legitimate place in the enterprise system, economists might do well to reconsider the power concept on which both theory and policy are based today. The limited usefulness of traditional theory in the shaping of workable policies stems in no small measure from the economist's preoccupation with the threat posed by monopoly power. This threat is real enough in numerous circumstances and must not be ignored. On the other hand, economists will have to learn how to live with monopoly power and noncompetitive practices. Past enforcement of antitrust legislation and the history of congressional action do not hold out much hope for the introduction of the kind of competition which seems to loom behind so many conventional policy proposals. Ways must be found to solve perennial economic problems—i.e., inflation, unemployment, etc.—in spite of monopolies and noncompetitive practices.


## II

If the solution does not lie solely in the eradication of monopoly power, where does it lie? Among other things, it lies in the fact that monopoly

---

[1] See also, [30], [65], [106], [161], and, in a different setting, [131].

power is not the only power worth studying. Every firm—as a matter of fact, every economic unit—has a certain amount of power to control its own destiny. This is the power, inherent in management, to make the right or the wrong, better or worse, decisions. For want of a better term, the author has called this elsewhere [88] the firm's *autonomous power*, chiefly because a firm's autonomy finds expression in the power it may have to manage itself freely [55].

Large corporations have a considerable amount of such power which need not be identical with or even related to their power to monopolize trade. As fewer firms can afford to be flown by the seat of their pants, this type of power will have to be looked at as a more and more important factor in determining the over-all performance of the economy. If we expect the latter to perform well, it makes a great deal of difference whether firms are scientifically managed or not. It would seem that the nation has an interest in the development of sound principles and practices of business management throughout the economy. Yet, public policy as formulated in the name of economics is not, at present, exploiting this type of autonomous power for improved over-all economic results. On the contrary, it has, sometimes unwittingly, sometimes deliberately, interfered with it to the detriment of an optimally operating economic system.

One of the reasons for this lies in a peculiarity of the theory of the firm as most contemporary economists know it. In it, autonomous power emerges with respect to the most basic of all economic problems, namely the question of how to allocate scarce productive resources so as to achieve specific ends. Economic theory has not ignored the power or ability a firm may have to manage itself wisely. The classical concepts of the *economic man* and the *entrepreneur* and, later, the *innovation principle*, recognize the existence of this power. So does the modern concept of the *production function*. However, traditionally, economics has not concerned itself with the continuous scientific scrutiny of the decision-making process which lies behind these concepts. Instead, it has left the task largely to other disciplines whose discoveries were not always incorporated into economic models [22, pp. 82 ff; 24, pp. 17 ff, especially p. 31]. As a matter of fact, there seems to exist some divergence between the assumptions of rational behavior in the theory of the firm and the actual decision-making process where rules of thumb, intuition, uneducated guesses, so-called sound judgment, and tradition, rather than the scientific method, appear to be the order of the day. T. C. Koopmans writes that "economics has suffered from looking at the production function as a boundary of its domain of competence" [97, p. 70].

If there does exist a recognizable best or most rational set of decisions for the achievement of specific business goals, it cannot be expected as a foregone conclusion that such decisions will be made. It is difficult to imagine a situation where a large corporation could ever reach a point of finding the best solution to its many problems. It is more likely, as time goes on, that better rather than the best decisions will be made.[2] Furthermore, the question still seems to be open as to whether firms are motivated by what is assumed in economic models.

Although there is always room for ideal and perfect models, the theory of the firm must ultimately describe more accurately how real-life firms behave. It is in the development of such a theory of the firm—particularly the large firm—that O.R. may be destined to play a key role. On the one hand, the economist may learn from O.R. how to adapt his models to a complex reality; on the other, the increasing use of scientific methods and tools of management—a trademark of O.R.—may bring business behavior closer to some recognized optimum standard, be the latter defined in strictly economic or considerably broader terms.[3] In view of the complexity of large modern enterprise, one is justified in asking why the economist's firm is not a more multivariate entity than are the models to which students tend to be exposed. The need for simplification in model construction is only a partial answer. In order to explain the operations of a large modern corporation in a theoretical model, it will be necessary to take a rather broad systems or organizations approach if an accurate picture is to be conveyed. Such models may have to be interdisciplinary and it is quite possible that the economist may have to provide models for different types of large corporations where the distinction is not made in terms of demand elasticities or relative degrees of monopoly power, but in terms of those key factors which define the firm's cost structure.

The restraints which are imposed upon different types of large corporations are not only internal and subject to managerial control. Many are institutional and result from the formal and informal social controls present in the economy. The rules of the game which govern the behavior of specific corporations vary[4] and many are so subtle that they are not now nor ever will be amenable to quantitative analysis [167]. Nevertheless, where institutional differences are substantial enough to account for variations in business behavior they will have to be acknowledged, and ways must be found to incorporate them into economic models. This is all the more important if we realize the impact which different behavior patterns of large corporations in particular and of business firms in general have on the performance of the economy.

---

[2] Charles Hitch, for one, questions the wisdom of the economist's dogged striving for *optimum* solutions; see his "Economics and Military Operations Research," in W. W. Cooper, *et al.* [41, pp. 199–209]. On a related point, Daniel Ellsberg suggests that it is not the economist's job to tell firms what their goals ought to be (i.e., profit maximization), but to show them how they might best achieve the goals which they have set for themselves; see his "A Final Comment," in [41, p. 227].

[3] The reader may wish to see what T. C. Koopmans has to say in this respect [97, pp. 183–6]. Of special interest, also, is his treatment of the old controversy concerning the need for realism in models and assumptions; see his essay entitled "The Construction of Economic Knowledge" [97, pp. 129 ff., especially pp. 135–42].

[4] An automobile producer can drop a line of cars from his regular production schedule with relative ease, but a railroad encounters serious obstacles in eliminating unprofitable segments of its network. See, for instance, [130].

Within less than a decade there has been a mushrooming of literature, much of which may eventually help the economist to formulate a satisfactory theory of the large corporation. In normative economics, activity analysis has been used to advantage in answering the question of how best to allocate scarce resources to specific tasks [96]. In business, both management science and O.R. have produced valuable models describing a variety of efficient operations. It is interesting to note that these advances in the theory of resource allocation have come about largely through the channels of applied economics and engineering.

In a sense, O.R. stands at the center of these new developments. Its inter-disciplinary character may prove to be one of the more significant aspects in the social scientist's attempts to construct a comprehensive theory of organizations of all types. It has already brought significant changes in the behavior of certain business firms, and some of these changes suggest effects which go far beyond the confines of the firm. Specifically, as new patterns of inventory and capital equipment management come into practice, the problem of the business cycle comes into evidence. From the point of view of national economic policy, therefore, O.R. may be regarded as a potential factor which might be subjected to "manipulation" in order to bring about desirable changes (and/or to prevent undesirable ones) in the practice of management for the good of the entire economy. The following exposition and especially the comments in Part Four of this chapter will attempt to explain this point in greater detail. While it is too early to predict whether a comprehensive theory of the large corporation can be developed, the ensuing remarks suggest both the possibility for this and some of the limitations.

## OPERATIONS RESEARCH:
## ITS NATURE AND SCOPE

In order to describe some of its important characteristics, an attempt will be made here to offer a definition and then a brief outline of the scope of O.R.

### I

In the words of the Earl of Halsbury, O.R. "is concerned with *optimizing the performance of a system*" [73, p. 239]. This requires "the application of scientific methods, techniques, and tools" [35, p. 18] and, according to Charles Hitch, normally involves "the use of systematic quantitative analysis" [41, p. 200]. A conspicuous feature of O.R. is the frequent use made of mathematical techniques, especially of linear programming. It is often stated that O.R. concerns the "organization as a whole," although, in practice, many O.R. projects and models do not honor this injunction. One of the features normally associated with O.R. is the so-called *mixed-team* approach to problem solving. However, the latter should not be viewed as a generic

characteristic of O.R.[5] Rather, it should be looked at as a convenient organizational device, necessitated by the complexity of certain problems or by
the lack of multiple skills in those hired to do the job. Some writers distinguish
O.R. from management science, where the latter represents general theory and
the former the application thereof.[6] The reader must be warned that such a
distinction is not easily substantiated by the contents of the leading professional journals in this area where the differences seem to be more in the type
of problem, in the nature of the mathematics and theories, and in the types of
organizations and activities studied, rather than between general theory and
its application. In the following, the term O.R. is used to describe the application of the scientific method, of quantitative analysis, and of mathematical
models in order to provide executives with the best possible answers concerning managerial problems under their control. In this sense, the really significant feature and contribution of O.R. is its emphasis on the optimization of
the performance of a system.

## II

The scope of O.R. can be evaluated on the basis of a number of criteria, such
as the range of industries and organizations, the number of specific activities
or processes, the variety of theories and techniques, and the types of systems
studied. Here, these four criteria will be taken up briefly in the order
stated.[7]

There is hardly an industry to which O.R. techniques have not been applied.
A partial alphabetical listing reveals the following: agriculture, amusement
parks, chemicals, commercial aviation, communications and computers,
food products, furniture, leather, lumber, machinery, mining, petroleum,
printing and publishing, public utilities, tobacco manufacturing, and various
forms of transportation. In addition, we encounter state and local government agencies, as well as such nonprofit organizations as libraries and
prisons. Of course, we must not overlook the vast amount of O.R. work
performed by a number of organizations for agencies of the federal government, especially in the military establishment.[8]

---

[5] Historically, mixed teams made up largely of nonmilitary personnel constituted the
first military O.R. groups whose members were often scientists trained in such disciplines
as biology, physics, statistics, mathematics, etc. They were sought for their scientific and
not for their specialized skills. Many of these teams came about as a result of improvisation
and last-ditch efforts to solve military problems. In business applications of recent years,
teams have become a normal sight, even to the point of obtaining their place in the
organizational structure of certain firms.

[6] For such a view, see [156]. For other definitions, see [123], [124], [125], and [151].

[7] In addition to the references listed in the bibliography, the reader will find helpful two
excellent bibliographies; see [133] and [139].

[8] In addition to many private consulting firms and university O.R. institutes, two out-
standing contributors are the Cowles Foundation at Yale University and the RAND
Corporation in Santa Monica, Cal.

According to R. L. Ackoff [3], [17, pp. 15–18], activities or processes which O.R. projects scrutinize most frequently fall into the following broad categories of which the first four are of particular importance to the economist:

a. *Allocation* problems; they arise when given sets of resources can be combined in different ways to achieve desired results or when there are not enough resources to perform all the necessary activities in the most efficient manner.

b. *Inventory* problems; they can be defined by a deceptively simple question: what or how much and/or when to order?

c. *Replacement* and *renewal problems*; this type of problem arises when a given machine, tool, or other form of investment deteriorates in use or becomes obsolescent for other reasons (such as changes in taste, in technology, etc.), and when an object (say, a light bulb, a spark plug) used in production is consumed or subject to failure.

d. *Competitive* problems or *situations of conflict*; these exist when two or more systems have goals which can only be reached in such a way that the decisions made on behalf of one system will render less efficient the outcome of the decisions of one, several, or all others. So-called games and bidding situations form two of the most frequently studied competitive problem types.

e. *Information-collection* or *search* problems; this type involves the minimization of the sum of the following two kinds of costs; the cost attributable to decision errors and the cost of assembling and analyzing the requisite data. These problems occur in a great variety of contexts: design of air-defense systems, construction of statistical indexes, and in auditing procedures, for instance, in the railroad industry, where revenues must be allocated to a given unit by many others.

f. *Queuing* or *waiting-line* problems; such problems are best defined by the expression "traffic-jam." They occur most frequently in the following fields: telephone and telegraph switching operations, machine breakdown and machine-service or -feeding (including conveyor and assembly lines), and traffic (vehicular and human).

g. *Routeing* problems; these exist when something or someone has to be transported from point A to point B in the most efficient manner, normally via a number of intermediate points. The classic mathematical case is known as the "traveling-salesman problem" [44], [47], [139, pp. 296–300, for additional references]. Another situation where this type of problem occurs is in production sequencing, particularly in connection with assembly-line balancing [141]. Routeing problems tend to be special cases of either allocation or queuing type problems or a combination of the two.

Normally, the problems which O.R. is trying to solve cannot be identified in the pure form which this classification suggests. For lack of a more ingenious term, we have come to speak of *combined* problems or processes. Yet, many seemingly different situations may have enough common characteristics so that the number of required models need not expand indefinitely. Linear and dynamic programming have contributed greatly to economy in model design. Among other things, it has become possible to transform problems requiring complex solutions into others of a more simple type. The use of linear programming to solve certain game problems is a case in point. S. Vajda [164] describes some of the most common situations as they are encountered either in practice or in the O.R. literature.[9]

This leads logically to the third criterion, namely the variety of theories and techniques available to assist in the solution of the many different problems [35]. The reader may be interested in the following: game and decision theory, general systems theory, information, communication, or servomechanism theory, inventory theory, linear and dynamic programming, organization theory, probability theory, queuing theory and stochastic processes, replacement and renewal theory, search theory, and statistics. This list gives an idea of the theoretical complexity and of the scientific scope of O.R., especially if we do not overlook the contributions made to it by such disciplines as psychology, sociology, economics, engineering, and many others.

The last criterion to be looked at here concerns the scope of the particular system under study. In this context, the term "system" refers to any *complex or organic unit of functionally interrelated elements*. A man is a system, and so are the following: a political party, the Roman Catholic Church, a bomber command, the sun with its planets. From the point of view of the manager, the firm is a system, be the latter a single proprietorship or a large corporation. Within a large corporation a myriad of systems of a lower order of subsystems exist. According to the available literature, subsystems seem to have received most of the attention from O.R. practitioners. The Ackoff classification represents subsystems within the broader concept of the firm. From the point of view of the economist, the firm is a subsystem, whereas the national economy—in some contexts even the world economy—constitutes the system of the highest order. Other subsystems in economics are industries and inter-industry sectors. If we look at this layer-cake of systems, we can notice how modern economists are penetrating to the lowest layers by means of linear activity analysis and other techniques. For instance, allocation problems are studied through input-output analysis in interindustry or intersectoral economics [13], and linear programming enables the business economist to suggest efficient allocation decisions concerning such subsystems as those defined by inventory and replacement processes. Thus, systems range in size

---

[9] Among the problems dealt with, we find the following: the caterer problem [87], the trim or trim loss reduction problem [61], [135], the blending of aviation gasoline [111], and various cases of the transportation problem.

and complexity from the cell to the universe. O.R. techniques can be appplied to any system susceptible to manipulation and quantitative analysis. If it is agreed that economics studies the operation of a system, applied economics— as the political economist sees it—has been a type of O.R. all along. In the following it may be well to remember that O.R. need not be restricted to the confines of the firm.

## SOME APPLICATIONS AND PROBLEMS

For the reader who is interested in the details of the various types of problems which O.R. is trying to solve, reference has been made to two comprehensive bibliographies in the foregoing section. In order to convey an idea of the ultimately very practical nature of O.R. work, this section contains (1) a brief description of a now famous case and (2) references to some business problems whose solutions became possible largely through the application of linear programming techniques.

### I

The case which has here been selected is known as the "Toll-Booth Case" [59] and has had considerable impact among O.R. practitioners. It concerns the New York Port Authority, a public enterprise which runs a variety of activities from shipping docks to air terminals. Its Operations Standards Division has applied O.R. techniques to many problems [58]. The first concerned the efficient use of the 1,000 man police force. The toll-booth study was part of the broader efficiency research, for about one-fourth of the Authority's police force is involved in the servicing of toll plazas.[10]

Service efficiency varied greatly. Manpower requirements were set by budget procedures. Budget requests were reviewed according to estimates of future traffic, past experience, and a rule of thumb concerning the number of vehicles one operator could service. Local toll sergeants would allocate personnel as events and experience told them. One of the requirements was to balance traffic requirements against the personal and meal reliefs of the operators. In a conflict, sergeants saw to it that traffic kept moving at the expense of the operator's comfort.

Three main objectives were set for the study: (1) to evaluate service quality and its variations for each toll lane as traffic volume changes; (2) to establish optimum service standards; (3) to develop a more precise service and expense control system and to assure the operators of well-spaced reliefs. An optimum solution of the manpower problem depended upon accurate predictions of traffic patterns. To obtain the latter, precise information had to be collected concerning traffic arrivals, traffic backup, and the number of toll transactions. From such measurements a number of strategic computations were made,

---

[10] For a more comprehensive treatment of queuing problems, see [126].

some of which were later chosen as criteria to determine the grade of service rendered at the toll plaza.[11]

The first step in the choice of suitable criteria consisted in an analysis of traffic arrivals. This culminated in the construction of observed and theoretical arrival frequency distributions which established the assumption that traffic was a *random variable*. Then, some comparisons were made, the first being between toll-booth occupancy and delay ratio,[12] another being between traffic patterns and holding time.[13] Such information makes possible the calculation of maximum booth capacity (total booth time in seconds divided by minimum holding time equals maximum number of vehicles per time period, say, an hour). This was found to apply when and where traffic can easily move out of the toll plaza. Thus, the George Washington Bridge proved to be very efficient in this respect, as well as traffic westbound out of the Lincoln Tunnel (no interfering traffic lights) as opposed to eastbound traffic in the latter and the Holland Tunnel.

The next step consisted in the construction of average delay curves, and this was followed by a frequency distribution analysis of traffic backup. The mean value of the backup was plotted for various lanes and both left- and right-hand booths. This led to the calculation of the probable maximum backup. This sequence of analyses aided in solving the *waiting-line* problem. This required a service standard, say, a top limit for average delay which, when reached, would signal the opening of another toll-booth. However, in O.R. procedures a less arbitrary method is suggested. A diminishing return method was chosen, where traffic volume represents the return and cost is equal to the delay. Inspection showed that a middle value of 11 seconds would constitute a reasonable service standard for the Lincoln and Holland Tunnels and the George Washington Bridge. This made possible the fixing of capacity standards "by equalizing the swing on each side of the standard delay as additional booths are provided" [105, p. 52].[14] If traffic volume is known and a standard for it exists, average delay and maximum backup can be predicted. In order to predict traffic patterns, charts were made which showed the hourly traffic pattern. The following spreads between median and peak volume were found

[11] Computations comprised the following: (1) over-all and average time used by all vehicles to clear the toll lanes; (2) total and average booth-holding time per vehicle; (3) average delay time per vehicle (over-all time minus booth-holding time); (4) delay ratio (average delay time divided by average booth-holding time); (5) percentage empty-lane-availability (number of times one or more lanes empty divided by total number of observations); (6) percentage occupancy of tool-booths (number of occupancies observed divided by total number of observations).

[12] This required the formulation of a delay theory and led to a comparison of empirical data with the theories of Erlang, Molina, and others. A direct result was the proof of the inefficiency of right-hand toll-booths, except during periods of high congestion. Therefore, the Port Authority will equip all major toll plazas with left-hand booths only.

[13] This proved to be less during congestion than in light traffic; holding-time also differs with the type of vehicle (smallest for passenger cars, longest for tractor-trailers).

[14] It was found that a backup of 12 cars is tolerated by patrons when 8 lanes are operating, but not when only 1 or 2 are in service.

through inspection: from 10 to 60 per cent at the George Washington Bridge, and from 10 to 30 per cent at the tunnels. "These variations limit how closely toll-booths can be scheduled in advance to provide optimum service" [105, p. 53]. From the figures on average delay for the median traffic volumes, the required capacity was determined. In cases where the maximum backup became too large, judgment determined that "backups up to three vehicles above the Poisson points" [105, p. 53] would be tolerated.[15] Thus, a schedule of booths for the entire day was set up from which the required number of booth hours could be calculated.

This leads to the last step, the scheduling of service personnel. For this the net working time, the minimum length of working time between reliefs (as well as the maximum length), meal relief time, and starting and quitting times must be known. From such information manpower can be scheduled with the aid of a Gantt-type chart, a trial-and-error procedure which is the more time consuming the more efficient the schedule is to be. One more question remained: will all this work? The answer: "During the entire week [of trial at the Lincoln Tunnel], the prearranged schedules were followed without a hitch. At no time did excessive backups occur, and at no time did reliefs have to be deferred. The movement of collectors and the opening and closing of booths took place without the attention of the toll sergeant" [105, p. 56].

The literature abounds with descriptions of other successful O.R. cases [6], [142], [159]. A lack of space prevents additional reporting here. The reader may find it worthwhile to consult the bibliographies mentioned above, also [104], and [105].

## II

Of all the business problems which have attracted the fancy of O.R. specialists, the inventory problem has produced the most spectacular burst of literature. A great deal of work has been undertaken in the mathematical theory of inventory which points toward further fruitful applications [10]. The methods of the calculus, of linear, and of dynamic programming have been used successfully in the solution of many types of inventory problems.

Inventory situations are well suited to describe the essence of the optimizing process typical of O.R., namely the bringing into balance of conflicting objectives and tendencies within an enterprise or an operation. In an automated plant, for instance, the manager may want to maintain continuous rates of output over as long a period as is necessary to gain the full advantages of mass production. On the other hand, the comptroller sees little reason in a volume of output which piles up inventory for lack of demand, thus tying up capital which earns nothing. Another conflict exists between the need for an adequate safety inventory to satisfy unexpected demand, thus assuring

---

[15] Traffic backup had been found to be approximately a Poisson-type frequency distribution [105, pp. 41–50].

customer goodwill, and the need to guard against excessive inventories and the threat of declining demand.

The inventory problem can be defined in terms of a cost-minimization criterion. This means that such conflicting tendencies as may exist will be expressed by appropriate costs some of which are: purchasing or production costs; the costs of holding and handling inventory; the cost and risk of the investment represented by inventory [108].[16] Purchasing costs per unit tend to increase as the amount ordered decreases, whereas inventory holding costs per unit normally vary directly with changes in the lot size. Basically, then, the inventory problem consists in finding ways to reconcile these opposite cost tendencies. This is accomplished by minimizing the value of the appropriate cost function.

The oldest and most frequently encountered model in inventory control concerns the economic lot size problem [108, pp. 44–66], [170, pp. 15–78, 230–4, 261–81]. An interesting finding of scientific inventory analysis is that "the appropriate order quantity and the average inventory maintained do not vary directly with sales" [108, p. 59, January–February issue]. This is in opposition to a prevalent rule of thumb guiding inventory decisions in many areas of everyday business enterprise. More precisely, the economic lot size changes, among other things, with the square root of sales [10, pp. 5–6], [107, pp. 58–9, January–February issue], [170, pp. 31–42]. Thus, as sales increase, assuming unchanging costs, the amount of inventory per unit of sales will decline. This is a strategic consequence upon which some comments will be made in the next section, "The Search for an Optimum."

For firms which produce their own products rather than to purchase them from the outside, the optimum solution of the economic lot size problem tends to affect the manner in which production is scheduled. It is unlikely that a firm which does not know its economic lot size is operating on an optimum production schedule. J. F. Magee describes a case where a joint analysis of inventory and production scheduling resulted in substantial savings above and beyond those brought about by the initial application of an optimum lot size system. From the economist's viewpoint it is of special importance that the combined system which Magee sets forth brought about a most significant stabilization of production [107, pp. 108–16, March–April issue]. In this connection it is interesting to note the so-called production smoothing models [82], [84], [86], [110], [122], [121] which have appeared in O.R. literature. As a rule, such models attempt to minimize some sum of inventory plus production costs within each of a number of time periods.[17]

It can, of course, be argued that the smoothing of production patterns is a

---

[16] For a detailed analysis of the costs involved, see [108, pp. 24–43].

[17] In the Modigliani-Hohn model, for instance, production costs vary with the rate, but not with changes in the rate of production, and marginal costs of production are assumed to be monotone increasing. Nonstochastic models have been presented in calculus and in linear programming versions, and Richard Bellman [18] has used dynamic programming. See also [17].

desirable objective both for business firms and for the economy. However, production smoothing is not, at the moment, a major O.R. criterion. The smoothing models which do exist are primarily cost-minimizing models, and the smoothing of production can almost be called a by-product resulting from the rigorous assumptions made concerning the behavior of the costs of production. In other words, when the conflicting tendencies of inventory and production costs are of a particular type, the result of minimizing the cost function is as smooth a pattern of production as can be allowed under the circumstances. This is quite different from setting production or even employment smoothing as the goal proper of production scheduling. While it would be wrong to underestimate the usefulness of current smoothing models, it would be equally wrong to attribute too much significance to them in an over-all scheme of national income stabilization, at least at the moment. Nevertheless, production smoothing—whatever the restraints of specific models may be—raises some important questions, some of which are touched upon in the next section.

There appear in O.R. literature a number of other problems which, like the inventory problem, have a special appeal to the economist because they are closely linked to the problem of cyclical fluctuations. Limitations of space do not permit elaboration except to state that one of the most crucial of these is the problem of capital replacement and renewal defined earlier [5], [8], [70], [152]. The lack of attention given to efficient depreciation policies both at the level of the firm and that of the economy is a conspicuous feature of traditional economic theory. George Terborgh and the Machinery and Allied Products Institute have developed some interesting theories and models, and they are pressing for a more realistic public policy [157]. Recent changes in emphasis may bring welcome innovations, and the contribution which O.R. has been and will be making may prove to be of great value to economic theory and policy formulation. In the next section some comments will be made on the role of O.R. within the broader context of the economy which the inventory and the replacement problems suggest, and some policy questions will be raised.

## THE SEARCH FOR AN OPTIMUM

The problems which have been mentioned in the preceding sections possess certain characteristics which are worth some brief comments; they also bring into focus some of the limitations and potentials of O.R. (1) All the problems are defined in terms of an optimal or best solution, a feature which has already been identified as typical of O.R. problems. This raises, among others, the crucial question of what the criteria are which define an O.R. *optimum*. (2) All the problems concern less than the whole enterprise. Thus, within the scope of a realistic theory of the firm they fall into the general classification of suboptimization problems. There exist O.R. studies whose scope is the whole firm, but the literature is weighted more heavily with the type of problem defined above. The question which will be asked here concerns the value of suboptimization within the broader systems complex. (3) Some of the problems, though limited in their immediate scope, concern variables whose macroeconomic magnitude is such that the performance of the entire economy is affected. This means that O.R., as applied to such problems, ceases to be of a strictly business interest. The question to which this leads here is what O.R. may or should mean to the political economist interested in the problem of how best to maintain full employment without causing inflation, though nevertheless assuring technological progress and economic growth.

I

The driver of a racing car is interested in the top speed he can safely reach for the duration of a given contest; the missile experts are looking for the apparatus which will eventually guide a payload to and not past the moon; a concert pianist may measure his success by the length of the ovation, the size of the audience, the number of engagements booked, or the amount of the check he receives for each performance. In each case, one or several criteria are at work on the basis of which efficiency or goal achievement can be evaluated more or less precisely. Where several criteria are at work, no permanent single preference ordering can be assumed to exist.

Business also has its criteria. They run from the relatively straightforward statement: "With us, profit is all that counts; the bigger, the better!" to this somewhat more complex situation: "We have social responsibilities which cost money. Somebody has to pay for them. Naturally, the prices of our products reflect this. But the competition knows, and we have—you might say—an industry-wide philosophy on this. It was quite a struggle getting this far, but this is only the beginning. The services we render are essential. If we don't do it, the government will have to come in." In business, as in many other places, a variety of criteria are often at work, giving more or less of a direction and purpose to management decisions.

As K. E. Boulding points out earlier in this volume, once we realize that a firm is an organization—and this especially for very large ones—the multiplicity of roles to be played and reconciled within this organization makes for a very difficult process of communication. Imperfections and inconsistencies will tend to obscure the firm's real objectives. Thus, as we learn more about the nature of organizations, a clearer definition of the criteria which define the optimum will emerge. In the meantime, our models will reflect the fragmentary nature of our knowledge in this key area.

It is one thing to construct models for optimum solutions without knowing what the actual objectives are but making educated guesses about them. It is quite a different thing to ignore known objectives, largely because they are not susceptible to quantitative analysis. Remarkable advances have been made during the last twenty years in quantitative studies. Nevertheless, there is a real danger in a development of the sciences devoted to the study of man and his relations with other men which professes to be either purely or predominately a quantitative endeavor. As the *optimum* appears in O.R. models today, it has been so packed with the economist's and the engineer's *quanta* that the soul has been all but squeezed out of it. There is ample room for precise science but there is also room for philosophy (in the classical sense of the word). An optimum which is defined in terms of criteria which have a purely quantitative flavor, though valid, will substantially limit the scope of fruitful applications. Intangibles must often be joined with tangibles, the unmeasurable with the measurable, in the definition of realistic optima.

If it is true that too much "quantitative social science" may harm the very thing it sets out to understand and improve, it is also true that there is a great need for further advances in the art of quantification itself. The overwhelming number of O.R. criteria are defined in terms of either minimizing a cost function or in maximizing some such performance criterion as physical output, sales, or profit. These are valid and very useful criteria. What we must ask ourselves is whether we have learned enough about them to give an accurate picture of the specific elements which constitute the cost and the performance factors themselves [20].

The theory of the firm offers an object lesson in this. The two basic elements around which most of the analysis is woven are *input* and *output*, supplemented by the concept of a *surplus*. Translated into monetary or accounting equivalents, these become cost, revenue, and profit (or loss), respectively. Whether the model of the firm is phrased in marginalist language or in the terminology of linear programming, its ultimate validity depends upon what is represented by cost, revenue, and profit in actual budgetary terms. Of the three, cost, rather than profit, appears as the crucial element. If we take the budget of any one of the well-known large corporations, we find expenditure categories which—from the point of view of a narrowly defined profit motive—have not the slightest connection with the basic purpose of the enterprise. Yet, not only are they there, but many of them tend to be substantial. The mixture of rational, irrational, and nonrational cost items is an expression of the firm's managerial ability and philosophy. With all its defects, it is the real-life organization's way of handling multivariate motivations, goals, and conflicts, *faute-de-mieux*, as it were.

This throws an interesting light on the traditional assumption in economic theory of profit maximization by the firm. If we start from a given cost setup, to maximize profits means chiefly to sell enough at the right price. Some of the cost decisions may have been made with a certain market price in mind. But when the cost function is given, as it is in the traditional textbook diagram, demand becomes the crucial variable. As a rule, demand does not fall within the immediate scope of managerial control. The solution which the marginalists suggest makes as much sense as any other. Its practical significance has probably been underestimated in some critical circles, and it may be followed more widely by firms than appears on the record. However, this sort of profit maximization is not at all what all the controversy has or should have been about. The heart of the matter is the economist's equally traditional assumption of cost minimization which underlies the production function analysis. When businessmen of sound mind object to the economist's assumption of profit maximization, they really may object not to the marginalists but to the principle of cost minimization narrowly conceived. *The key to profit maximization does not lie so much in the balancing of costs with revenues as it lies in the initial decisions which define a given organization's cost structure.* Thus, the allocation of scarce resources by the firm occupies the center of the stage.

Cost minimization involves at least two types of decisions. The first is characterized by activity analysis in economics and by O.R. in the theory and practice of business management. It involves optimization with given cost factors. The second relates to the choice of the cost factors proper, particularly their number and quality. This area of decision-making is not very well understood at present, and it is here that intangibles are most conspicuous. For instance, so-called social responsibility expenditures by big business fall into this category. At the moment, O.R. has relatively little to offer in this area. From the point of view of the role to be played by large (and other) firms in the broader social environment, this may well be the key realm in the over-all managerial decision-making process and, therefore, in determining the true nature of the over-all optimum standard.

If economics through the theory of the firm and the science of management through O.R. are to lead to optimum solutions of their respective problems, the criteria defining this optimum must be a composite of the aspirations and values characteristic of the organization to which they apply. *The managerial decisions and what lies behind them, culminating in the economist's production function, are the true indicators of the firm's objectives.* For large organizations, the latter are bound to be multivariate. Therefore, the criteria defining the optimum will be multivariate, containing both tangible and intangible values to be achieved.

## II

Because and as long as so many O.R. problems are of the suboptimization type, it is important to synchronize the optimum solution of the particular problem with the criteria complex which defines the over-all optimum standard of the organization. If anything, this is perhaps the most demanding task facing O.R. specialists who work on problems confronting large corporations and other similarly complex systems for which cost minimization and profit maximization in the narrow sense do not represent accurate definitions of the over-all optimum standard, but where the latter is better described by multivariate criteria.

Piecemeal suboptimization is perhaps all that can properly be expected of O.R. at the present time. One of the reasons for this is the relative newness of systems analysis and thus the lack of sufficient data for the understanding of large complex systems. Another reason is that large systems can only be studied carefully over a very long period of time, whereas the businessman is interested in getting results quickly. This leads him to sponsor research in areas where the payoff can be expected shortly. Of course, the time and money factors are closely related in their effect upon the scope of O.R. in direct business applications.

If it is correct that suboptimization will be one of the chief aspects of O.R. for some time to come [81], [79], failure to synchronize the various optimum standards within a given large system would drastically limit O.R.'s usefulness, confining its application to organizations of a relatively simple structure. From this, a good case can be made for the contention that O.R., at present at least, seems to be better suited to further an optimal solution of the problems of small enterprises, especially those operating in a highly competitive environment, than to assure the optimum performance of very large corporations. This conclusion is supported by certain activity analysis models [97, pp. 7–66, also 66–104].

In contrast, it is interesting to note that O.R. has made its most conspicuous inroads in big business circles. It must be pointed out, however, that in spite of multiple goals, there are many problem areas in large corporations where a single optimum criterion can readily be identified and pursued without the danger of violating some over-all multivariate optimum standard. Although big business is at times quite complex in its motives and goals, it would be wrong to exaggerate this complexity. After all, there is a great deal of straightforward engineering in the management of large-scale manufacturing and plenty of old-fashioned economizing in commerce and banking. Nevertheless, when it is difficult to be precise about the over-all optimum standard, the danger of choosing the wrong criteria for suboptimization is enhanced [95].[18]

Sometimes the wrong suboptimum criterion is chosen for reasons which must be found in the imperfect organizational and communications structure within the system. For instance, decentralization in the decision-making process can become a major handicap in this respect.[19]

---

[18] In the case of the "Traveling-Salesman Problem," for instance, time, distance, or costs appear to be sound criteria. Yet, if such things as personal contact, service, availability loom high in the firm's list of the objectives which it hopes will lead to greater sales, the minimization of an objective function in terms of any of the three variables listed is bound to run counter to the firm's over-all goal.

[19] As one corporation president puts it: "We must have hired too many individualists." A typical illustration is afforded by a routine personnel problem. A sales department discovered that, contrary to company policy, they were hiring candidates for their training program who did not have a background of liberal education. The company analyzed the problem and discovered that some of its tests and interviewers were biased in favor of vocationally trained men; furthermore, it was found that the over-all objective had never been clearly communicated to the sales department. See, for instance [28].

Finally, it should be pointed out that the choice of the appropriate or "right" suboptimum criterion is in itself no guarantee for optimum performance of the over-all system. Among other things, it is essential that the requisite data be available. A case in point are the cost minimizing models. The traditions of cost-accounting are such that firms do not always have an accurate picture of the actual costs of the various operations, and this in spite of elaborate bookkeeping. O.R. can perform a real service by calling attention to the type of cost data which large corporation accounting systems in particular and business accounting in general must provide before cost-minimizing models can have their full practical impact. It would be wrong to lay the blame entirely at the doorsteps of the accounting profession which has contributed much to improved knowledge of what it costs to do business. The responsibility lies elsewhere as well; for instance, with the various legislative and regulatory bodies who perpetuate antiquated accounting methods often as a matter of sacred principle. In this they are frequently assisted by the courts which tend to live by precedent. The economics of public utilities and railroading offer ample evidence of this. Here again, O.R. may be able to serve the public interest by discovering those practices which promise optimum results scientifically.

Though many obstacles exist, suboptimization has a crucial role to play in bringing about greater over-all efficiency, be the latter defined from the point of view of economics or from the broader one of all the social sciences. It must remain clear, however, that the random choice of suboptimum criteria does not necessarily lead to an over-all optimum; as a matter of fact, the chance is that it will not. Over-all systems optimization—assuming that the requisite data are available—depends upon the simultaneous and cumulative optimization of subsystems. In other words, *the over-all optimum of a complex system is equal to the sum of correct suboptimizations*, provided the optimum standards of the latter reflect the multivariate standard of the total system.

### III

Since the problem of cyclical fluctuations concerns everyone, it is not surprising that the managers of some of our largest corporations are asking themselves what role they might play in order to help tame the beast. After all, every business has a vital interest in a prosperous economy. The executives of large corporations in certain key industries are becoming aware that their policies may well determine whether there shall be prosperity in the land or not. For purposes of public policy, as well as economic analysis, it is appropriate to look at the performance of the economy, in part, as the result of countless executive decisions, most of them made consciously though not always with the benefit of complete information nor with full, if any, knowledge of the consequences. O.R. brings precision to these decisions, thus affecting the performance of the economy.[20] Whether or not its impact will be substantial depends largely upon how widespread its use will be throughout the economy. What the nature of its impact will be, on the other hand, will be determined chiefly by the types of models put into practice and by the type of criterion which defines the optimum standard these models aim to achieve.

It has already been pointed out that inventory models are among the most popular O.R. concerns. Within the confines of the firm, inventory models are normally of the suboptimization type. A noticeable change in the inventory component of the GNP may take place if the use of scientific models should necessitate—as it often does—a change in inventory practice. For instance, the convention of a fixed inventory-to-sales ratio would lead to a new convention of, say, the square-root type, mentioned above. Although this specific change also signifies increased stability in production under certain circumstances, such an outcome is by no means certain. If inventory stability is not necessarily in the cards, the change nevertheless may mean a different behavior of one of the key business indicators [2]. In *The Theory of Inventory Management*, T. W. Whitin discusses some of the connections between inventories and cyclical fluctuations [170, pp. 109–61]. Similarly, where the application of scientific *replacement models* would tend to lead to a change in the performance of the capital consumption and/or the investment components of the GNP, the question of economic stability would again be raised because once more a crucial economic indicator is involved. Thus, to the extent to which O.R. through suboptimization models succeeds in affecting the performance of the economy, its specific solutions become a key element in the attempt to understand how the economy functions.

The popularity of the inventory model in O.R. and the strategic nature of the replacement model suggest that a desirable or directed impact upon the economy through certain types of suboptimization models need not be a matter of the distant future. Inventory and replacement processes are and have for some time been amenable to public controls. This means, among other things, that certain desired changes can be encouraged, thus giving public policy significance to O.R. models. The application of certain O.R. models may help a business firm to contribute to greater economic stability. Or, as the smoothing problem mentioned earlier makes clear, certain types of O.R. models will enable firms to prevent avoidable economic instability. One may be charged with having an overly active imagination, but it is attractive to think of an ever more widespread use of such models throughout the economy as a matter of deliberate countercyclical policy.

However, most of this is in the future as far as political reality is concerned. Furthermore, O.R. as we know it today is not as such designed to bring stability to the economy; it probably never will be. One of the reasons for this has to do with the uncertainty of economic events. O.R. is a device or method

---

[20] See the debate between Ackoff [4] and Hitch [80].

through which management is able to control certain variables. But not every variable which must enter into the calculations of management falls under this internal control. There are many random variables, and as a result economic stability cannot be achieved—if at all—through private business policy alone. The uncertainty of future events is a serious limitation and prevents the most scientifically managed firm from contributing to economic stabilization all that society might find desirable.

Another reason why economic stability will not naturally flow from the application of O.R. methods has to do with the nature of the optimum standard common to so many models, namely the minimization of production costs. A review of the available literature suggests that many O.R. applications lead not only to automation, but more generally to a deliberate minimization of the wage factor as a cost of production. The replacement of men by machines can be accomplished most discreetly during the transition period merely by not hiring new workers as old ones retire and others leave for greener pastures. An occasional bout with a recession will prove most helpful in this respect, for the machine will pick up during the recovery where men used to work. The minimum number of permanently unemployed workers may tend to be on the high side, and this not only during the recovery period. The modern scientific revolution is of a different mettle than previous ones have been in that it tends to make a potentially large portion of unskilled labor into a more or less obsolete factor of production. Unless the unskilled labor force is either absorbed into the service trades or re-educated, it will join the ranks of the permanently unemployed. It is not at all certain whether we are prepared to carry through the job of re-education which this scientific revolution requires [26]. Thus, as O.R. contributes to and accelerates the use of automation, it may make business more efficient, but at the same time it may make the economy vulnerable to cyclical maladjustments and perhaps to social upheaval. As long as a large portion of O.R. models stress the minimization of costs, the increased efficiency of particular firms may well be bought at the cost of rising social costs. The only certain way in which O.R. would contribute to ever greater economic stability is to make stabilization proper the criterion for the various models. At the moment, this does not look like a feasible nor a very sound suggestion.

If O.R. may pose long-range problems because of its effect upon the level of employment, its cost minimization emphasis may nevertheless prove to be one of the most tangible forces acting against inflation. This raises the interesting question of how to reconcile the need for a stable dollar with the un-desirability of a relatively high level of permanent or recurring unemployment. Within the broader setting of the entire economy, the solution falls within the realm of systems analysis where the subsystems are firms and consumers and the over-all system is the national economy. Maybe what has been said earlier about the need for co-ordinating the criteria of subsystems is relevant here. As far as large corporations are concerned, we are also entitled to ask the question of whether their goals and values may not have to be brought into closer harmony with the objectives of the national economy, and if so, whether and how this can be done. It is encouraging that some corporation executives seem to think that a constructive answer exists. O.R. may well be adapted to the task once the objectives can be or have been defined. It is well to remember, however, that business is not the sole protagonist in the economic drama. Other groups have social responsibilities, too, like labor, for instance. But this raises another problem altogether.

## CONCLUSIONS

### I

O.R. is one of the newest tools available to those who have to organize men and resources into meaningful operating entities for the express purpose of achieving specific desired goals. As a scientific discipline or method, it is commonly associated with the management of what the economist calls *producing units* or *firms*. The latter can be public or private, large or small. On a somewhat broader front, O.R. methods can be applied over even larger organizations and operational units such as the entire economy, for instance. As applied to the firm, O.R. represents an important phase in the current industrial revolution. One of its major virtues is the precision which it brings to the process of management.

To the economist, O.R. is significant for a number of reasons. First, it opens up the possibility for a better understanding of how real-life firms operate. This should help in the formulation of a theory of the firm which more accurately than ever describes the performance of an important segment of our economy. At the same time the economist's ability to predict business behavior may be enhanced because of more realistic models. This *rapprochement* may come about because under the impact of linear activity analysis and other techniques the firm will behave more readily in ways prescribed by pure science or because the economist has learned how to adapt his models to actual behavior.

Second, O.R. may ultimately be able to provide the economist with the kind of data he needs for the formulation of a comprehensive theory of the large modern corporation. A significant element in such a development is the fact that O.R. is systems oriented. This means that the operations which it studies and attempts to render more efficient are looked at as organic units or as being part of such units. The modern corporation is an organic unit. Its purpose is multivariate, and its organization is a complex of conflicting tendencies and forces. One of the key characteristics of O.R. is to try to resolve such conflicts for optimum operational results.

Third, O.R. affects the performance of the economy. By influencing the making of managerial decisions it shapes, among other things, the pattern of expenditures and the allocation of resources. Some of the decisions will tend to influence key business indicators, such as employment, investment, inventories, and personal income. This suggests that O.R. has significance to the economist in his endeavor to understand and control cyclical and other economic fluctuations.

## II

O.R.'s power to affect the performance of the economy can have either desirable or undesirable results, depending upon one's point of view or the social goals and values which can be identified with a given economic system. This is especially important in the application of O.R. techniques to problems faced by the large modern corporation, chiefly because of the substantial impact of its activities on the economy.

In the past virtually the only public policy question raised by economics in connection with the operations of large corporations had to do with the existence of monopoly power and its exercise through a variety of restrictive practices. The power inherent in large corporations to be well or badly managed did not attract much attention and has not become a subject of economic policy. Monopolies were condemned (or regulated) as a matter of principle on the assumption that they represented less efficient entities in the over-all economic framework than firms operating in a competitive environment. The ingenious device of the price system became the center of the analytical framework. The complex forces which determine the relative degree of efficiency within the corporation's organizational structure were not considered. With the advent of linear programming in business and activity analysis in economics there are no longer sufficient reasons not to make what we have called *autonomous power* an integral part of economic theory and policy. As a matter of fact, not to do so would mean that an important policy tool is left idle in our efforts to make the economy perform better.

O.R. offers public policy the opportunity to strike a favorable attitude toward large corporations and to exploit the power to manage so as to strengthen the economy. By framing legislation (i.e., fiscal policy) and public regulation in a way which creates appropriate incentives, the practice of O.R. may be drawn toward the type of process which, like inventory and replacement processes, may enhance the stability of the economy and further technological development. Other types of incentives may foster the application of optimum models whose practical result will be the economizing of scarce natural resources. Still another important impact public policy may have is to foster research and data collection in an impartial and extensive manner so as to develop a science of management with at least the fervor we now see being put into research connected with space travel and other less celestial occupations.

O.R. is a relative newcomer in the economic arsenal. If it is viewed with optimism for its positive contributions to a stable and growing economy, to technological development, to the conservation of resources, to better business performance, it may come to play an ever greater role in the shaping of American capitalism, and one which goes far beyond the relatively modest scope which the scientists have assigned it at the moment. O.R. has a future in economic policy formulation and, therefore, in economic theory. It deserves the attention of the best thinkers in the social sciences if the human values are not to be sacrificed to the materialistic and mechanistic ones.

| Chapter | MULTIPLE GOALS |
| 6 | IN THE THEORY |
| | OF THE FIRM |

## by C. MICHAEL WHITE

The goal or objective of the firm most widely accepted by economists and businessmen is the maximization of profit. Unfortunately, at least a part of this general agreement stems from a diversity of interpretations of the term profit and of the conditions under which this quantity is maximized. As Frank Knight expressed it, "Perhaps no term or concept in economic discussion is used with a more bewildering variety of well-established meanings than profit."[1] In fact, all business decisions can be justified on the basis of profit maximization, given a suitably broad interpretation of this objective.

It is the thesis of this essay that the universally accepted goal of profit maximization is in reality a heterogeneous collection of multiple goals of firms used either in place of profit maximization or in some weighted combination with it. The intent here is to segregate and classify the major objectives sought by business firms so that profit maximization may be interpreted in its proper perspective in the modern theory of the firm. The recognition of the existence of multiple goals of firms presents the possibility of removing some of the ambiguity associated with profit maximization at the present time.

It is hoped that the following discussion will clarify the proper status of the goal of profit maximizing by bringing together some of the current thought on the diverse objectives found in contemporary business policy. It also is hoped that the suggestions for analyzing alternate goals will be helpful, particularly insofar as some of these goals can be quantified and adapted to the linear programming frame of reference along with the generally accepted linear programming goal of profit maximization.

### THE DEFINITION OF PROFIT

Depending upon the source chosen, the definition of profit varies from the gross margin concept in marketing to the residual return idea implicit in

[1] Knight [93], p. 480.

some economic interpretations. In between these extremes there is the widely used accounting approach based on the income statement in which profit is the total net revenue per period of time. The financial idea of profit typically is expressed as a percentage return on total investment. Each of these as well as many other ideas of profit is subject to diverse interpretations. If a continuum could be constructed out of all these variations it undoubtedly would stretch across the entire breadth of economic and business thought!

Historically, these ideas of profit have evolved out of the hazy preclassical notion which made little or no distinction between interest and profit and which usually included proprietorship wages. Adam Smith and J. B. Say attempted to clarify these terms but without great success. However, they did make a contribution in recognizing that profits varied in relation to the risk involved in an enterprise. With the development of the marginal analysis in the last half of the nineteenth century the first precise, though abstract, concept of profit evolved. Alfred Marshall conceived of profit as a return resulting from market disequilibrium which would disappear when the balance of perfectly competitive forces was reached. So long as differential conditions prevailed among firms, those which correctly anticipated the uncertainty involved were rewarded with a pure profit over and above Marshall's necessary profit. Thus, pure profit became a return to some differential advantage possessed by a firm. Marshall referred to this pure profit as quasi-rent which emphasized the monopoly element present. In this sense the monopoly or differential advantage might be any superiority of one firm over other firms such as more accurate decision making by management, better location or labor relations, limited entry to the industry. These differences could be transient or relatively permanent. They could be external in origin or created by the firm itself.

Following the Marshallean tradition, F. H. Knight made the first significant contribution of the twentieth century to the theory of profits in his *Risk, Uncertainty, and Profit*. Knight substituted the term "uncertainty" for the broader meaning associated with the term "risk" since the days of Adam Smith. He defined "risk" as a special case of "uncertainty" characterized by sufficient quantitative precision to yield a statistical probability of the outcome.[2] In contrast, true uncertainty is an unmeasurable risk and is the cause of profit. According to Knight, this unmeasurable and therefore uninsurable risk is associated with economic change. These changes either result from managerial decisions or involve managerial adaptations. Knight's concept of profit has been modified by J. F. Weston who has stated that "the relevant distinction for profit theory is not between risk and uncertainty, but between transformable risks and nontransformable risks."[3] A transformable risk in Weston's thesis is one which can be reduced, substantially eliminated, or converted into a definite cost. The remaining nontransformable risks give rise to profits.

[2] Knight [94], p. 20.                                [3] Weston [168], p. 44.

If profit arises only out of Knight's uncertainty or Weston's nontrans-formable risk, we have the disturbing situation that profit would be reduced (or eliminated) insofar as management is able to increase the predictability of its actions and lessen the lack of certainty for its firm. Under such circumstances profit maximization becomes incongruous since profit would vary directly (and only) with the degree of uncertainty involved. It would seem that the emphasis should be placed on the *differential advantage* accruing to a given firm. Such an advantage might well be a smaller degree of uncertainty than competing firms experienced. It also might involve the Schumpeterian idea of a return to innovation or any disequilibrating force or imperfection in the market. Kenneth Boulding has pointed out that profits arise *both* from uncertainty and from imperfections in the market.[4]

Many contemporary writers have made much over the fact that pure profit must not include any return to entrepreneurs for wages or invested captial. Attention is focused upon the residual return after such imputed costs are deducted. The French economist, Jean Marchal, has pointed out that entrepreneurs typically do not follow this economic distinction in their decision making. He claims that "what [entrepreneurs] call profit and what influences their activity is the *gross amount* which remains in their hands when their collaborators have been paid."[5] In following this objective, Marchal contends that entrepreneurs seek to influence the market structure through various pressures so as to increase their gross return. Such action would tend to increase the market imperfections or differential advantages enjoyed by a given firm. These actions or pressures would be exercised upon consumers, upon the innovation process, and upon public authority to create an environment more favorable to the firm.

To a certain extent Marchal's theory of profit is a functional one including elements of what Weston has classified as "(a) payment for the entrepreneural function, (b) payment for ownership, and (c) payment for entrepreneurial or managerial efficiency."[6] These and other writers also recognize monopoly or market imperfections as sources of profit. The above bases of profit are rather clearly distinguished from theories such as Knight's where some interpretation of risk or uncertainty accounts for profit. It would seem that in a system as complex and dynamic as ours, profit can and does arise from all of these causes and for most firms no one cause can be isolated as the sole source of profit.

Since the sources of profit are so heterogeneous, is it possible to find an acceptable and useful meaning for the profit concept? Marchal's "gross amount" appears to have validity in this connection. Other writers refer to profit as the difference between the cash value of the enterprise at the beginning and end of the period.[7] While technical differences exist between these

---

[4] Boulding [21], p. 548.
[5] Marchal [113], p. 550.
[6] Weston [168], p. 40.
[7] Spencer and Siegelman [153], p. 97.

ideas of profit, for practical purposes they amount to the same basic approach. In each case profit may be defined as the aggregate residual change per period of time in the resources under the control of the entrepreneur.

While the above discussion is intended to be suggestive rather than comprehensive, perhaps it will be helpful in delineating the role of profit in the theory of the firm. This role is best understood if attention is focused upon the determinants of managerial decisions. After all, it is these determinants which account for the differential advantages among firms. Profit must be a return to a firm resulting from some element either within the firm or in its environment which differentiates it from other firms. This return must be expressed in quantitative terms and subject to calculation from other quantitative aspects of the firm. It also must relate to some finite period of time. Two questions are suggested in this formulation. First, what quantitative aspects of the firm are to be considered? Secondly, what time period is relevant?

### Impact of Valuation on Profit

As soon as the question of quantitative elements is raised, the entire problem of valuation is introduced into the analysis. Boulding's *Reconstruction of Economics* treats this valuation problem in considerable detail and points up its significance for profit theory. He emphasizes that profit determination is contingent upon a system of valuation of assets which will permit the derivation of changes in net worth. When business activity involves changes which do not entirely begin and end with money, an arbitrary element is introduced in the valuation of changes in nonmoney assets.

Several accounting adjustments involved in the periodic calculation of net profit on the income statement point up the impact of valuation on profit determination. In the first place, business activity is a continuous, not a periodic process. For any period (short of the entire life of the firm) some activities are started but not completed while other activities are completed which were undertaken in a prior period.[8] The valuation of the cost allocatable to a given period must, of necessity, be arbitrary. While production and other variable costs usually are allocated with reasonable accuracy, fixed costs such as research, market development, public relations, and most managerial activities are allocated to the period in which the costs are incurred rather than the future period in which sales, production costs or the position of the firm will be influenced by the present research, market development, etc. Obviously, these practices are dictated by expediency since who, except an omnipotent oracle, can say when the benefits of an institutional advertisement will be realized? However, the fact remains that the profit in any current period can be increased or decreased substantially by the amount of future oriented activities undertaken.

[8] Spencer and Siegelman [153], p. 94

Two other valuation problems influencing profit determination should be mentioned. These are inventory valuation and depreciation. In both of these instances an element of managerial discretion exists in the valuation determination, and the accepted practice favors the choice which minimizes current profit. While tax considerations undoubtedly exert an influence here, there is reason to believe that managerial practices would be in the same direction without tax pressures. With a long-run tendency toward rising prices most firms in the mid-twentieth century choose to value inventory on a LIFO basis, the result of which is to understate current profits. Depreciation practice favors procedures which provide for as rapid a write-off of assets as can be justified. The larger depreciation charges per period of time have the effect of reducing the income statement profit.

Insofar as the above and similar valuation practices tend to understate present profits, they tend to increase future profit *potential*. Jean Marchal's suggestion that entrepreneurs are influenced by the gross amount remaining in their hands might well be extended. It appears that they are influenced by the net aggregate amount of physical assets (including cash) remaining in their hands at the end of any given period. A lower dollar valuation on remaining inventory or machinery does not reduce the actual units of inventory on hand or the remaining productivity in a machine. However, in each case, insofar as physical value exceeds dollar value, future profit potential is increased.

Current business activities whose benefits can be realized only in future periods have an effect remarkably similar to the valuation decisions discussed above. For instance, an extensive advertising campaign designed to strengthen the market position of a particular product (as contrasted with advertising to increase current sales) of necessity reduces present profit. However, at the end of the campaign the firm hopes to have a more secure market for the product—a better profit potential. Product and process research, public relations activities, etc., all have the same sort of orientation.

Capital expenditures for new plants and equipment also involve present expenditures in anticipation of future benefits. However, unlike the above examples, new capital goods exist after their acquisition as physical assets at some valuation on the books of the firm. They also differ in that their productive value during future periods is reasonably determinate. Just how determinate depends upon the accuracy of estimates of expected life and future productivity.

### Time Element in Profit Determination

Throughout the above discussion of the valuation problem in profit determination, the second problem of the relevant time period for profit calculation has been implicit. The term profit has meaning only in relation to some finite time period, and yet this approach distorts the continuous nature of a firm's activity. When the firm was essentially a sole proprietorship its meaningful planning period paralleled the life of its owner. The perpetual life of a modern corporation extends its planning period indefinitely. The corporate firm may be expected to act as if it always has a future. It still has the problem of how much of that future should enter into its planning. Realistically, all planning must be limited to the pertinent economic horizon; the firm must have some image of its future position toward which it seeks to plan. Given this image it is assumed that a firm can calculate the flow of net income which its future position will yield. Its horizon is limited by the reliability of its estimate of its future positions.

In one sense the time problem is solely one of capital investment involving the determination of the present value of expected future net income, given an appropriate rate of capitalization. However, there is a deeper significance for profit theory. The longer the profit planning period, the more likely these plans are to include all future profit potential of present activities. On the other hand, the farther into the future a firm seeks to plan, the less accurate its estimates become. Profit planning can involve such a potentially wide range of possible outcomes as to make the estimates of little value. Theoretically, if the planning period is long enough, all actions of a firm could be justified on a profit basis. But meaningful estimates of relevant variables cannot be made this far in advance. Therefore, future profit calculation has to be limited to a period of time within which sufficient precision can be achieved to make the calculations useful. For most firms profit would be a relatively short-run objective on this basis.

Present activities of a firm designed to increase profits in the long-run can best be measured in terms of changes in *profit potential*. While the total future profit potential may not be amenable to calculation, it is possible to measure certain present characteristics of firms which are likely to influence their profit potential. Such characteristics may well be regarded as alternative goals to profit within the planning periods considered. These goals would include those concerned with a firm's image, those which affect its markets, those related to its economic and sociological position in the structure of the economy, and those dealing with its financial position. If such diverse objectives are available to firms as alternatives, how and why are particular ones selected? In the next section some of the bases of choosing goals are examined.

## THE CHOICE OF ENTREPRENEURAL GOALS

### The Formulation of Goals

From a practical standpoint goals of firms or of individuals typically are expressed in optimal terms. That is to say, an objective is a desirable target ordinarily formulated in optimum terms—one aims for the bull's eye, not just the target itself. If profit is a desirable target, under most circumstances a firm will seek to maximize its profit, not just try to make "some" profit. If sales volume is the criterion of success, then it is this measure which will be maximized. Frequently in business practice, goals are stated in precise units (such as a sales quota of an exact dollar volume). In reality such precise goals are top management's estimate of the maximum attainable level of the criterion. The effect is to maximize the criterion chosen while setting what appears to be a precise level to be achieved.

The formulation and analysis of goals requires that at least one goal be optimized. Given a single goal of an organization, it is essential that it be optimized. Where two or more goals exist simultaneously, it is necessary for all but one goal to be limited by one or more constraints allowing the remaining goal to attain its optimum level. That is to say, multiple goals must be placed in an ordinal sequence at least to the extent that one is primary and the others secondary.

### The Choice of Profit Maximization

Businessmen are inclined to accept profit as the measure of business success because of the obvious necessity of avoiding losses to survive. If losses are undesirable then profit should be desirable and the optimum situation would be the maximization of profit. Although this line of reasoning has an intuitive appeal and widespread acceptance, Peter Drucker contends that it is fallacious. Drucker claims that "the guiding principle of business economics . . . is not the maximization of profits; *it is the avoidance of loss.*"[9] According to his thesis there is a minimum level of profit for each firm which is vital to its survival, but this does not imply a compulsion to maximize profit. Of course, the more competitive a firm's situation the more closely its maximum possible profit approaches the minimum necessary for its survival. In other words, Drucker's distinction is academic until profit-producing differentials separate substantially the maximum profit from the minimum necessary profit.

The profit motive is deeply ingrained in the folklore of modern business. The universally used financial statements of business focus attention on the amount of profit as the primary measure of business performance. A substantial amount of managerial attention centers on the effect of all decisions on profitability. Even our corporate tax laws use the amount of profit as the basis of ability to pay taxes.

Like businessmen, economists have a strong predilection toward the goal of profit maximization, but for somewhat different reasons. In economic theory the goal of profit maximization is almost always used in a first approximation model because of its convenience and simplicity of analysis. At least some economists defend this goal in all levels of their analysis as the best single criterion available. However, others deviate from this first approximation in their more complex models by introducing the possibility of alternative goals which modify the profit-maximizing assumption. John Due has summed up the basis of the profit maximizing goal in economic analysis

---

[9] Drucker [55], pp. 46–7.

in his statement that "it is the most satisfactory single assumption which can be made about goals of business behavior."[10] Just how satisfactory an assumption it is depends upon the uses of the analysis and how well the underlying implicit qualifications are understood.

### Qualifications and Modifications of Profit Maximization

Much of the confusion concerning the goal of profit maximization in economic theory could be eliminated if economists were more inclined to specify the assumptions implicit in their models and the extent to which they assume that these assumptions approximate reality or the extent that they regard them simply as conveniences in theoretical models. The frequent criticism by businessmen that economic theory is unrealistic misses the point. Theoretical models are employed precisely because they are unrealistic; because they simplify reality sufficiently so that analysis is possible. Unfortunately though, readers are not always forewarned as to the simplifying assumptions involved in particular models.

Tibor Scitovsky has added a clarification to the entrepreneural psychology underlying profit maximization. He contends that "the entrepreneur's choice between more and less activity—or between more income and more leisure—must be independent of his income."[11] That is to say, his motivation for additional profit cannot be increased or decreased by the present amount of his income. Insofar as a higher income is an index of greater success this condition is easy to accept. However, if an entrepreneur measures his success on some basis other than money income, Scitovsky's point raises a question about the effectiveness of profit as entrepreneural motivation and introduces the possibility of alternative objectives.

Other economists have questioned the usefulness of the profit-maximizing goal as a guide to entrepreneural decision making. Stephen Enke has pointed out " . . . in the face of future uncertainty, the profit-maximizing motive does not provide the entrepreneur with a single and unequivocal criterion for selecting one policy from among the alternatives open to him. The desire to maximize profits does not constitute a clear and unique behavior prescription."[12] According to Enke this lack of precision arises out of the impossibility of predicting the behavior of an *individual* firm faced with uncertainty even though the aggregate behavior of such firms might be determinate. Essentially, this is a problem of uncertainty due to ignorance of the state of nature on the part of the entrepreneur. Strictly speaking Enke is correct in his criticism. However, modern statistical decision theory provides systematic guides to action for decision makers which tend to limit the range of unpredictability involved.[13]

[10] Due [56], p. 33. See also Coppock [42], p. 6.
[11] Scitovsky [146], p. 356.
[12] Enke [62], p. 567.
[13] Chernoff and Moses [33], Chap. 5.

The interesting possibility that goals other than profit maximization are consistent with rational behavior has been suggested by A. G. Papandreou in his statement that "profit maximization does imply rationality of course; but rationality is consistent with maximization of other things as well as profits."[14] He draws a distinction between efficiency and profit maximization showing that even though efficiency is implicit in profit maximization a firm may be efficient without seeking to maximize profits. On this basis, profit is simply one possible ranking criterion in a broader system of preference-function maximization. Under perfect competition, profit is the only ranking criterion consistent with survival. In the absence of perfect competition the long-run survival of a firm may be achieved best (or at least as well) through the maximization of goals other than profit.

Firms deliberately avoid maximum profits for a variety of reasons. Some of the more important ones are the fear of attracting new competitive firms, the fear of provoking government antitrust action against the firm, and the feeling that a "satisfactory" or "average" rate of profit is more desirable than maximum profit from the standpoint of public relations, union demands, etc. Corporate tax laws have the effect of encouraging firms to limit present profit in favor of future profit potential by incurring larger present costs which are future oriented. Profit maximization not only may be modified or limited but it may be replaced by or combined with alternative goals in which profit appears only as a minimum limiting factor on the net revenue of the firm. Although a profit-maximizing objective usually promotes survival it provides no assurance that a firm will survive. Indeed, survival may depend upon *not* maximizing profits as the following section indicates.

## SURVIVAL OF THE FIRM—HOMEOSTASIS

The firm as a social and economic organization, like many other organisms, has a compelling urge to survive. More fundamental than the profit motive, the motive to survive is implicit in most decisions within the firm, though the possibility of organizational suicide should not be ruled out entirely. In the long-run a firm that survives will make a positive profit. However, a firm might maximize its profit and not survive. Obviously, sufficiently large losses will bankrupt a firm. It is also possible for a profitable firm, due to inadequate liquidity, etc., not to survive. Thus, the goal of survival must take precedence over all other objectives of firms. In the short-run, all positive profit may have to be sacrificed to permit survival.

Once a firm is organized and is a going concern, survival is usually associated with maintaining the status quo. Boulding appropriately uses the term "homeostasis" to describe this action.[15] Any functioning organism has a tendency to maintain itself in its existing state. Much of the activity of any

[14] Papandreou [134], p. 206.
[15] Boulding [23], pp. 26–7.

firm is designed to restore a previously existing state once its actions alter this state. Indeed, the normal flow of business activity is a circular pattern which tends to perpetuate itself. Cash is converted into inventory, sales convert inventory into receivables, and these in turn become cash again. As equipment depreciates, it must be replaced; as debt is liquidated, it is replaced with more debt.

In addition to its internal state a firm has a status in relation to its environment which also must be maintained. A going concern has a tendency to maintain its relative position within its industry and in the economy. In a dynamic, growing environment a firm must grow at a rate comparable to its competitors to retain its relative position. These tendencies of firms toward homeostasis are revealed quite clearly in the usual financial analysis. Such an analysis makes use of few, if any, absolute bases of evaluation. Rather, a firm's present position and performance is compared with its own past record and with the position and performance of other similar firms.

Survival, including the consequent homeostasis concept, is seldom an explicit primary goal of a firm but instead provides a pervasive set of limitations upon all other goals including profit. As suggested above in connection with financial analysis there is no absolute guide to survival. The prescription is unique for each firm at each point in time and must be defined on the basis of managerial estimates. These estimates typically include a set of survival conditions plus a "safety factor" or margin of error.[16] Both the limiting conditions and the size of the safety factor involve value judgments by management. However, these subjectively evaluated conditions must be translated into quantitative guides such as "our current ratio must never be less than 2.3 to 1." At times these quantitative guides will be wrong (else firms would seldom fail). But the important consideration here is that through the value premises of management, survival conditions can be and are quantified. These quantitative measures can be introduced into a linear programming problem as additional constraints on whatever primary objective is chosen to be optimized.

But who wants to be associated with "just another firm" that seeks only to survive? American mores place a premium on being on a winning team or at least being above average. Firms, like individuals, seek to differentiate or distinguish themselves in some respect. While the preference functions used differ widely, firms strive to optimize some magnitude considered desirable by their decision makers. This optimization of some index or criterion such as Papandreou's utility-index[17] is aimed at creating a differential for a given firm when it is compared to other firms. These differentials may result in greater profit but they are more likely to increase profit potential. Of course the result need not involve profit or profit potential at all. Typically, greater product loyalty is evidenced in a less elastic demand enabling a firm to protect

[16] Fellner [65], pp. 146–57.
[17] Papandreou [134], pp. 188–89 and pp. 205–10.

its profit potential in the face of changing conditions. On the other hand, greater prestige of a firm may simply increase the personal satisfaction of its executives. In the next section some of the more important differentials sought by firms will be considered.

## ALTERNATIVE GOALS CREATING DIFFERENTIALS FOR FIRMS

It would be difficult for any treatment of the goals of firms to be all-inclusive and space does not permit such an attempt here. In a limited survey of firms' objectives there are both problems of selection and of classification. The goals discussed below are grouped roughly into those that are primarily external to the firm itself and those that deal mainly with internal organization and operation of firms.

### External Goals

Three major types of external goals are those relating to a firm's markets, those dealing with the creation of appropriate images, and those which concern a firm's power over its environment.

MARKET GOALS. The horizontal demand curve faced by a firm under perfect competition limits marketing decisions to a simple sell or not sell choice at the market price. As product differentiations increase and the number of competitors decreases, the range of entrepreneurial alternatives expands. Price is no longer a given factor. Nonhomogeneous products can be varied without limit. Customers can be selected as to location, size, or ability to pay. Private "rules of the game" evolve within markets or are agreed upon by participants. The relative position of competitors becomes a resultant of strategic maneuvers rather than impersonal market forces. The single marketing decision of a perfect competitor has been expanded into a complex set of closely interrelated alternatives. What guide to action or goal can serve as a criterion for these decisions?

Given an existing marketing situation for a firm, the initial objective typically will be homeostasis—maintenance of the present position. Assuming that a firm seeks to better its position, how is a better position defined? In practice it is defined in terms of any one or more of the variables involved. That is to say, a "better position" may mean either a higher or a lower price, a larger volume of sales, a better product mix, a larger or different market area, a larger or more stable share of the market, etc. The problem is how to abstract from these diverse variables a useful quantitative measure of "better market position."

It appears that the one quantitative measure of market position which is most representative and therefore most useful is the volume of sales of the firm. To be sufficiently inclusive this measure will need several alternative formulations. The volume of sales can be expressed either in unit sales or dollar sales. Maximum unit sales might be used when maximum market penetration is sought. Maximum dollar sales would be more valid when the product mix is particularly heterogeneous. One other modification of this objective is needed. Market position involves not only a current flow of sales but also a future sales potential. The goal of maximizing sales volume could be stated in terms of maximum sales potential as well as actual sales volume. This is not the same thing as *expected* future sales. The difference is that expected sales is the volume which the entrepreneur feels is most likely to materialize, while the sales potential is a volume which can be realized only if certain changes occur to bring it about.

Almost all marketing goals can be expressed in terms of one of the above formulations of sales volume. For instance, the best product mix would be either the one producing the largest volume of expected sales or the largest sales potential. In the latter case, an improved mix might be one less sensitive to innovation by competitors because of a better patent position. Expected sales might not be larger but the firm would be less susceptible to inroads by competitors.

Once a useful objective other than maximum profit can be stated in quantitative terms it may be possible to incorporate it into a linear programming framework. A goal of maximum sales volume can be handled in this way. Naturally, no firm would seek to maximize its sales volume without regard to its profit position. Some constraint on the minimum permissible profit would have to be included. The linear programming formulation of this marketing objective is developed in the Appendix to this essay.[18]

IMAGE CREATION. A most interesting and useful approach to the behavior of a firm is suggested in Boudling's treatment of the organizational image of the firm.[19] The idea is particularly useful in understanding some of the organizational objectives sought by decision makers. As mentioned earlier, the tendency of a firm to perpetuate its present position depends upon the manager's image of the firm as it now exists. When a firm seeks to improve its position, such improvement must be defined in terms of a change from its existing state.

Several types of images are of significance in relation to firms' objectives. Ultimately, all decisions result from some sort of an image in the mind of the decision maker. However, this image is partially a reflection of what the decision maker thinks is the image of his firm and its products that is held by various other groups. These groups include customers, employees, competitors, stockholders, government officials, and the general public. Decisions result not from the actual images held by these groups but by what managers *think* these images are. The reaction of management to the images of various groups is not a passive one because it is generally recognized that a firm's actions can and do influence these images. Management's role thus includes

[18] See Appendix, p. 199.
[19] Boulding [22], pp. 82–96.

the following sequence: first, the nature of the existing images of relevant groups is assessed; second, the images which management would like for these groups to hold is determined; third, the action by the firm needed to change the present images into the desired ones is planned; finally, the costs of these actions are weighed against the expected benefit from having the groups hold more desirable images of the firm or its products. Although the entire process is highly subjective at every stage, a substantial volume of the public relations and advertising expenditures of major firms is devoted to image creation.

Depending upon the group involved, various types of images may be considered desirable by a firm. A desirable consumer image might include such aspects as service, quality of products, fairness of price, leadership in innovation. The image held by competitors would involve fair dealing, efficiency, leadership in volume of sales, etc. Whatever the elements in particular images held by groups, each corporate decision must be evaluated in terms of its impact on these images. The entire problem of image creation is complicated by the fact that the existence of a characteristic does not necessarily create an image of it nor does an image insure the presence of the elements involved. Actual service may not create a consumer image of service. The image of economy in a product may best be created not by a low price per unit but rather by a package that *appears* to give more units for a given price.

The objective of creating desirable images in associated groups can rarely be a primary one. Ordinarily such objectives will operate as additional constraints upon other primary objectives. For instance, while profit is regarded as highly desirable and proper in our system, excessively large profits are condemned as the connotation of profiteering suggests. But when are profits "excessively large"? Firms seek to avoid the image of a profiteer and large firms sometimes consciously avoid profits in excess of some level. The motivation might be fear of either an unfavorable public image, of attracting additional competitors, or of encouraging a governmental investigation of monopolistic practices. Of course the effect of an upper limit on profit is achieved by regulatory bodies in the field of public utilities when they set rates to yield a fair rate of return on a fair value of invested capital.

Even though some firms might place an upper limit on profit, all firms try to impose a lower limit on profit. There is always a minimum profit (possibly negative in the short-run) below which control is jeopardized. The goal of survival discussed earlier ordinarily is expressed as a minimum profit level and the example of maximizing sales volume also made use of such a constraint. Thus, in a linear programming problem any goal including profit maximization could be subject to upper and lower limits on profit.[20]

POWER GOALS. Throughout man's history, both as an individual and in groups, he has sought power in the form of control over other individuals, over other groups or organizations, and over material objects. In a capitalistic

[20] See Appendix, p. 200.

system, profit is an obvious source of power to its recipients. There are those who consider it the primary if not the sole source of power in our economic system. Undoubtedly profit must be ranked high on any scale of power sources. However, Marchal has reversed the usual direction of causality in his theory of profit in which profit results from the exercise of power by the firm over various aspects of its environment.[21] Effective power will produce differentials capable of altering an existing equilibrium.

The neoclassical theory of the firm recognizes impersonal, disequilibrating market forces as a source of temporary profit. Marchal has extended this idea to include forces or pressures consciously exercised by firms which can create a differential advantage over other firms. Essentially, all such forces are an evidence of a monopoly power of some kind. Advertising designed to increase product differentiation and innovations of products and processes are two major areas of firm-created power differentials. However, it should be noted that an *image* of a superior product creates a more effective monopoly power than a product which is in fact superior but does not have the corresponding image.

Firms can create and exercise power in the factor markets as well as in the markets for their products. Notably, most wage determination today is a result of the exercise of power by management and labor. Effective collective bargaining is an interplay of the potential power of the participants. Similarly, a position of financial power tends to yield capital on more favorable terms.

The existence of power is a complex phenomenon with ramifications extending into psychology and organizational theory as well as price and value theory. In antitrust decisions United States courts have tended to distinguish between the existence of monopoly power and the exercise of such power by firms. In the Standard Oil and American Tobacco cases of 1911,[22] the Supreme Court established its famous "rule of reason" which, in effect, sanctioned monopolies so long as they did not *unduly* restrain trade. Although bigness is generally associated with monopoly power, the Court in its 1920 decision in the U.S. Steel case held that "the law does not make mere size an offense. It . . . requires overt acts and trusts to its prohibition of them and its power to repress and punish them."[23] Even though U.S. Steel was admittedly large, controlling over one-half of the supply of steel, the Court ruled that it had not misused this monopoly power. In effect, bigness was not badness.

Corwin Edwards has spelled out rather clearly the power of large firms in his statement that:

To create a large corporation may be to gain something in central-office economies, in marketing efficiency, or in organizational skill. It is certainly to gain much in

---

[21] Marchal [113], pp. 549–65.
[22] *Standard Oil Co. of N.J. v. U.S.* 221 U.S. 1, and *U.S. v. American Tobacco Co.*, 221 U.S. 106.
[23] *U.S. v. U.S. Steel Corporation*, 251 U.S. 451.

control over customers, coercive power over competitors, preferential status before banks and other service organizations, and ability to turn law and politics to business advantage. The bargaining advantages of bigness are sufficiently great and obvious to account for the existence of large enterprises, apart from any economies which these concerns may achieve.[24]

Whether the power involved is exercised or not, large corporate size is probably the most effective measure of all types of corporate power. To be sure, the size of a firm is relative to the size of other firms in its industry and the share of the market controlled. The goal of maximizing the volume of sales considered above would give one measure of size especially when this volume is expressed as a share of the total market. The next most satisfactory measure of the size of a firm would be its total value of assets. Firms seeking to increase their differential advantage of power over other firms are most likely to increase the amount of assets controlled. This could be accomplished either through internal growth or through mergers or combinations with other firms.

A large firm represents a power potential which may or may not be exercised by its management. While a power potential may be acquired or exercised for reasons other than profit, it is difficult to overlook the implicit profit potential in such a position. It is possible to use such power to produce large monopoly profits but it is more likely to be used to increase the stability of earnings of the firm. Thus, a monopolistic position might be most valuable in avoiding conditions adverse to the firm. There is little agreement among independent economists or government experts on a satisfactory criterion for measuring economic concentration or monopoly power.

### Internal Goals

A distinction between the external and internal aspects of a firm is not clear-cut. To some extent all of the external goals above involve the internal operation of firms. However, it is felt that production and financial management may properly be regarded as largely internal in their consequences when compared with the marketing, image creation, and power goals above.

PRODUCTION GOALS. There is little doubt but that efficiency is a widely used criterion in evaluating production. Like profit maximization the universality of the appeal of maximum efficiency depends in part upon diverse interpretations of what is meant by "efficiency." As J. M. Clark recognized, usage varies from the technical or engineering concept to the broad idea of social efficiency.[25] Any measure of efficiency is a ratio of outputs to inputs. Perhaps the most meaningful efficiency ratio for the firm is the ratio of the *value* of outputs to the *value* of inputs which combines the engineering concept with the unit prices of inputs and outputs.

[24] Edwards [60], p. 118.
[25] Clark [36], p. 73.

Although most economists refer to the ratio of the value of outputs to the value of inputs as economic efficiency, Scitovsky calls it technological efficiency.

The firm is technologically efficient if it produces the greatest output with given resources or—what amounts to the same thing—a given output with the least input of resources. Technological efficiency is in a firm's own interest, since it is a condition of maximum profit. This is true regardless of the firm's market position, that is, regardless of what prices are and whether the firm is in a perfectly or imperfectly competitive position.[26]

It is generally agreed that under conditions of perfect competition the position of maximum efficiency is one of maximum profit. However, under noncompetitive conditions a number of economists introduce the possibility that maximum profit may be made with less than optimum efficiency. As Richard Leftwich states it, "the scale of plant and the output which maximize the monopolist's long-run profits are not necessarily the optimum scale of plant or the optimum rate of output of the scale of plant which he does build."[27]

Institutional economists have long questioned the efficiency of noncompetitive firms in maximizing their profits. Usually these writers are concerned with social efficiency although sometimes they also include the ideas of economic efficiency. Allan Gruchy in describing J. M. Clark's ideas states that:

Whereas in the orthodox interpretation collective efficiency is nothing more than the reflection of individual efficiencies, in Clark's dynamic economics "narrow commercial efficiency" does not lead to "economic efficiency in the large." Clark observes that the efforts of individual business enterprises to achieve efficient operation do not now result in the furtherance of collective or social efficiency, but instead their efforts bring about "the convulsions that sap the strength of business as a whole." The simple connection between individual and collective efficiency established by the economists of the last century has been destroyed by the new conditions of the twentieth-century economy, with the result that high efficiency in private profit-making is now correlated with a very low level of social efficiency.[28]

Insofar as the institutional economists and some contemporary economists such as Leftwich and Bain are correct in assuming that maximum efficiency and maximum profit need not be coincident, it is possible for firms to seek to maximize economic (or even social) efficiency even though such a goal might yield less than maximum profit.

The concept of efficiency need not imply profit maximization if some ranking criterion other than profit is chosen. Papandreou has stated that "efficiency relates to rationality, that is to maximizing a utility index. It implies

---

[26] Scitovsky [147], p. 148.
[27] Leftwich [100], p. 218.
[28] Gruchy [71], pp. 365–66.

maximization of ends with a given set of means or the minimization of means in the attainment of a given set of related ends. . . . A business firm may be efficient without seeking to maximize profits."[29] The problem of a ranking criterion for efficiency free from some of the above criticisms has been clarified by Boulding.

> But what are the significant concepts of output and input from the economic point of view? The ultimate product or output of all economic activity is, as we have seen, an intangible, unmeasurable, but nevertheless real quantity which we call "utility." The ultimate resource which we have to spend in the production of utility is human time; it is the inexorable fact that a day is only twenty-four hours long, which ultimately limits our ability to do what we want. The most significant concept of economic efficiency, therefore, is that of the production of utility per man-hour of life.[30]

Boulding points out that while production of utility per man-hour of life is not amenable to quantification, it is possible to use an index of physical output expressed in output per man-hour of human productive activity for this purpose.

Under many of the conditions where firms for one reason or another do not choose to maximize profit, they may find it desirable to maximize efficiency. Frequently, the usual orthodox interpretation of economic efficiency is a suitable form of this goal. It is felt that insofar as firms strive for optimum efficiency in the future, they are likely to use Boulding's "output per man-hour of human productive activity" as their measure of this objective. It is the formulation of this ratio which comes closest to encompassing all of the diverse interpretations discussed above.

FINANCIAL GOALS. Financial management includes a variety of goals which can be generalized by stating that the financial requirements of all possible future conditions of the firm should be met adequately. No firm can realize this objective completely; to prepare for one contingency adequately often limits a firm's ability to meet other situations. For instance, the relative amount of debt and equity financing should be determined on the basis of the worst possible earnings position which can reasonably be expected within the firm's economic horizon. Any larger debt position would threaten ownership control of the firm.

In most instances financial objectives are evidenced as additional constraints on other objectives. Some of the major types of financial limitations would be the maximum amount of short-term or long-term debt, the minimum ratio of current assets to fixed assets, the maximum amount of inventory or receivables in relation to sales, and the minimum level of working capital. In addition to these basic relationships financial managers make use of a wide

[29] Papandreou [134], p. 206.
[30] Boulding [21], pp. 717–18.

variety of comparisons and ratios between the major components of the balance sheet and income statement. All of these financial yardsticks can be applied as constraints in the solution of any nonfinancial problem of the firm.

Occasionally, in the short-run a financial objective may take precedence over all other objectives so that a firm would seek to optimize the relationship involved. The liquidity position of a firm can be of prime importance and at times might be crucial. While cash is the only truly liquid asset, most firms regard receivables (and sometimes inventory) as liquid assets. It would be possible to maximize cash and receivables as a percentage of total assets in a linear programming formulation.[31] If desirable, other financial ratios or relationships might be optimized in a similar manner.

## SUMMARY

The goals of firms represent a wide array of alternative objectives of which profit maximization is only one, although without doubt a most significant one. In those instances where firms strive to maximize profit all other aspects of the firm's behavior impose restrictions and limitations on this goal. The difficulty of estimating with accuracy the long-run prospects of a firm makes survival or homeostasis (when interpreted as a relative position within an environment) the most likely long-run objective.

Though difficult to express in quantitative terms the goal of maximizing the power of a firm appears to have the widest application. If differential advantages are viewed as types of power, it is appropriate to regard such differentials as the primary source of profit in our system. Any differential, whether external to the firm or created by it, provides a source of potential power (and of profit) which may or may not be exercised by the firm. In fact, firms may regard a profit potential as more important than realized profit from a long-range standpoint.

This essay is largely an effort to bring together diverse current ideas and writings which have a bearing on the objectives of firms. It is hoped that it has pointed up the need for integrating developments in the areas of business management and organizational theory with the traditional economic theories of profit. It is only insofar as such integration is accomplished that the potentialities of modern quantitative techniques such as linear programming can be utilized in a modern theory of the firm.

## APPENDIX

The preceding discussion was designed to introduce the possibility of goals other than profit maximization into the modern theory of the firm. While some valid objectives of firms do not lend themselves to quantitative interpretation, most of them can be quantified through the subjective evaluations of decision makers. The decision maker must make these evaluations

---

[31] See Appendix, p. 200.

even though his analysis may not force him to use precise formulations. It is hoped that the possibility of taking advantage of the powerful tool of linear programming will encourage decision makers to analyze the bases of their decisions in quantitative terms. Once business goals are quantified, it usually is possible to incorporate them into the linear programming framework. The following illustrations suggest some techniques by which this may be accomplished.

In general, the usual mathematical notation and formulation of a linear programming problem will be followed in the examples below.[32]
Let:

$n$ = number of activities of the firm, some of which yield marketable products or services and all make some change in available resources,

$c_j$ = market price or unit value of the $j^{th}$ activity ($j = 1, 2, \cdots, n$),

$x_j$ = optimum number of units of the $j^{th}$ activity,

$m$ = number of resources (includes all things of value used by firm),

$b_i$ = maximum units of the $i^{th}$ resource available ($i = 1, 2, \cdots, m$),

$d_i$ = unit value of the $i^{th}$ resource,

$a_{ij}$ = units of resource $i$ used per unit of activity $j$,

$a_{ij}x_j$ = units of resource $i$ used for the optimum output of activity $j$,

$a_{ij}x_jd_i$ = total cost of resource $i$ used for the optimum output of activity $j$,

$c_jx_j$ = gross revenue from the total sales of the $j^{th}$ activity,

$p$ = minimum net profit permissible.

The above notation differs from that usually used in that $c_j$ is the market price rather than the net return of the $j^{th}$ activity. This change requires the addition of $d_i$ as the unit cost of the $i^{th}$ resource. On this basis $\sum_{j=1}^{n} c_jx_j$ will be the total sales volume for the firm.

## Maximization of Sales Volume

The goal of maximum sales volume subject to some minimum level of net profit expressed as a percentage of sales would be formulated as follows:
Maximize

$$Z_1 = \sum_{j=1}^{n} c_jx_j$$

Subject to:

(1)
$$\sum_{j=1}^{n} c_jx_j - \sum_{j=1}^{n} \sum_{i=1}^{m} a_{ij}x_jd_i \geq p$$

(2)
$$\sum_{j=1}^{n} a_{ij}x_j \leq b_i \qquad (i = 1, 2, \cdots, m).$$

[32] For example, see Harrison [74], pp. 217–21.

Thus for the first activity where $j = 1$ the profit constraint would show the net profit of this activity. That is to say, $c_1x_1$ would be the gross revenue from activity 1 while $\sum_{i=1}^{m} a_{i1}x_1d_i$ would be the total cost of resources 1, 2, $\cdots$, $m$ used to carry out activity 1. The summation of the net profit for all of the $n$ activities would be the total net profit of the firm for the period under consideration. Depending upon the inclinations of management the constraint $p$ could be either a minimum arbitrary amount of profit or an amount calculated as some minimum percentage of sales or total investment.

### Upper and Lower Constraints on Profit

Whatever goal is chosen for optimization it sometimes is desirable to have an upper as well as a lower limit on the level of profit. If $p'$ is used to designate an upper limit on profit and $p''$ a lower limit, these constraints can be expressed as follows:
Subject to:

(3)
$$\sum_{j=1}^{n} c_jx_j - \sum_{j=1}^{n} \sum_{i=1}^{m} a_{ij}x_jd_i \leqq p'$$

(4)
$$\sum_{j=1}^{n} c_jx_j - \sum_{j=1}^{n} \sum_{i=1}^{m} a_{ij}x_jd_i \geqq p''.$$

### Maximization of the Value of Assets

If the goal of maximizing the value of assets is used in a linear programming form two changes are necessary in the notation used above. The symbol $b_i$ used for the maximum units of the $i^{\text{th}}$ resource includes both quantities of the resource on hand and quantities which can be acquired during the period under consideration. In the example below, $b'_i$ will identify the total quantity of resource $i$ on hand. Resources such as labor and other services would always have a zero value for $b'_i$ since these resources cannot be stored or kept on hand. The quantities of the $i^{\text{th}}$ resource which can be acquired during the period under consideration would be designated $b''_i$ so that $b_i = b'_i + b''_i$. In other words, the total resources available would be equal to the amounts of resources on hand plus the quantities which can be acquired.

The resource series will be divided so that as $i$ varies from 1 to $k$ all resources with positive $d_i$ values (assets) would be included. As $i$ varies from $k + 1$ to $m$ all resources with negative $d_i$ values (liabilities) will be included. Thus, $\sum_{i=1}^{k} b'_id_i$ would be total assets and $\sum_{i=1}^{m} b'_id_i$ would be net worth. It follows that $\sum_{i=1}^{m} \Delta b'_id_i$ would be net profit in balance sheet terms.

The generalized form of a linear programming problem using a goal of maximizing value of assets would be:

Maximize

$$Z_2 = \sum_{i=1}^{k} b'_i d_i$$

Subject to:

(5)
$$\sum_{i=1}^{m} \Delta b'_i d_i \geq p$$

(6)
$$\sum_{j=1}^{n} a_{ij} x_j \leq b_i \qquad (i = 1, 2, \cdots, m)$$

Such a formulation also would measure the maximum growth in assets and firms are more likely to think of this objective in terms of growth.

## Maximization of Financial Ratios

Liquidity of assets is an important consideration in any firm and at times in a short-run situation a firm might choose to make decisions so that its quick assets (cash and receivables) were as large a percentage of total assets as possible. Such an objective could be stated in the mathematical notation of linear programming as follows: Let $b'_1 = $ cash and $b'_2 = $ receivables. The sum of $b'_1 + b'_2$ would be the quick assets of the firm.

Maximize

$$Z_3 = \frac{b'_1 d_1 + b'_2 d_2}{\sum_{i=1}^{k} b'_i d_i}$$

Subject to:

(7)
$$\sum_{i=1}^{m} \Delta b'_i d_i \geq p$$

(8)
$$\sum_{j=1}^{n} a_{ij} x_j \leq b_i \qquad (i = 1, 2, \cdots, m).$$

It would be possible to make use of other financial ratios which it might be desirable to optimize in a similar formulation. Typically, these would be short-run objectives for a firm.

Chapter

7

# A SHORT ESSAY
# ON A MANAGERIAL THEORY
# OF THE FIRM

*by* SHERRILL CLELAND

The "traditional" theory of the firm, as Boulding points out in his introductory essay, does not have a very long tradition. With the possible exception of Cournot, there was no theory of the firm in economics before Marshall. The classical economists were mainly interested in the market system and how it allocated various resources. They believed that competitive pressures would either force a firm to operate at maximum efficiency or force it out of business and, therefore, they were not interested in the combination or the organization of these resources once they had been allocated. For this reason, the classical economist neglected the internal organization of the firm in his theorizing, and never seriously considered the possibility that administrative authority might act as a possible alternative to the market mechanism. The firm was a passive reactor to market events.

The more recent contributions of the Chamberlin-Robinson revolution to the theory of the firm expanded the area of decision-making from price-quantity adjustments to include promotional adjustments, and Abbott[1] has added recently product adjustments. Even these advances in the theory still mean decision-making is limited by the constraints of the market and the greatest concern is how the market is organized rather than how the firm is organized.

## THE TRADITIONAL FIRM

Figure 1 shows the firm in its market environment according to the traditional theory of the firm. External constraints limited firm behavior and reduced entrepreneural decision-making to the choice of what line of business to enter. There was no organization theory, because the market eventually destroyed all firms that were not organized in the most efficient manner. There was no information theory because in a perfectly competitive society

---

[1] Abbott [1], *passim.*

the important pieces of information were assumed to be known. The information that the entrepreneur acted upon referred to the profit levels of different industries. Beyond that, factor prices and product prices were given

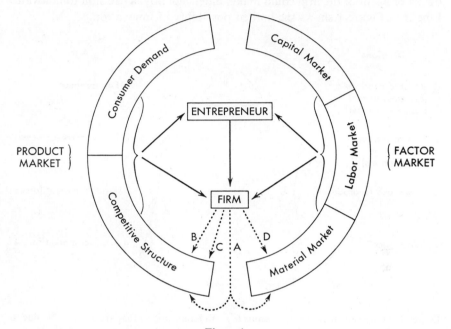

**Figure 1**

Solid lines represent market pressures on the entrepreneur and the firm. Dotted lines show the limits on the firm's activity. Line A is the limited path by which the innovator may make an important decision (e.g., an innovation). Dotted lines B, C, and D represent unsuccessful attempts to innovate.

by the markets and in the theory of the firm (at least in its marginal analysis form) it was assumed that the entrepreneur-manager would have to organize his resources most efficiently in order to maximize profits.

The decision-making process as limited by the "traditional" theory of the firm can be illustrated by a tree as in Figure 2. Figure 2 shows, on the left branch of the tree, the initial decisions to be made in a firm, and, on the right branch of the tree, the agents which will make the corresponding decision. Only the decisions above curve $AB$ are made by the agents of the firm. In order to understand the decision-making process or the sequence of decisions that lie below curve $AB$, the economist must understand the market, not the firm, for the market is the decision-making agent, not the firm or its officers. Once path $M$ is chosen by the owner of the firm as the particular industry he will enter (decision 1), paths $R$, $S$, and $T$ are then determined for him by market constraints (decisions 2, 3, and 4).

According to the traditional theory of the firm, there was, however, one additional avenue of freedom of action open to the owner (or agent) of the firm. Although competition in the factor market and product market provided an environment that restricted the activity of the firm almost completely, the owner or agent of the firm could make, independently, a decision to innovate. Line *A* in Figure 1 shows the limited possibility of innovation.

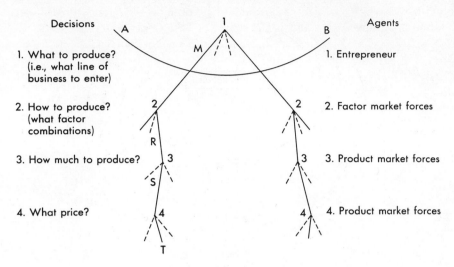

**Figure 2**

Dotted lines indicate alternative decisions (e.g., different prices) that are not feasible due to market restraints.

Lines *B*, *C*, and *D* indicate attempts for the independent action by the firms which were rendered unsuccessful by the market environment. The incentive to innovate, none the less, was great, for as Line *A* shows, it was this type of dynamic decision, made within the firm, that could actually have an impact on the environmental constraints of the product and/or factor markets and give the innovating firm more market freedom. In reality, the successful innovation provided the firm with a temporary monopoly advantage. This monopoly advantage gave the firm some freedom in decision-making so that alternative choices were available to the firm without extreme penalty, at least temporarily. But the successful innovation was rare for a specific firm, so the market mechanism was still the economists' main field of study.

## A RESTRUCTURED FIRM

While the economist was studying the operation of the market in order to understand the allocation process, the businessman was developing a strong propensity to innovate in order to gain temporary monopoly control over market forces. As the businessman learned by doing, his propensity to innovate shifted to a propensity to monopolize and temporary monopoly became more permanent. The pattern of internal decision-making which he followed was designed to minimize the external constraints which had theoretically limited his decision alternatives. The initial managerial revolution, then, was an attempt by the businessman to control or influence the external forces (the product market and the factor market) that had been controlling and limiting him. That he was successful, and patently so, is evidenced by our antitrust laws. He wished to expand his field of choice, his set of alternatives, while simultaneously reducing the degree of uncertainty which he faced.

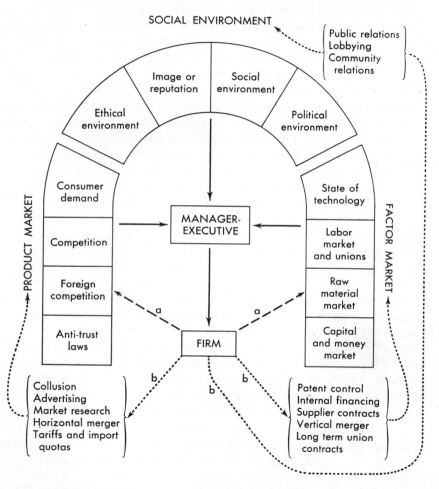

**Figure 3**

a. Dashed lines show that there is still some market restraint on the firm, but generally it enjoys significant freedom of action.

b. Dotted lines indicate the kinds of activity engaged in by the firm and based on internal decisions. The activities are designed to reduce the uncertainty which the firm faces, by reshaping the various aspects of its environment.

To do this the businessman made decisions internally which were designed to change his external environment. The changes that he made in his firm's environment took such forms as the tariff to limit his foreign competitors, collusion to foil the market temporarily, or horizontal merger to foil the market permanently. On the factor market side, he encouraged immigration (at least in the United States) to maintain a large supply of labor, he used patents to control the state of technology, and he promoted vertical mergers to insure his firm a source of supply. What developed was a firm which, although not completely immune from outside market forces, was not totally controlled by them either. Further, the manager-executive of this firm had much wider decision-making alternatives. His field of choice had expanded with his success in gaining monopoly power. At the same time his firm, his decisions, and his propensity to monopolize had an impact on the external environment in such a way as to reduce the degree of uncertainty which he faced in making his decisions. The new framework of the firm as it might be visualized after consideration of the above changes is shown in Figure 3.

As can be seen in the figure, the manager-executive or peak co-ordinator has greater latitude in his decision-making due to the wider environmental freedom which develops as a result of his partial monopoly power. However, he is also faced initially with greater uncertainty due to the possibility of other firms in his industry or area having some partial monopoly powers as well. There may not be a market price or a market wage, but a range of prices or wages instead. There may not be one technology, but several. The manager-executive will, of course, try to make decisions which will minimize the greater uncertainty. In a very real sense then, the firm is operating in an environment where both the limitations of the market *and* the protection of the market have been reduced. This different market environment, reflecting some degree of monopoly power, provides the manager-executive with alternative choices so that the internal organization and the internal and external information systems of the firm become important.

To see the difference in the decision-making process that now confronts the restructured firm of Figure 3, another decision process tree is shown in Figure 4. In Figure 4, the same decisions are made as were made in Figure 2, but the agents corresponding to a specific decision are now different.

Decisions which were made more externally by the market than internally by the management group have been minimized. Now all of the decisions lie above the curve *AB*, not, as in Figure 2, just the entrepreneur's decision on what line of business to enter. One could consider curve *AB* in Figures 2 and 4 as the lower edge of a window blind. In the traditional theory (Figure 2), an economist with a knowledge of the market could understand and predict the outcomes of specific decisions—the window pane is clear and the window blind is up. In Figure 4, the blind is down and knowledge of the market is no longer enough. To understand and predict firm behavior, the economist must go inside the firm and see what lies behind the darkened window. His market knowledge will help considerably, but he will also need supplementary knowledge of the internal structure and the internal procedures of the firm, found only behind the blind.

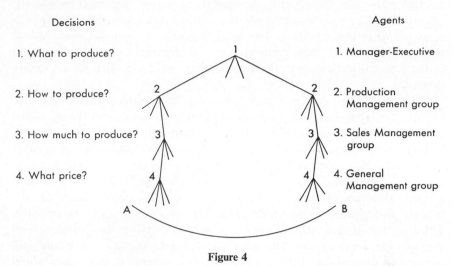

Decisions

1. What to produce?
2. How to produce?
3. How much to produce?
4. What price?

Agents

1. Manager-Executive
2. Production Management group
3. Sales Management group
4. General Management group

**Figure 4**

Comparisons of the traditional firm of Figures 1 and 2 with the restructured firm of Figures 3 and 4 should give a better understanding of the environmental structure within which the firm really operates and the internal, sequential decision-making process that takes place.

Although the market limitations are still important, they are not controlling. The modern firm has grown so in size and complexity that the traditional theory of the firm which described a single-product, single-plant, single-owner enterprise operating in a competitive environment is no longer always applicable. As Shubik has recently pointed out:

There are few individual-bachelor, owner, entrepreneurs running small single-product firms as unincorporated enterprises in our economy. The facts of life force us to recognize the presence of large multiproduct firms operating in a welter of different market structures, under a host of legal and social restraints, operating under several types of institutional forms such as corporations or partnerships, owned jointly by many individuals and often controlled by men who are either fractional owners or have no capital invested in the firm they control.[2]

This does not mean that our knowledge and insights gained from the traditional theory of the firm are useless or that theory should be discarded for an institutional approach. Rather, it means that the traditional theory of the firm should be expanded, reconstituted, or replaced by a different theory of the firm. It is with this thought in mind and within the framework here presented that the managerial theory of the firm needs to be examined.

[2] Shubik [149], p. 219.

## TOWARD A MANAGERIAL THEORY OF THE FIRM

To develop and describe a managerial theory of the firm, one must look beyond economic theory and incorporate some of organization theory, information theory, cybernetics, and the institutional material of the business schools and of business itself. This is no simple task, even for those economists willing to tread these relatively unfamiliar paths. But as the discussion in the previous section suggests, there is strong indication that such a theory is needed.

The firm as portrayed in Figure 3 has significant decision-making power executed, of course, by the manager-executive. A managerial theory of the firm then would become a theory of management decision. This theory would be built on three legs. First is the external environment (including the product market and the factor market), which provides real limits but which is also subject to countervailing pressures by the firm. Second is the internal organizational structure of the firm, which must be developed in order for the process of decision-making under conditions of uncertainty to be effective. Third is the communication system, which transmits information to and through the organization. The managerial theory of the firm would still demand an understanding of how the market is organized, but it also would demand an understanding of how the firm is organized. The *manager* would be substituted for the *market* as the key element.

This means that the managerial theory of the firm would be a departure from the traditional theory of the firm. As J. P. Miller has recently pointed out, there are several implicit assumptions in the traditional theory of the firm. These are:

1. *The stationary assumption*—it assumes that wants, resources and the body of knowledge are given and unchanging.
2. *The independence assumption*—it assumes that wants, resources and the body of knowledge are independent of one another and of the actions of the firm.
3. *The motivational assumption*—the purposes or goals of the firm are assumed to be maximizing of net benefits (or profits).
4. *The informational assumption*—it assumes that there is a well-organized system for the acquisition and dissemination of relevant information to the firm and within the firm, whether this be concerning technical processes, human relations, the markets for products and raw materials, or facilities for production.
5. *The organizational assumption*—it assumes a process for decision and action within the firm by which the decisions and actions of various individuals are related to one another in terms of the maximizing purpose of the firm.[3]

The managerial theory of the firm would maintain the motivational assumption, the informational assumption, and the organizational assumption *as categories* but would modify the nature and content of these assumptions. It, however, would substitute a "growth assumption" for the stationary one

---

[3] Miller [119], pp. 135–6.

and an "influence assumption" for the independence one. The assumptions implicit in the managerial theory of the firm, then, would be as follows:

1. The motivational assumption—the goals and purposes of the firm are assumed to be satisficing or minimaxing ones.
2. The informational assumption—it assumes that the normal information system is unorganized, distorted, and full of noise and that the acquisition and dissemination of relevant information to the firm and within the firm is a problem that must be solved internally.
3. The organizational assumption—it assumes that the decision process is determined by the organizational structure of the firm which in turn determines the information system.
4. The growth assumption—the wants, resources, state of technology, and body of knowledge are assumed to be changeable and changing.
5. The influence assumption—it assumes that the wants, resources, state of technology, and body of knowledge are not independent of one another and can be influenced by the actions of the firm.

In spite of these different assumptions, the managerial theory of the firm would maintain much of the form of the traditional theory. For example, if we include the possibility of innovation as part of the traditional theory of the firm as I have in Figure 1, then the growth and influence assumptions are little different than the modifications suggested by the Chamberlin-Robinson contributions. Furthermore, both the traditional theory and the managerial theory rely upon control devices for maintaining the firm in equilibrium. According to the traditional theory, if there was a change in factor prices this information would be fed into the firm and this would set off the automatic substitution of factors which would minimize cost and restore equilibrium. The external *control* of the markets would tolerate no other adjustment (except death).

The managerial theory of the firm would also rely upon control devices for maintaining the firm in equilibrium. However, these control devices would be internal to the firm. They would be part of its organizational and informational structure, and a factor price change would result in *internal* decisions which would re-establish the firm in equilibrium.

Where the managerial theory would differ basically from the traditional is in terms of goals. The managerial firm is not a maximizing firm. It may be a satisficing one or a minimaxing one. A satisficing firm is one that attempts to achieve "satisfactory" profits rather than maximum profits.[4] Often "satisfactory" is explained in terms of a target rate of return on investment concept.[5] It reflects the fact that a firm will usually have some leeway between its "survival position" and its "maximum position" and what profit level it

---

[4] Although one might contend that a firm seeking "satisfactory" profits would still be a maximizing firm in that it is maximizing satisfaction, such a goal is certainly different than the maximum profit goal of the traditional firm.

[5] Kaplan [90], Chap. 2.

seeks may depend upon its fear of antitrust activity, the manner in which it exerts its "influence," and the pricing orientation it may follow (e.g., low mark-up, high volume or high mark-up, low volume). If the firm attempts to achieve a target rate of return on its investment (a satisficing goal), it may choose to raise product prices in response to the factor price rise rather than engage in a substitution of factors as the traditional theory of the firm would require. The decision, however, would be made internally by the manager-executive and not forced externally by the market.

If the firm chose to follow an offensive and defensive decision-making policy, it would be termed a minimaxing firm. A minimaxing firm is one strongly aware of the implications of the "influence" assumptions. The firm's manager-executive recognizes that not only can he influence wants or events to a degree, but that his competitors can also. Therefore he is trying to make his decisions in such a manner that if all the wrong things happen, he still would hope to salvage maximum results under the circumstances. The minimaxing firm is trying to minimize losses and maximize gains. Decisions which are designed to reduce the degree of uncertainty which the firm faces (by trying to change the external environment) are offensive. Decisions which attempt to protect the firm from uncertainty (e.g., by buying insurance) are defensive. A minimaxing firm when faced with a factor price change would probably try to sign long-term supplier contracts so that the uncertainty of another factor price rise would be reduced.

The managerial theory of the firm, by shifting the motivational assumption from one of maximizing to one of satisficing or minimaxing, may provide a better framework for understanding, explaining and predicting some of the so-called uneconomic decisions of industry. Such decisions as gifts to liberal arts colleges or active community affairs spending, which are difficult to justify within the framework of the traditional maximizing firm, are understandable in a satisficing firm. This kind of activity by the firm is often referred to as social responsibility. Social responsibility activity by the firm makes more sense if the firm has some measure of market power (the influence assumption) to be responsible with, and has achieved a satisfactory profit level, though not a maximum one, to share socially. And it certainly implies an internal decision by the manager-executive of the firm.

A key element of the managerial theory of the firm must be the locus of control. In the managerial firm the control mechanism will more often be internal than external. Naturally, since the market environment is a basic underpinning for the managerial theory of the firm, the market will provide some constraints and limits. However, there will ordinarily be a range of possible decisions over which the market would exert little influence. The internal control mechanism may appear at first glance to be a simple homeostatic model on the order of Boulding's balance sheet model.[6] In effect, there

---

[6] Boulding [23], Chap. 2.

would be an "internal invisible hand" guided by company policy and industry or firm convention that would provide the constraints which would limit the alternatives of the manager-executive.

These company policies and business conventions are highly important factors in the managerial theory of the firm. Unfortunately, because they are often unrecognizable to the economist or are considered by him as trite listings of the obvious, they have been overlooked or neglected. Nonetheless, they often provide the internal constraints to guide decisions. As Margolis points out in his discussion of a deliberative model of the firm (which has some similarity to my managerial model of a firm), "the managers, rather than being either omniscient at one extreme or mechanically random at the other extreme, are deliberating leaders of a firm who adopt procedures and rules because of the lack of information necessary to be fully 'rational'."[7]

The adoption of these internal company policies and conventions is only a recognition of the fact that information is not costless. The manager-executive is forced to decide on the basis of limited information how worthwhile it may be to expand the amount of his information and thereby his field of choice. He makes this decision well knowing that the additional, costly, information may be useless or may indicate a much more intelligent line of action. Because of this uncertainty, when enough information is available to justify a decision which falls within the range of acceptable firm practice or convention, extra information will be considered uneconomic and the decision will be made. Accepting this description of internal control and of the internal decision-making process, the effectiveness of this control and of the decisions will be dependent upon the amount and reliability of the information received. It is at this point that information theory would make its contribution.

### The Role of Information

Information theory has emphasized the process of feedback of distasteful data to an action source. In the firm this action source is the manager-executive or his subordinates. Assume the information of an external event, a factor price rise, comes into the firm. The resulting action due to internal control methods will follow the pattern as indicated in Figure 5. The special insight which the managerial theory of the firm would give in this type of situation is that the executive's action on receipt of the message will be generally quite predictable, based on the internal controls of company policy and business convention.

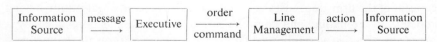

**Figure 5.**   Information moving through a firm.

[7] Margolis [114], p. 189.

Information theory provides a number of important insights into a managerial theory of the firm. For example, information theory shows that there is a strong likelihood that there will be excess capacity in terms of information received. That is, more information will be transmitted through the channels than can be used, while at the same time there will be no guarantee that all the relevant information has been transmitted. Information as an input of the firm will often be as indivisible as a large machine.

A second insight that information theory provides is the importance of noise.[8] Noise will be present and may distort the information input so that important pieces are lost, while excess unimportant pieces may come through and be used as a guide in decision making. We might even suggest that one reason why the traditional theory of the firm with its costless information assumption still remains in vogue is that noise, in the form of incantations of the "conventional wisdom," has distorted the relevant bits of information that might have forced abandonment of that assumption. At any rate, it is the existence of noise and the excess capacity of the information input that make the manager-executive's reliance on company policies and conventions a fairly rational action.

Ideally then, the information received will result in "predictable" executive action. However, the reliability of the information received is dependent upon the structure of the firm's organization. The manager-executive will attempt to organize the firm in such a manner as to filter out as much noise as possible and to utilize the capacity of the information input as efficiently as possible. It is here that organization theory would come into the picture.

### The Role of Internal Organization

The economist has been highly resistant to organization theory. He has either accepted the traditional theory of the firm, which means he believes the organization of the market, not the organization of the firm, is key, or he considered organization theory as the static drawing of organizational charts found in management textbooks.

The firm as an entity does not make decisions nor does it "behave" in the strict sense. Decision-making and behavior are attributed to the people in the organization, especially the manager-executive. However, as Boulding points out in his introductory essay, the behavior of the individual differs as he takes on the different roles demanded of him by the organization to which he belongs. The "traditional" theory of the firm circumvented this problem by talking of the entrepreneur in the one-man firm. Moving out of this limited concept of the firm, one must then examine the firm as an organization having control, co-ordinating, and communicating functions, and dominated by a manager-executive who follows different roles as he performs these functions.

---

[8] Noise may be defined as any change or unintended distortion in the information input which is not intended by the information source.

Actually the firm might be visualized as a specific case within the framework of general organization theory. By studying the firm in this framework, one would be forced to re-examine the motivational assumption, which I have already done, and the organizational assumption. The managerial firm is an economic structure organized under an agent with authority who must develop a control and co-ordination system and an informational system. In this type of economic structure the agent or manager-executive would develop specific policies and establish standard procedures which would enable subordinates in the organization to make numerous operating decisions. These standard policies and procedures would serve as organizational constraints and would replace in many cases external market constraints.

By standardized policies and procedures I mean that the manager-executive would develop a specific strategy in anticipation of a wide range of possible events and that the particular decision to be made would be predetermined by the strategic plan. Tactical activity by subordinates would be discouraged except in certain narrowly defined areas and the strategic plan would provide the internal constraints to the decision-maker regardless of his position in the organization. The middle management man to whom a decision had been delegated would usually operate within the constraints of the strategic plan even though in some cases he might feel the prescribed decision is wrong.

This distinction between strategy and tactics is quite important. Tactics mean spur-of-the-moment decisions at the time of an event, based on individual judgment and past experience (if the decision-makers have them). Strategy means examining the possible alternatives, setting policies and standards, and deciding, *in advance*, how specific tactical decisions will be made. Strategy takes the uncertainty out of which decision will be made, once the facts of an event are known.

As the managerial firm adopts specific strategies and as these strategies become institutionalized and better known outside the firm, the possibilities of predicting the decision or action of the managerial firm would expand. However, this would presuppose a knowledge of the firm's organizational structure that determines how and by whom the strategies are set as well as an understanding of the decision-making process itself.

### A Decision-making Process

The decision-making process is defined as a series of steps designed to identify a problem and then find the most satisfactory solution. In the traditional theory of the firm this "most satisfactory solution" would have been determined once and for all and be demanded by market constraints. In the managerial theory of the firm, the solution may also be determined once and for all by business convention or rigorous internal company policy. Then the decision-maker's job would be to locate the solution and make the "proper" strategic decision. However, the managerial theory does not assume that the solution has to be a once and for all decision.

The managerial theory would try to explain why the proper solution *usually* would be a once and for all one. In the firm the decision-maker operates within a specific organizational structure and activity program which limits his alternatives and tends to produce the proper solution from him or from his subordinates. Firms attempt to standardize their decision-making process and in so doing, it will develop that there will be a certain number of steps involved and that choice will be limited by a fixed number of alternatives. The expected number of steps in the decision-making process should be an indicator of the difficulty of the decision involved in a given task. And the number of steps in the process will depend on the size and efficiency of the organizational structure and its activity program.

Once the organizational structure which best handles the flow of information and facilitates the reaching of decisions in the firm has been established, some value can be gained by examining the activity of the firm's manager-executive who operates within the structure. The basic activities or functions of the manager-executive are organizing, controlling, and planning.

The organizing function of the manager-executive refers not only to his role in establishing the specific structure of the firm but to the organizing of inputs, workflow, output, and the decision process, as well. Although this organizing function is a vital one, it is not a continuing activity that demands the day to day direction of the top man. It does, of course, demand intermittent reappraisal of the organizational structure since the structure of the managerial firm is both changing and changeable.

The control function deals with the establishment of a control mechanism or process, internal to the firm, to serve as a substitute for the external market restraints which have been reduced by the firm's activity. The control process, which is dependent upon an adequate information system, is a four-part process. The specific steps in the process are the development of standards, the gathering of performance results, the evaluation of results against standards, and the corrective action. The development of standards is a basic activity of the manager-executive although, as Margolis[9] has pointed out, the standards may be long-used business conventions that have become institutionalized and, therefore, the decision-making activity of the executive could be minimal in this area since much of it would be delegated according to predetermined strategy. The collection of information will be routine if the manager-executive has done his organizing job well and the evaluation of results will cause corrective action that should be close to automatic if he has set his standards well. The control function, then, like the organizing function, is not a continuing activity for the manager-executive. Each part of the control operation will be intermittently reappraised and re-evaluated and attempts

⁹ Margolis [114], pp. 190–1.

will be made to minimize the time and activity involved between steps 3 and 4 of the control process so that they will almost blend into one.

Once the manager-executive has performed his basic organizing and controlling activity and delegated the routine work in these areas to subordinates, he will have greater time for planning. This is, of course, only true for the managerial firm, not the traditional one, for a firm's internal activity is dependent upon its environmental freedom. The firm of Figure 1 has almost no environmental freedom, so the structure of the organization and its internal activity is of limited importance. It follows that if the organizational structure of the firm is not important, then the internal informational flow will also be unimportant, and the internal control process which relies on information will be both ineffective and unnecessary. The market is king.

The managerial firm of Figure 3, on the other hand, has significant environmental freedom and even some power to *influence* its environment. This means that there is wide leeway in the manner in which the firm may be organized. The organization of the firm to provide the free flow of near noiseless information would then allow the internal control process to operate effectively and free the manager-executive for planning or decision-making activity pointed toward the future and towards growth. It is in this manner that the managerial theory of the firm would introduce the potentiality for firm growth and the organizational relationships by which it would take place.

The organizational assumption, the influence assumption, and the information assumption are all important in providing a framework for examining the growth of the managerial firm. As Penrose has pointed out, "Successful expansion must . . . be preceded by planning on the part of the firm. Firms do not just grow automatically, but in response to human decisions."[10] These plans are made and can be made, because, due to the influence of the managerial firm on its environment, the firm has some degree of monopoly power and some control over its own future. This degree of environmental influence reduces the uncertainty which a firm faces and puts confidence in its plans. Cooper[11] has pointed out that the distinction between operations and planning in a firm's activity is a significant one. The managerial theory of the firm attempts to provide a framework within which this significant distinction can be pursued. This is not a theory of firm growth, but an outline of a framework which may allow the study of growth as one of many aspects of a dynamic, managerial theory of the firm.

## SUMMARY

The traditional theory of the firm considered the firm as a passive reactor to market events, intent upon maximizing profits. The managerial theory of the firm considers the firm as an organized information system, intent upon a

[10] Penrose [136], p. 532.
[11] Cooper [39], p. 532.

satisfactory profit level operating in an external and internal environment which allows the manager significant decision-making power. By organizing the firm and its information system and establishing control techniques which make limited decisions on the basis of this information, the manager-executive has: (1) the time to plan for future growth; (2) the power and insight to attempt to influence his external environment; (3) and the ability to make decisions whose sequential aspects can be carried out by subordinates.

This discourse has not set forth a finalized (to use a managerial word) model of the managerial firm. It is primarily a map of where to go or a sketch of how to proceed and as such it is certainly not the last word. It may, however, be an interesting beginning.

## BIBLIOGRAPHY

1. Abbott, L., *Quality and Competition*, Columbia University Press, New York, 1955.
2. Abramovitz, Moses, *Inventories and Business Cycles with Special Reference to Manufacturers' Inventories*, National Bureau of Economic Research, Inc., New York, 1950.
3. Ackoff, R. L., "The Development of Operations Research as a Science," *Operations Research*, June 1956, pp. 265–95.
4. ———, "Operations Research and National Planning," *Operations Research*, August 1957, pp. 457–68.
5. Alchian, A. A., *Economic Replacement Policy*, The Rand Corp, Santa. Monica, Calif., April 12, 1952.
6. Allais, M., "Method of Appraising Economic Prospects of Mining Exploration Over Large Territories: Algerian Sahara Case Study," *Management Science*, July 1957, pp. 285–347.
7. Allendoerfer, C. B., and Oakley, C. O., *Principles of Mathematics*, McGraw-Hill Book Company, New York, 1955.
8. American Management Association, *Capital Equipment Replacement*, American Management Association, Special Conference, May 3–4, 1954.
9. Arrow, K. J., Hurwicz, L., and Uzawa, H., *Studies in Linear and Nonlinear Programming*, Stanford University Press, Stanford, 1958.
10. ———, Karlin, Samuel, and Scarf, Herbert, *Studies in the Mathematical Theory of Inventory and Production*, Stanford Mathematical Studies in Social Science 1, Stanford University Press, 1958.
11. Artin, E., *A Freshman Honors Course in Calculus and Analytic Geometry*, Charlottesville, Va., Committee on the Undergraduate Program, Mathematical Association of America, 1957.
12. Barankin, E. W., and Dorfman, R., *On Quadratic Programming*, University of California Press, Berkeley, 1958.
13. Barna, Tibor, *et. al.*, *The Structural Interdependence of the Economy*, John Wiley & Sons, New York, 1954.
14. Bassie, V. L., *Economic Forecasting*, McGraw-Hill Book Company, New York, 1958.
15. Baumol, W. J., "Activity Analysis in One Lesson," *American Economic Review*, December 1958, pp. 837–73.
16. ———, *Economic Dynamics: An Introduction*, Macmillan, New York, 1951.
17. Bellman, Richard, *Dynamic Programming*, Princeton University Press, Princeton, 1957.
18. ———, "Dynamic Programming and the Smoothing Problem," *Management Science*, October 1956, pp. 111–13.
19. Bennion, E. G., "Capital Budgeting and Game Theory," *Harvard Business Review*, September–December 1956.
20. Bodenhorn, D., "The Problem of Economic Assumptions in Mathematical Economics," *Journal of Political Economy*, February 1956, pp. 25–32.
21. Boulding, K. E., *Economic Analysis*, 3rd ed., Harper & Brothers, New York, 1955.

22. Boulding, K. E., *The Image*, The University of Michigan Press, Ann Arbor, 1956.

23. ———, *A Reconstruction of Economics*, John Wiley & Sons, New York, 1950

24. ———, *The Skills of the Economist*, Howard Allen, Inc., Cleveland, 1958.

25. Breuer, J., *Introduction to the Theory of Sets,* Prentice-Hall, Inc., Englewood Cliffs, New Jersey, 1958.

26. Bright, J. R., "Does Automation Raise Skill Requirements," *Harvard Business Review*, July–August 1958, pp. 85–98.

27. Browne, E. T., *Introduction to Determinants and Matrices*, The University of North Carolina Press, Chapel Hill, 1958.

28. Carroll, T. H., "Toward a Liberal Education for Business," *California Management Review*, Spring 1959, pp. 73–8.

29. Chamberlin, E. H., *The Theory of Monopolistic Competition*, 1st ed., Harvard University Press, Cambridge, 1933.

30. ———, *The Theory of Monopolistic Competition*, 5th ed., Harvard University Press, Cambridge, 1946.

31. Charnes, A., and Cooper, W. W., "Nonlinear Power of Adjacent Extreme Point Methods in Linear Programming," *Econometrica*, January 1957, pp. 132–53.

32. ———, and Lemke, C. E., "Minimization of Nonlinear Separable Convex Functionals," *Naval Research Logistics Quarterly*, December 1954, pp. 301–12.

33. Chernoff, Herman, and Moses, Lincoln E., *Elementary Decision Theory*, John Wiley & Sons, New York, 1959.

34. Christian, R. R., *Introduction to Logic and Sets*, Ginn and Company, Boston, 1958.

35. Churchman, C. W., Ackoff, R. E., Arnoff, E. L., *et al.*, *Introduction to Operations Research*, John Wiley & Sons, New York, 1957.

36. Clark, J. M., "The Socializing of Theoretical Economics," *The Trend of Economics*, Alfred A. Knopf, New York, 1924.

37. Clemence, R. V. (ed.), *Readings in Economic Analysis*, Vol. II, Addison-Wesley Press, Cambridge, 1950.

38. Committee on the Undergraduate Program, *Elementary Mathematics of Sets with Applications*, Mathematical Association of America, Buffalo, New York, 1958.

39. Cooper, W. W., "Limits to the Growth and Size of Firms, Discussion," *American Economic Review, Proceedings*, Vol. 45, pp. 559–65.

40. ———, "Revisions to the Theory of the Firm," *American Economic Review*, December 1949, pp. 1204–22.

41. ———, *et al.*, "Economics and Operations Research: A Symposium,' *Review of Economics and Statistics*, August, 1958, pp. 195–229.

42. Coppock, J. D., *Economics of the Business Firm*, McGraw-Hill Book Company, New York, 1959.

43. Cournot, A. A., *Recherches sur les Principes Mathematiques de la Theorie des Richesses* (English translation by N. T. Bacon), Macmillan, New York, 1897.

44. Croes, G. A., "A Method for Solving Traveling-salesman Problems," *Operations Research*, November–December 1958, pp. 791–812.

45. Dantzig, G. B., "Application of the Simplex Method to a Transport Problem," *Activity Analysis of Production and Allocation*, T. C. Koopmans (ed.), John Wiley & Sons, New York, 1951, pp. 359–73.

46. ———, *Computational Algorithm of Revised Simplex Method*, Rand Report, RM–1266, October 26, 1953.

47. ———, Fulkerson, D. R., and Johnson, S. M., "On a Linear Programming Combinatorial Approach to the Traveling-salesman Problem," *Operations Research*, January–February 1959, pp. 58–66.

48. ———, and Johnson, S. M., "A Production Smoothing Problem," *Proceedings of the Second Symposium in Linear Programming*, George Washington University, Washington, D. C., Vol. 1, January 27–29, 1955, pp. 151–76.

49. Dauten, C. A., *Business Fluctuations and Forecasting*, Southwestern Publishing Company, Cincinnati, 1954.

50. Davis, Chandler, "Linear Programming and Computers," *Computers and Automation*, July and August 1955, pp. 10–17 and pp. 10–16.

51. Davis, R. M., "The Current State of Profit Theory," *American Economic Review*, June 1952, pp. 245–64.

52. Dorfman, Robert, "Mathematical, or 'Linear,' Programming: A Nonmathematical Exposition," *American Economic Review*, December 1953, pp. 797–825.

53. ———, *Application of Linear Programming to the Theory of the Firm*, University of California Press, Berkeley, 1951.

54. ———, Samuelson, P. A., and Solow, R. M., *Linear Programming and Economic Analysis*, McGraw-Hill Book Company, New York, 1958.

55. Drucker, P. F., *The Practice of Management*, Harper & Brothers, New York, 1954.

56. Due, J. F., *Intermediate Economic Analysis*, rev. ed., Richard D. Irwin, Inc., Homewood, Illinois, 1955.

57. Edgeworth, F. Y., *Mathematical Psychics* (1881), reprinted for the Economists' Book Club, Augustus M. Kelley, New York, 1954.

58. Edie, L. C., "Operations Research in a Public Corporation," *Operations Research*, February 1957, pp. 111–22.

59. ———, "Traffic Delays at Toll Booths," *Operations Research*, May 1954, pp. 107–38.

60. Edwards, Corwin, *Maintaining Competition*, McGraw-Hill Book Company, New York, 1949.

61. Eisemann, Kurt, "The Trim Problem," *Management Science*, April 1957, pp. 279–84.

62. Enke, Stephen, "On Maximizing Profits: A Distinction Between Chamberlin and Robinson," *American Economic Review*, September 1951, pp. 566–78.

63. Federal Reserve Bank of New York, *Annual Report*, 1958.

64. ———, *Monthly Review*, January 1959, p. 12.

65. Fellner, William, *Competition Among the Few*, Alfred A. Knopf, New York, 1949.

66. Flood, M. M., "The Traveling-salesman Problem," *Operations Research*, February 1956, pp. 61–75.

67. Frank, M., and Wolfe, P., "An Algorithm for Quadratic Programming," *Naval Research Logistics Quarterly*, March and June 1956, pp. 95–110.

68. Gass, S. I., *Linear Programming: Methods and Applications*, McGraw-Hill Book Company, New York, 1958.

69. Good, R. A., "Systems of Linear Relations," *SIAM Review*, January 1959, pp. 1–31.

70. Gordon, M. J., and Shapiro, E., "Capital Equipment Analysis; the Required Rate of Profit," *Management Science*, October 1956, pp. 102–10.

71. Gruchy, A. G., *Modern Economic Thought*, Prentice-Hall, Inc., New York, 1947.

72. Haberler, G., *Prosperity and Depression*, United Nations, Lake Success, New York, 1946.

73. Halsbury, the Earl of, "From Plato to the Linear Program," *Operations Research*, August 1955, pp. 239–54.

74. Harrison, J. O., Jr., "Linear Programming and Operations Research," in 104, pp. 217–37.

75. Harrod, R. F., "Doctrines of Imperfect Competition," *Quarterly Journal of Economics*, May 1934, pp. 442–70.

76. Hausdorff, F., *Set Theory*, Chelsea Publishing Company, New York, 1957.

77. Henderson, Alexander, and Schlaifer, Robert, "Mathematical Programming: Better Information for Better Decision Making," *Harvard Business Review*, May–June 1954, pp. 73–100.

78. Hicks, J. R., *Value and Capital*, 2nd ed., Oxford University Press, New York, 1946.

79. Hitch, Charles, "An Appreciation of Systems Analysis," *Operations Research*, November 1955, pp. 466–81.

80. ———, "Operations Research and National Planning—a Dissent" (letter), *Operations Research*, October 1957, pp. 718–23.

81. ———, "Suboptimization in Operations Problems," *Operations Research*, May 1953, pp. 87–99.

82. Hoffman, A. J., and Jacobs, W., "Smooth Patterns of Production," *Management Science*, October 1954, pp. 86–91.

83. Hohn, F. E., *Elementary Matrix Algebra*, Macmillan, New York, 1958.

84. Holt, C. C., Modigliani, F., Simon, H. A., "A Linear Decision Rule for Production and Employment Scheduling," *Management Science*, October 1955, pp. 1–30.

85. Hotelling, Harold, "The Economics of Exhaustible Resources," *Journal of Political Economy*, April 1931, pp. 137–75.

86. Hu, Te Chiang and Prager, W., *Network Analysis of Production Smoothing*, Division of Applied Mathematics, Brown University, March 1958.

87. Jacobs, W., "The Caterer Problem," *Naval Research Logistics Quarterly*, June 1954, pp. 154–65.

88. Jenny, H. H., "Big Business in Modern American Capitalism: the Concept of Autonomous Power," Paper read at the Annual Meeting of the Ohio Association of Economists, April 1956, Columbus, Ohio, abstract published in *Proceedings*, mimeographed.

89. Kamke, E., *Theory of Sets*, Dover Publications, Inc., New York, 1950.

90. Kaplan, A. C. H., Dirlan, J. B., and Lanzillotti, R. F., *Pricing in Big Business*, The Brookings Institute, Washington, D. C., 1958.

91. Kemeny, J. G., Snell, J. L., and Thompson, G. L., *Introduction to Finite Mathematics*, Prentice-Hall, Inc., Englewood Cliffs, New Jersey, 1957.

92. Kershner, R. B., and Wilcox, L. R., *The Anatomy of Mathematics*, The Ronald Press Company, New York, 1950.

93. Knight, F. H., "Profit," *Encyclopedia of the Social Sciences*, Vol. XII, Macmillan Company, New York, 1934.

94. ———, *Risk, Uncertainty, and Profit*, Houghton, Mifflin Company, Boston, 1921. (London School of Economics, Reprints of Scarce Works, No. 16.)

95. Koopman, B. O., "Fallacies in Operations Research," *Operations Research*, August 1956, pp. 422–6.

96. Koopmans, T. C., *Activity Analysis of Production and Allocation*, Cowles Commission Monograph No. 13, John Wiley & Sons, New York. 1951.

97. ———, *Three Essays on the State of Economic Science*, McGraw-Hill Book Company, New York, 1957.

98. Kuhn, H. W., and Tucker, A. W. (eds.), *Linear Inequalities and Related Systems*, Princeton University Press, Princeton, 1956.

99. ———, and ———, "Nonlinear Programming," in *Proceedings of the Second Berkeley Symposium on Mathematical Statistics and Probability*, University of California Press, Berkeley, 1951, pp. 481–92.

100. Leftwich, R. H., *The Price System and Resource Allocation*, Rinehart & Company, New York, 1955.

101. Leontief, W. W., "The Use of Indifference Curves in the Analysis of Foreign Trade," *Readings in the Theory of International Trade*, Blakiston, Philadelphia, 1949, pp. 229–38.

102. Lorie, J. H., and Savage, L. J., "Three Problems in Rationing Capital," *Journal of Business*, October 1955, pp. 229–39.

103. Lutz, Vera and Lutz, Friedrich, *The Theory of Investment of the Firm*, Princeton University Press, Princeton, 1951.

104. McCloskey, J. F., and Trefethen, F. N. (eds.), *Operations Research for Management*, Vol. 1, The Johns Hopkins Press, Baltimore, 1954.

105. ———, and Coppinger, J. F., *Operations Research for Management*, Vol. 2, The Johns Hopkins Press, Baltimore, 1956.

106. Machlup, F., *The Economics of Sellers' Competition*, The Johns Hopkins Press, Baltimore, 1952.

107. Magee, J. F., "Guides to Inventory Policy," *Harvard Business Review*, January–June 1956, pp. 49–60, 57–70, 103–16.

108. ———, *Production Planning and Inventory Control*, McGraw-Hill Book Company, New York, 1957.

109. Makower, Helen, *Activity Analysis and the Theory of Economic Equilibrium*, St. Martin's Press, New York, 1957.

110. Mann, A. S., "A Note on the Modigliani-Hohn Production Smoothing Model," *Management Science*, July 1957, pp. 317–29.

111. ———, *Scheduling of Petroleum Refinery Operations*, Harvard Economic Studies No. 48, Harvard University Press, Cambridge, 1956.

112. March, J. G., and Simon, H. A., *Organizations*, John Wiley & Sons, New York, 1958.

113. Marchal, Jean, "The Construction of a New Theory of Profit," *American Economic Review*, September 1959, pp. 549–65.

114.  Margolis, J., "The Analysis of the Firm: Rationalism, Conventionalism, and Behaviorism," *Journal of Business*, July 1958, pp. 187–99.

115.  Markowitz, Harry, "The Optimization of a Quadratic Function Subject to Linear Constraints," *Naval Research Logistics Quarterly*, March and June 1956, pp. 111–33.

116.  ———, and Manne, A. S., "On the Solution of Discrete Programming Problems," *Econometrica*, January 1957, pp. 84–110.

117.  ———, "Portfolio Selection," *Journal of Finance*, March 1952, pp. 77–91.

118.  Marshall, Alfred, *Principles of Economics*, 8th ed., Macmillan, London, 1947.

119.  Miller, J. P., "Contributions of Industrial and Human Relations to Economists' Theory of the Firm," *Industrial Relations Research Association, Proceedings*, Vol. 11, pp. 134–42.

120.  Mitchell, W. C., *Business Cycles*, University of California Press, Berkeley, 1913.

121.  Modigliani, F., and Hohn, F. E., "Production Planning over Time and the Nature of the Expectation and Planning Horizon," *Econometrica*, January 1955, pp. 46–66.

122.  ———, and ———, "Solution of Certain Problems of Production Planning over Time, Illustrating the Effect of the Inventory Constraint," Appendix Cowles Commission Discussion Paper No. 2,038.

123.  Morse, P. M., and Kimball, G. E., *Methods of Operations Research*, rev. ed., John Wiley & Sons, New York, 1951.

124.  ———, "The Operations Research Society of America," *Operations Research*, November 1952, pp. 1–3.

125.  ———, "Statistics and Operations Research," *Operations Research*, February 1956, pp. 2–18.

126.  ———, *Queues, Inventories, and Maintenance*, Publications in Operations Research, No. 1, John Wiley & Sons, New York, 1958.

127.  Munroe, M. E., *Introduction to Measure and Integration*, Addison-Wesley Publishing Company, Cambridge, Mass., 1953.

128.  Murdoch, D. C., *Linear Algebra for Undergraduates*, John Wiley & Sons, New York, 1957.

129.  National Council of Teachers of Mathematics, *Insights into Modern Mathematics*, Washington, The Council, 1957.

130.  Nelson, J. C., *Railroad Transportation and Public Policy*, The Brookings Institution, Washington, D.C., 1959.

131.  Neumann, John von, and Morgenstern, Oskar, *Theory of Games and Economic Behavior*, Princeton University Press, Princeton, 1947.

132.  Newman, P., "Some Calculations on Least Cost Diets, using the Simplex Method," *Bulletin of the Oxford Institute of Statistics*, September 1955, pp. 303–20.

133.  Operations Research Society of America, *A Comprehensive Bibliography on Operations Research, through 1956, with Supplement for 1957*, Case Institute of Technology, ORSA publication No. 4, John Wiley & Sons, New York, 1958.

134.  Papandreou, A. G., "Problems in the Theory of the Firm," *A Survey of Contemporary Economics*, Vol. II, Richard D. Irwin, Inc., Homewood, Illinois, 1952.

135. Paull, A. E., and Walter, J. R., "The Trim Problem An Application of Linear Programming to the Manufacture of Newsprint Paper," *Econometrica*, July 1955, abstract, p. 336.

136. Penrose, Edith, "Limits to the Growth and Size of Firms," *American Economic Review, Proceedings*, Vol. 45, pp. 531–43.

137. Reinfeld, N. V., and Vogel, W. R., *Mathematical Programming*, Prentice-Hall, Inc., Englewood Cliffs, New Jersey, 1958.

138. Richardson, M., *Fundamentals of Mathematics*, rev. ed., Macmillan, New York, 1958.

139. Riley, Vera and Gass, S. I., *Linear Programming and Associated Techniques, A Comprehensive Bibliography of Linear, Nonlinear, and Dynamic Programming*, Operations Research Office, The Johns Hopkins University, Chevy Chase, Md., 1958.

140. Robinson, Joan, *The Economics of Imperfect Competition*, Macmillan, London, 1934.

141. Salveson, M. E., "The Assembly-line Balancing Problem," *Journal of Industrial Engineering*, May–June 1955, pp. 18–25.

142. Sandiforn, P. J., Bernholtz, B., and Shelson, W., "Three Applications of Operations Research in a Large Electric Utility," *Operations Research*, December 1956, pp. 663–73.

143. Sasieni, M. W., Yaspan, Arthur, and Friedman, Lawrence, *Operations Research: Methods and Problems*, John Wiley & Sons, New York, 1959.

144. Schelling, T. C., "The Strategy of Conflict," *Journal of Conflict Resolution*, September 1958, pp. 203–64.

145. Schreier, O., and Sperner, E., *Introduction to Modern Algebra and Matrix Theory*, Chelsea Publishing Company, New York, 1955.

146. Scitovsky, Tibor, "A Note on Profit Maximization and Its Implications," *Readings in Price Theory*, Richard D. Irwin, Inc., Homewood, Illinois, 1952.

147. ———, *Welfare and Competition*, Richard D. Irwin, Inc., Homewood, Illinois, 1951.

148. Shackle, G. L. S., *Expectation in Economics*, Cambridge University Press, 1949.

149. Shubik, Martin, "Economics, Management Science, and Operations Research," *Review of Economics and Statistics*, August 1958, pp. 214–20.

150. ———, *Strategy and Market Structure*, John Wiley & Sons, New York, 1959.

151. Smiddy, H. F., and Naum, L., "Evolution of a 'Science of Managing' in America," *Management Science*, October 1954, pp. 1–31.

152. Smith, V. L., "Economic Equipment Policies: An Evaluation," *Management Science*, October 1957, pp. 20–37.

153. Spencer, M. H., and Siegelman, Louis, *Managerial Economics*, Richard D. Irwin, Inc., Homewood, Illinois, 1959.

154. *Standard Oil Company of N. J. v. U. S.* 221 U.S. 1.

155. Stigler, G. J., *The Theory of Price*, Macmillan, New York, 1946.

156. Symonds, G. H., "The Institute of Management Sciences: Progress Report," *Management Science*, January 1957, pp. 117–30.

157. Terborgh, George, *Dynamic Equipment Policy*, McGraw-Hill Book Company, New York, 1949.

158. Thielman, H. D., *Theory of Functions of Real Variables*, Prentice-Hall, Inc., New York, 1953.

159. Thornthwaite, C. W., "Operations Research in Agriculture," *Operations Research*, February 1953, pp. 33–8.

160. Tintner, G., "Monopoly Over Time," *Econometrica*, April 1937, pp. 160–70.

161. Triffin, Robert, *Monopolistic Competition and General Equilibrium Theory*, Harvard University Press, Cambridge, 1941.

162. *U.S. v. American Tobacco Company*, 221 U.S. 106.

163. *U.S. v. U.S. Steel Corporation*, 251 U.S. 451.

164. Vajda, S., *Readings in Linear Programming*, John Wiley & Sons, New York, 1958.

165. Vazsonyi, Andrew, *Scientific Programming in Business and Industry*, John Wiley & Sons, New York, 1958.

166. Weintraub, Sidney, *Price Theory*, Pitman Publishing Company, New York, 1949.

167. Weinwurm, E. H., "Limitation of the Scientific Method in Management Science," *Management Science*, April 1957, pp. 225–33.

168. Weston, J. F., "A Generalized Uncertainty Theory of Profit," *American Economic Review*, March 1950, pp. 41–60.

169. ———, and Beranek, W., "Programming Investment Portfolio Construction," *Analysts Journal*, May 1955, pp. 51–5.

170. Whitin, T. M., *The Theory of Inventory Management*, 2nd ed., Princeton University Press, Princeton, 1957.

171. Whittaker, Edmund, *Economic Analysis*, John Wiley & Sons, New York, 1956.

172. Wiener, Norbert, *Cybernetics*, John Wiley & Sons, New York, 1948.

# INDEX

225